Zonia K. Porter

Geneva '33

Test. Amoeba = Rhizopoda
Mastigophora
Sporozoa.

OUTLINES OF GENERAL ZOÖLOGY

THE MACMILLAN COMPANY
NEW YORK · BOSTON · CHICAGO · DALLAS
ATLANTA · SAN FRANCISCO

MACMILLAN & CO., LIMITED
LONDON · BOMBAY · CALCUTTA
MELBOURNE

THE MACMILLAN COMPANY
OF CANADA, LIMITED
TORONTO

A Portuguese Man-of-War Capturing a Fish

OUTLINES

OF

GENERAL ZOÖLOGY

BY

HORATIO HACKETT NEWMAN

PROFESSOR OF ZOÖLOGY

IN THE UNIVERSITY OF CHICAGO

Revised Edition

𝔑𝔢𝔴 𝔜𝔬𝔯𝔨

THE MACMILLAN COMPANY

1930

SET UP, ELECTROTYPED, AND PRINTED BY T. MOREY & SON
IN THE UNITED STATES OF AMERICA

PREFACE TO THE REVISED EDITION

In the five years that have elapsed since this book was issued, teachers have had a sufficient opportunity to discover its stronger as well as its weaker points. The outstanding feature of the book was its judicious blending of the principles method and the type method of presenting the materials of General Zoölogy. This feature has stood the test of time and needs no modification in principle. Several teachers, however, have asked for the introduction of more types and have specified those most desired by them. Others have requested more material about some of the types already in use, notably the earthworm and the frog.

In general, it now appears that the main criticism of the first edition was that it did not contain quite enough material for a two-semester course. Closely following the needs that seem to be most commonly felt by teachers, the writer has introduced several new types: the sponges, the clam, parasitic roundworms of man, and the grasshopper. Rather extensive additions have been made to the chapters on the earthworm and the frog.

Prompted by the splendid new edition of *The Cell*, by E. B. Wilson, the chapter on the MORPHOLOGY AND PHYSIOLOGY OF THE CELL has been completely rewritten. The chapter on THE ANIMAL KINGDOM has been materially enlarged by the addition of a discussion of the interrelations of the animal phyla along the lines of the new *Diphyletic Tree Theory*. This idea seems to add unity and coherence to the whole section of the book dealing with animal types.

The most important improvement in the book involves the materials presented in Part IV, which was formerly entitled GENERAL PRINCIPLES OF ZOÖLOGY. Competent critics suggested that this part of the book, while it contained materials indispensable for a beginning course, was loosely organized and lacked sequence and coherence. This section of the book has now been rearranged and extensively rewritten under the general title of DYNAMIC ASPECTS OF ZOÖLOGY. It was found that nearly all of the materials formerly treated as principles could readily be dealt with as biological mechanisms for regulating the interactions of

v

the parts of the organism, for adapting the organism to the environment, and for racial change and adjustment. A few old sections seemed not to fit into this scheme and were omitted, while three new chapters on BIOLOGICAL MECHANISMS, COÖRDINATING AND REGULATING MECHANISMS, and SENSE ORGANS have been added. A criticism of the first edition was that it did not give enough material on physiology. It will now be seen that the new Part IV carries a physiological tone throughout.

In its present form this text is now believed to be as well adapted for courses lasting a whole college year as for those confined to one semester or one quarter. For those covering the subject in a briefer way it is suggested that a good many of the chapters on types be omitted and that Part IV be dealt with only in brief outline. Selections and omissions will, of course, depend upon the individuality of the teacher.

In revising this text the writer has had the advantage of kindly criticisms of several of his colleagues, especially Professors W. C. Allee and B. H. Willier and Dr. L. H. Hyman, for which he is duly grateful.

The book in its present form is a tangible expression of the writer's appreciation of the many kindly suggestions and constructive criticisms on the part of the users of the first edition. Everything has been done to comply with requests and suggestions in so far as these have been compatible with the general purpose, plan, and scope of the book. The publication of a *Laboratory Guide and Review Manual* to be used especially with this text constitutes a response to one of the most oft-repeated requests on the part of teachers using the first edition.

H. H. NEWMAN.

March, 1929

PREFACE TO THE FIRST EDITION

During more than a score of years the writer has had an exceptional opportunity of studying the changing styles of teaching employed in courses in General Zoölogy in representative American universities and colleges. In the earlier days it was the fashion to use the *type method* exclusively, conducting the student through a cursory survey of the animal kingdom with the idea of affording him at least a speaking acquaintance with as many as possible of the representative animal types. The superficiality of this method became increasingly apparent as time went on, and the natural remedy was to abbreviate the list of types studied and to concentrate on a few of the most important forms, these selected so as to represent the various levels of organic complexity. The idea underlying this departure—an idea not without justification—was, that a few animals intensively studied illustrate the essential principles of the subject as well as or better than a much larger number studied superficially. Intensive work, moreover, tends to inculcate ideas of exactitude in observation and skill in laboratory technique.

Out of the type-study method there gradually evolved another method—that of the study of principles. At first, the principles were merely brought in as side issues to lend interest to types. Gradually, however, the principles came to assume larger and larger proportions until they overshadowed types altogether. Thus evolved the *principles method*. According to this method types, as such, were abandoned, and the subject matter of zoölogy at least as much of it as admitted of such treatment, was presented as a series of principles. Animal forms were mentioned only incidentally as illustrative materials, no one animal being studied at all completely. This method had a measure of success in some institutions, but the common experience has been that the student can go just so far in a study of principles before he begins to feel an insistent demand for a more concrete knowledge of animals themselves. He asks: "What is this Amœba, this Hydra, this Planaria?" The instructor is then forced to stop and introduce some of these real animal types before he can profitably go ahead with his teaching of principles.

The experience of the writer and of his colleagues has, we understand, not a few points in common with that of the majority of teachers who have tried the principles method. We have been forced to revert to some of the tried and proven features of the type method, while retaining what seem to us the best features of the principles method. Thus we have adopted a workable compromise between the old and the new methods; and the present text is an embodiment of our experience as to the content and arrangement of materials for a well-rounded course in General Zoölogy.

Our method is, in general, as follows: We begin with a historical survey; we follow this up with a general discussion of the problems associated with life, protoplasm, and the cell; it then becomes necessary to present a series of animal types, ranging from Amœba to the frog, each type being used as a concrete illustration of one or more principles; finally, a return is made to matters of general biology, the topics leading logically up to the principle of organic evolution.

If the instructor prefers to introduce the vertebrates first, he may, without any other adjustment of materials, take out bodily the section on the frog and transfer it to a position in advance of that on the Amœba, and then proceed through the other topics in the order given. There may be too much material in the book for a major or a semester course as offered in some institutions. In that case various chapters, according to the judgment of the instructor, may be omitted without impairing the unity of treatment. There is, on the other hand, sufficient material for courses given throughout the year; and this certainly would be the case if some of the shorter chapters were to be expanded by the instructor.

It need hardly be said that the author has drawn upon a great variety of sources for the data presented in the book. In some cases the materials of other authors have been incorporated with little change in thought or point of view and with only sufficient modification in language or in order of presentation to make it fit into the place assigned to it. In general, it is hoped that old facts have been presented with at least an added touch of newness either of expression or of point of view.

The author has tried to avoid the error of overillustration not uncommon in textbooks of the present day. No figures are used except where an illustration seems necessary to supplement the material given in the text. In this place the author would like once more to acknowledge his indebtedness to Mr. Kenji Toda, whose skill with the pen has done much to lend freshness to the book.

For constructive criticism the author is indebted to his colleagues, Professors W. C. Allee and A. W. Bellamy, who read considerable parts of the manuscript, and to the skilled reader employed by the publishers.

Most of the illustrations used in the book, other than those drawn or redrawn, have been borrowed from The Macmillan Company's publications; and acknowledgments are due to the following authors: T. J. Parker and W. J. Haswell, E. B. Wilson, R. W. Hegner, S. W. Holmes, Ulric Dahlgren and W. A. Kepner, R. S. Lull, L. L. Woodruff, H. E. Walter, W. B. Scott, A. E. Shipley and E. W. MacBride. Some of the most valuable illustrations have been borrowed, with permission, from books published by other companies, and we herewith express our indebtedness to both authors and publishers of the following books: *Evolution and Animal Life*, by D. S. Jordan and V. L. Kellogg (D. Appleton & Co.); *Genetics in Relation to Agriculture*, by E. B. Babcock and R. L. Clausen (McGraw-Hill Book Co.); *Principles of Animal Biology*, by A. F. Shull *et al.* (McGraw-Hill Book Co.); *Biology*, by G. N. Calkins (Henry Holt & Co.); *General Biology*, by W. T. Sedgwick and E. B. Wilson (Henry Holt & Co.); *Zoölogy*, by T. D. A. Cockerell (World Book Co.); *Biology, General and Medical*, by J. McFarland (W. B. Saunders Co.); *Individuality in Organisms*, by C. M. Child (University of Chicago Press); *Animal Communities in Temperate America*, by V. E. Shelford (University of Chicago Press); *The Biology of Twins*, by H. H. Newman (University of Chicago Press). Finally, a considerable number of illustrations and much valuable data have been obtained from books, monographs, and shorter articles published either in journals or privately. While a complete list of these cannot well be given here, the author would like to acknowledge his indebtedness to the following: C. O. Whitman, E. B. Wilson, E. G. Conklin, T. H. Morgan, F. R. Lillie, C. M. Child, W. E. Ritter, J. A. Thomson, A. Dendy, A. E. Shipley, E. W. MacBride, H. S. Jennings, D. S. Jordan, V. L. Kellogg, S. J. Forbes, V. E. Shelford, R. W. Hegner, A. F. Shull, L. L. Woodruff, R. S. Lull, J. Loeb, W. E.

Castle, H. E. Walter, W. M. Wheeler, H. F. Osborn, G. N. Calkins, S. W. Holmes, W. B. Scott, J. McFarland, E. B. Babcock, R. L. Clausen, the authors of the Cambridge Natural History, and many others.

The writer is not unmindful that some controversial matters have been handled in more or less partisan fashion, but he feels that the purely neutral position is a deadly one for a teacher to take. If the instructor feels called upon to take an opposed view as to any or all of the points at issue, he will at least have a good opportunity of starting a class discussion; and discussion is the very life of class work.

H. H. NEWMAN

THE UNIVERSITY OF CHICAGO
June, 1924

CONTENTS

PART I

ELEMENTARY BIOLOGICAL PHENOMENA

PART II

ANIMAL TYPES (INVERTEBRATES)

PART III

THE FROG (A TYPICAL VERTEBRATE)

PART IV

DYNAMIC ASPECTS OF ZOÖLOGY

CONTENTS

APPENDIX

PART I

ELEMENTARY BIOLOGICAL PHENOMENA

CHAPTER I

INTRODUCTION

A. The Biological Point of View

THE biologist looks upon himself as a seeker after truth, as one striving to get a glimpse behind the veil of the mystery of life. If he is partially successful in his efforts, he comes to have a vision of himself and his fellows as but one kind of organism in the midst of an almost infinite variety of other organisms, some of which bear unmistakable resemblances to himself. He is impressed with the strong likeness, amounting almost to caricature, between the anthropoid apes and man. The likeness exhibited by the lower vertebrates, though obvious, is not nearly so striking; and when he compares the invertebrates with man, he finds resemblances, to be sure, but these are only of the most general character. Yet through all the intricate maze of living forms there is a certain unescapable community of fundamental structure and function that compels the realization of the inherent oneness of all life. Man is part of one great organic system, each part of which has some relation to the whole. Thus the genus Homo is not to be looked upon as the center of all creation, nor the sole criterion of values; but merely as a part—at present a very important part—in a vast coherent system of living beings.

B. Zoölogy as a Science

Biology may be defined as the Science of Life. Zoölogy deals with the biology of animals; Botany, with that of plants. The division of Biology into these two main subsciences is somewhat arbitrary and in some respects unfortunate, for the same broad principles underlie both branches. A well trained biologist must, therefore, be familiar with both fields, for certain facts about one throw much light on the other. Hence, although in this volume our chief attention will always be focused upon animal life, we shall, whenever the needs of the case demand it, have recourse to plant materials. When, for example, we are dealing with the

3

simplest organisms, we often find ourselves in doubt as to whether certain types under discussion are animals or plants. The zoölogist claims them and classifies them as animals; the botanist considers them plants—so close do the two great subkingdoms of living organisms approach each other at their lower levels. To classify such indeterminate forms unreservedly as either animals or plants would be quite arbitrary. Far better would it be to recognize the fundamental oneness of all life and to regard the classification of types into categories as merely a matter of convenience leading toward better organization of knowledge.

We humans are inveterate classifiers. We like to pigeonhole our facts and our ideas so that we can find them again when we want to use them. The classifying instinct is a valuable one so long as we continue to recognize that we ourselves made the classification and that therefore it is fallible and subject to modification. When we take our pigeonholes too seriously, we sometimes get into the same difficulties as those encountered by peoples who make arbitrary laws that they do not wish to obey. In this book, then, we shall not be too arbitrary about classification. While we must recognize animal groupings to some extent, our main interest will be focused upon the principles that underlie the science. We shall use animal groups as convenient hooks upon which to hang the ideas of the subject, incidentally introducing some of the facts about various sorts of animals that are representative of the animal kingdom as a whole. We hope to focus attention primarily upon principles, but we shall try not to forget that animals themselves are also significant realities.

C. The Complexity of the Subject

At the risk of seeming to glorify our own particular science, it may be said, with the assurance that few will disagree, that Zoölogy is the most intricate of all the sciences. It may be thought of as a sort of superstructure built upon the solid foundations reared by the physical sciences (Physics, Chemistry, Geology). Its framework is Philosophy; the sciences of Mathematics and Engineering furnish the tools and the instruments of precision. Training for advanced work in Zoölogy involves a preliminary training in all of the sciences mentioned, and frequently more. Ofttimes the zoölogist has had to turn inventor in order to equip himself with the necessary instruments with which to carry on his researches. Thus biologists have had much to do with the gradual improvement of the compound microscope and with microphotography. Many temperature regulating and temperature registering instruments of great delicacy have been the self-made tools of biological explorers.

The rather widespread impression that Zoölogy is merely a study of "bugs" and that zoölogists are "bug-hunters," is gradually giving way before a growing conviction that Zoölogy is a serious and valuable subject. Its problems are the most complex and difficult of solution among the problems of science, and they require the best efforts of the best intellects for their successful solution. Zoölogy is a science of unsolved or only partially solved problems, many of them baffling in their elusiveness and intangibility. Some of our very earliest and most pressing problems are still unsolved, and progress in many other lines is retarded by our failure to solve them. Such an unsolved problem is the perennial mystery: what is life? Until we can answer this, the ultimate solution of many another knotty problem will be held in abeyance. A list of some of the larger problems and principles and theories that constitute the framework of the science of Zoölogy will perhaps make plain to the uninitiated reader something of the nature and content of zoölogical science.

D. Some of the Problems and Principles of Zoölogy

1. When and how did life first begin?
2. The problem of abiogenesis. Can life arise under present conditions out of inorganic materials?
3. What is life? The problem of the nature of life.
4. The problems of the exact physical and chemical constitution of protoplasm.
5. The problem of the nature of death. Is death inevitable or may it be indefinitely postponed?
6. Mechanism versus Vitalism: a controversy of long standing.
7. The Cell Theory: one of the three guiding principles of biology.
8. Problems as to the nature of cell organization and as to the functions of the various cell organs.
9. The problem of the mechanics of mitosis.
10. The problems as to the rôles of mitosis and of amitosis in development and heredity.

11. The organismal versus the elemental points of view: an important biological controversy.

12. The nature of individuality in organisms.

13. The Axial Gradient concept: an important modern physiological interpretation of the basis of organization.

14. The problems as to the essential distinctions between Protozoa and Metazoa, and of the genetic relations of these two groups.

15. The problem of the mechanics of amœboid locomotion, and of spontaneous protoplasmic motion in general.

16. Tropism versus Trial and Error: the problem of the nature of the behavior of lower organisms.

17. The rôle of conjugation in the life cycle of the Infusoria, and its bearings on the function of sex.

18. The Protozoa and the Cell Theory.

19. The nature and significance of metagenesis—alternation of generations.

20. The physiology of asexual (agametic) reproduction.

21. The problem of metamerism.

22. The problem of asymmetry.

23. The principle of homology.

24. The nature of social organization in insects.

25. The relation of insects to disease.

26. The immunity problem.

27. Preformation versus epigenesis.

28. Modes of reproduction and their interrelations.

29. The Germ-plasm Theory. To what extent is it justified?

30. The Chromosome Theory of Heredity.

31. The fertilization problem in its various phases.

32. The general problem of sex, including those of sex determination and sex differentiation.

33. The problem of the modes of origin of mutations, and their causes.

34. The problem of the rôle of mutations in evolution.

35. The problem of the ultimate mechanism of Mendelian heredity.

36. Problems involving the relationship of the organism to the environment.

37. The general problem of adaptation.

38. How much of adaptation is the result of ontogenetic response?

39. How much of adaptation is strictly hereditary?

40. The significance of the concept, the Web of Life.

41. What are the factors governing the distribution of animals over the face of the earth and in the waters?

42. To what extent does behavior affect distribution?

43. Why is there so much popular opposition to the principle of evolution?

44. Is the principle of evolution proved? If so, what is the nature of the proof?

45. The great assumption underlying all of the evidences of evolution: that homologies are the result of heredity. Is this assumption justified?

46. What is the exact nature of the contribution of each of the main bodies of evidence toward the demonstration of the validity of the principle of evolution?

47. What are the causes of the extinction of animal species?

48. The factors of organic evolution in general.

49. Orthogenesis: the problem as to the causes of definitely directed evolution.

50. The Lamarckian doctrine: the perennial controversy as to whether somatic modifications are heritable; or the problem of the inheritance of acquired characters.

51. The Darwinian doctrine: the problem as to the exact rôle of Natural Selection in species forming and in the production of adaptations.

52. The rôle of Isolation in species forming.

53. The relative potency of heredity and environment in development.

54. The exact rôle of the environment in the production of hereditary change, and thus in shaping the course of evolution.

55. Instinct and Intelligence: the problem of nature and origin of innate and of acquired intelligence.

56. Problems of the special physiology of nervous activity.

57. The rôle of endocrine glands in growth and coördination.

58. The sense organs as adaptations to the environment.

59. The ancestry of man.

60. The problem of the future of man on the earth.

These are only a few of the problems that confront the student of the science of Zoölogy. Another writer might, and probably would, considerably modify this list, leaving out some of the items and adding others that seem to him of more importance; yet there would doubtless be very general agreement on more than half of those in the list. The beginning student is hardly expected to understand the nature or the content of the subjects thus briefly mentioned, but he should at least gain the impression of the multiplicity of questions and problems that form part and parcel of the science he is beginning to study, and acquire some degree of appreciation of the intricacy and difficulty of the subject. Hardly one of the problems listed above can be said to be fully solved; only a few of them are as much as half solved; many of them are still entirely unsolved. Many special or minor problems that are corollaries of or accessory to the major problems mentioned have been studied intensively and may be considered, at least tentatively, as solved. Many both major and minor problems, doubtless capable of solution, have as yet never been adequately explored. The field of Zoölogy then is untilled ground. We zoölogists are just beginning to catch glimpses of what the future has in store for us. Zoölogy is a splendid field for young and able investigators, for there is no dearth of problems worthy of their best endeavors. Every new discovery throws light on several other points and thus paves the way for further discoveries. All of the problems are so interrelated that they require for their solution a massed attack on some few of the major problems and minor attacks from various angles on the secondary strategic points.

This outlook upon Zoölogy as a body of insistent problems demanding solution is beyond question most stimulating both to novices and to veterans. It lends life and interest to the discussion of the numerous phenomena that make up the factual basis of the subject. The student must learn to view knowledge as to a large extent tentative, subject to correction, and ready for complete revision in the light of new discoveries. This is the spirit of modern science, and this should be the spirit of each student of Zoölogy.

E. The Subdivisions of Zoölogy

When Zoölogy was young and in its formative period, the whole field could have been grasped by one man. But now the subject matter has grown so amazingly that its literature comprises hundreds of thousands of books and monographs. Hence, no one man can possibly familiarize himself with more than a small fraction of the total field. The necessity for specialization has grown out of this fact, and in modern times workers in the vanguard of progress have come to confine their attention to restricted fields of research in which they may become expert.

We have come to recognize that some of the problems are in a sense purely academic, inasmuch as they appear to have no practical significance; while other problems are closely allied to human welfare and are therefore considered more practical. We have come to speak of the academic aspects of our science as PURE ZOÖLOGY and of its more practical aspects as APPLIED ZOÖLOGY. Thus the great majority of the zoölogists in the universities and colleges, and at least half of those in research institutions, are engaged in attempts to solve the fundamental problems of Zoölogy, with little thought as to the practical bearing of their work; while the greater part of those working in government bureaus, agricultural schools, and commercial laboratories are interested, primarily, in making practical applications of the discoveries made by the pure zoölogists. The pure zoölogist, however, never knows when some discovery which he makes in the pursuit of truth may turn out to be of immense practical value. Conversely, the applied zoölogist may unexpectedly run across some new principle in pure Zoölogy. One does not always find what he is looking for, but if he seeks with a will, he seldom fails to find some new thing. Important as are the numerous phases of applied Zoölogy, such as Medicine, Sanitation, Eugenics, Euthenics, Agronomy, Economic Entomology, and economic aspects of animal life in general, this book is intended to deal primarily with pure Zoölogy and to take only incidental notice of the applied aspects of the subject, and then only when these appear to be especially significant from the pure-science point of view.

When we limit our outlook to the field of pure Zoölogy, we find that we must still recognize several distinct points of view. Thus, one may interest himself chiefly in the structures of animals, in their functions, in their distribution in space and in time, in their relations with one another and with the environment, in their genetic relationships, and in the philosophical aspects of the subject.

Certain of the major concepts of the science, though not strictly separable from the other aspects of the subject just mentioned, are to be viewed as the warp of the complex fabric of the science of Zoölogy.   Thus the concepts of Organic Evolution, the Organismal Theory, and the Cell Theory are interwoven throughout the whole fabric, and they serve to bind together, to unify, and to rationalize all of the branches of the subject.

For convenience, we may subdivide Zoölogy into six subsciences, being careful not to imply that these branches are self-sufficient or independent:—

I. MORPHOLOGY—the science of form or structure.
II. PHYSIOLOGY—the science of function.
III. ECOLOGY—the science of the interrelations of the organism and the environment.
IV. DISTRIBUTIONAL ZOÖLOGY—including:—
    a. PALÆONTOLOGY—the science of ancient life, or that of the distribution of animals in time.
    b. ZOÖGEOGRAPHY—the science of the distribution of animals in space.
V. TAXONOMY—the science of the classification of organisms.
VI. GENETICS—the science of the origin of organisms.

All of these aspects of Zoölogy will receive attention in the body of the text, but it will not be possible to subdivide the book according to the above plan.   Rather, it is our intention to break away from formal lines of demarcation and to present the ideas of the subject in the order in which they will, in our judgment, best subserve our scientific and pedagogical ends.

CHAPTER II

HISTORY OF ZOÖLOGY

BEFORE entering upon a systematic study of various problems of Zoölogy or of the various types of animals, it is well for the student to take a brief historical survey of the history of the science we are dealing with, to learn how and when and at whose hands the great problems arose, and in how far they have been solved. All history is one: no longer can the church historian understand his subject without a knowledge of political, educational, and scientific history. Similarly, we find that the history of Zoölogy—and particularly the philosophical aspects of it, such as the Principle of Evolution—has been inextricably bound up with religious and secular history. During times of peace and prosperity, when thinkers had leisure to think and were unhampered by artificial religious restrictions, science made great strides. During and after wars, in periods of severe religious dominance and intolerance, in periods of social laxity and overindulgence, science was prostrated and made little progress. The history of Zoölogy has been characterized by long periods of stagnancy and depression. These ups and downs are now to be brought to our attention.

A. THE BEGINNINGS OF ZOÖLOGY

The earliest writers on zoölogical subjects, except possibly the Egyptians, were the early Greeks, but they were not really zoölogists. Rather, they were philosophers, interested in speculations as to the origins of things both living and lifeless, in religion, in astronomy, and in every phase of human experience. In their speculative flights they were untrammeled by any need of keeping within the bounds of fact. To them such mythological creatures as centaurs, mermaids, hydra-headed monsters, were nearly as real as were the animals from other parts of the world, known to them only through the descriptions of travelers. We must not judge these forefathers of Zoölogy too harshly, however, for they were beginners, and in many ways, scientifically speaking, mere children.

11

All of their ideas were beclouded by superstition, legend, and folk-lore. In this respect they were in no way different from the mass of unscientific minded people today. One might easily list a score of popular fallacies that have long been known as such to science, but which live in the minds of the people. The scientific point of view is unnatural and hard to acquire, and few possess it even in this enlightened twentieth century. Superstition and dogmatism still blind the mental vision of vast numbers, some of whom are people of ability and many are endowed with at least average intelligence. Let us then be lenient with our pioneer zoölogists, who were as free-minded, compared with their fellow men, as are the scientists of today in contrast with the great mass of people living in intellectual bondage.

These earlier Greek writers—some of them philosophers, others poets—were members of a race of sea people. "Along the shores of the blue Ægean," says Osborn, "teeming with what we now know to be the earliest and simplest forms of animals and plants, they founded their hypotheses as to the origin and succession of life. . . . The spirit of the Greeks was vigorous and hopeful. Not pausing to test their theories by research, they did not suffer the disappointments and delays which come from one's own efforts to wrest truths from Nature." The very first problems which they tackled were the ones that are still farthest from solution: the problems of the origin of living creatures, including man. They did not lack mental audacity, but they did lack judgment. Some of their theories seem quite ridiculous today, but in a few of their ideas we see the germs of modern principles.

Thales (624–548 B.C.) had a theory that the ocean was the mother of all life; that living creatures of all sorts, even terrestrial animals, arose from the womb of the ocean. Questions as to how and why did not suggest themselves.

Anaximander (611–547 B.C.) had a vague, highly mythical idea of transformation of species. Adopting the idea of aquatic origins of all creatures, he thought that each terrestrial species was a transformed aquatic type that had acquired adaptive features necessary for land life.

Empedocles (495–435 B.C.) went much further than his predecessors in his conceptions as to the transformation of species, inquiring even into the cause of adaptive structures and the general fitness of organisms. Assuming the spontaneous generation of living

creatures, he thought that at first there existed merely discon-
nected organs and parts scattered here and there. These parts of
animals were attracted or repelled by the forces of Love and Hate,
resulting in all sorts of weird and impossible combinations so out
of harmony that they could neither survive nor reproduce. Only
the sufficiently harmonious and adaptable combinations persisted
and multiplied. Thus is fitness explained; and we may look upon
this fairy story as a sort of vague prophecy of Darwin's "survival
of the fittest" idea, one of the most striking of modern evolutionary
theories.

Aristotle (384–322 B.C.) has been called the Father of Natural
History. A wealthy man for those times, he was able to maintain
an extensive private library and, doubtless, a laboratory. He was
the first true scientist in that
he adopted the inductive
method: that of first securing
facts and then basing his
principles upon these facts.
Aristotle was an original investigator. Many an animal
was for the first time in human
history dissected and de-
scribed by him, and some of
these descriptions would stand
today as fair models of careful observation and inference.
In spite of many errors, he
had a good understanding of
the structure and development of the main groups of
animals, and some of his observations were so far ahead of
his time that they have been

Fig. 1. Aristotle.

confirmed only within the last century. As an example of his
acumen, it may be mentioned that he discovered the fact that
some sharks are viviparous and that the embryo, in a manner
not unlike that of the placental mammals, acquires a nutritive
connection with the membranes of the maternal uterus—facts
that were rediscovered only a few decades ago by Johannes
Müller.

Aristotle became acquainted with so many kinds of animals—about 500 species are mentioned in his writings—that he felt the necessity of classifying them. He recognized eight large groups roughly corresponding to: 1, Mammals; 2, Birds; 3, Oviparous quadrupeds (corresponding to lizards and turtles); 4, Fishes; 5, Mollusks; 6, Crustaceans; 7, Insects; 8, Animals with shells. This was, of course, a very incomplete and inaccurate classification, but it is interesting as a first effort to develop a taxonomic system.

Aristotle reached a high level of attainment in zoölogy beyond which there was little further progress until comparatively recent times.

B. The Decline of Zoölogy

The history of zoölogical progress was profoundly influenced by world movements, and it is therefore natural enough that, when the great Greek civilization declined and ultimately collapsed, the sciences declined and collapsed with it. No zoölogical writers of consequence appeared among the later Greeks, and the Romans did little better. Even *Pliny,* who was considered by his contemporaries as the greatest living zoölogist, is now known to have been only an indiscriminate compiler of data—half false and half true—from the writings of his predecessors. He borrowed extensively from Aristotle and attempted to substitute for the latter's relatively scientific effort at classification a purely superficial one based on the habitats of organisms. He divided all animals into three groups—flying animals, land animals, and water animals.

The Dark Ages.—The rise of Christianity, turning the minds of man from material to purely spiritual interests, had a profoundly depressing influence upon scientific activities of all sorts. The idea became prevalent that the Bible was a universal compendium of all knowledge and that it was irreligious to make original investigations after truth. The clergy, for reasons of their own, fostered this spirit of subservience to authority and exercised a dominating influence in all matters, not merely religious but intellectual and political as well. Men ceased to think for themselves, preferring to be told what to believe. When a simple observation might readily have settled a controversy, they preferred to look up authorities on the matter in question. A series of acrimonious debates, leading almost to bloodshed, was waged over the question —How many teeth has a horse? After all of the authorities had been consulted, a freethinker finally settled the debate by looking into a horse's mouth. This, however, was considered an unsportsmanlike procedure. In those days if a person found that his own observations were contrary to authority, he did not doubt authority, he merely doubted the accuracy of his own senses. Even today there are many who hold tenaciously to authority as against the vast accumulation of facts, easily confirmed by any intelligent person, that contradict ancient authority.

During the millennium and a half of deference to authority, we find little progress in Zoölogy. It was only in the medical schools that we find any interest being taken in Zoölogy, and even here animals were used merely as aids in understanding human anatomy. *Galen, an anatomist* of the second century (A.D.), came to be the authority in human anatomy, and students of medicine for centuries merely studied their anatomy from his books. Dissection of the human body was against the laws and therefore Galen had to learn his human anatomy by analogy with that of other animals. He made numerous mistakes because there are many details of human structure quite unlike those of other animals. The errors, however, became authority and were taught for centuries. Instead of doing laboratory work, the student merely listened to lectures, with occasional demonstrations upon cat or dog materials. Galen's works were read as authority and if the demonstrations failed to agree, it was explained that these particular specimens were in some way abnormal. Even today explanations of this sort are not unknown in our zoölogical laboratories.

C. The Revival of Science

Individual initiative and freedom of thought and speech had been suppressed for many centuries before release came some time during the sixteenth century. Revulsion against religious, intellectual, and political authority went hand in hand. Independent thinkers here and there throughout civilized Europe dared to step out and speak forth their views. Zoölogy, which had been confined to the medical schools for a thousand years, was destined to have its revival in connection with the teaching of human anatomy.

Vesalius (1514–1564), the father of modern anatomy, was responsible for the revolt against authority in the medical schools of Paris. While a student of medicine there, he became dissatisfied with the timeworn methods of anatomical instruction then in vogue. He is said to have pushed aside the barbers, who were hired to make the demonstration dissections, and to have per-

formed this service himself. Subsequently, in the University of Padua in Italy, he studied anatomy and became professor of this branch in that institution. Daring to use human material, he taught anatomy from actual demonstrations only, abandoning all previous authority. His treatises on anatomy are today so accurate in detail as to need little correction.

Just as Vesalius broke away from the bonds of authority in anatomy, certain natural philosophers, *Francis Bacon* (1561–1626) in England and *Bonnet* (1720–1793) in France,

FIG. 2.   Andreas Vesalius.

daring spirits in an age when daring often meant persecution and death, freed themselves from the trammels of scholasticism and gave free rein to their speculations and deductions from facts. All three played a large part in the revival of interest in the Principle of Evolution, the greatest concept of biological science.

D. PROGRESS IN VARIOUS LINES

1. *The Origin of Experimental Methods in Zoölogy*

The spirit of free inquiry soon led from the earlier observational methods of study to those of experimentation. Today we consider no hypothesis of value unless it subjects itself to experimental proof. The usual procedure is as follows: One sees in an array of data some semblance of order and one wishes to know what are the factors responsible for the observed lawful arrangement. A working hypothesis suggests itself. This is tried out upon the available data and if it is consistent with the facts it is then ready for final testing by experiment. Conditions are so arranged that such and such a result must be obtained from a given set-up of experimental conditions. If the result accords with anticipation the theory is believed to be sustained; if not, it must be modified. A science is in an undeveloped or in a mature state in proportion as it is merely observational or purely experimental.

Simple experimentation had been practised in Zoölogy even by Aristotle, but during the Dark Ages the spirit of inquiry died, and it is to *William Harvey* (1578–1657) that we owe the revival of experimental methods in Zoology. Harvey is frequently called the founder of Physiology. To him is attributed the discovery of the circulation of the blood. In his physiological work he constantly made use of experiments and it is this method, rather than any outstanding discoveries made by him, that constitutes Harvey's chief contribution to the advance of zoölogical science.

Fig. 3.   William Harvey.

2. *The Beginnings of Specialization*

Not long after the Revival of Science was fully accomplished the various workers in zoölogical fields began to specialize, some becoming systematic zoölogists, others microscopists, others comparative anatomists and embryologists. This tendency to specialize has proved a great boon in Zoölogy, since one can go much deeper into a single field than he can into many. Perhaps the earliest of the biological subsciences to attain a fairly advanced condition was that of Taxonomy, or Classification.

3. *Progress in Taxonomy*

We have seen how Aristotle made the first attempt to classify animals and how Pliny reverted to a less scientific criterion of classification. The accumulation of further facts about animals made the task of classifying them progressively more difficult, and there was a long period of confusion. It is to *Linnæus* (1707–1778) that we owe the bringing of order out of chaos in this field. He was the son of a Swedish clergyman. During his youth he was adjudged good for nothing as a student and was therefore apprenticed to a cobbler. Later, however, coming under the influence of a physician, he gained an interest in biological matters and soon grew to be a man of high attainment in his chosen field of medicine. After a time, we are told, his interest in pure biology came to outweigh his love of medicine and he became professor

FIG. 4.   Carolus Linnæus.

of Natural History in the University of Upsala. Linnæus' greatest work was entitled "*Systema Naturæ*," first published in 1735. It passed through twelve editions. In this book we find the groundwork of our modern taxonomic methods. Linnæus made distinct advances in several ways. His introduction of scientific terminology, his clear definitions, his precise diagnoses, and above all his perfection of the system of BINOMIAL NOMENCLATURE, mark an epoch in zoölogical advance. The custom hitherto had been to give animals merely common names like catfish, gray squirrel, earthworm. The same name was frequently applied in different regions to quite unlike species, just as today the word "pike" is used for one species in the Middle West, another species in the South, and still another in Canada. Linnæus decided to give each species a distinctive Latin name consisting of two parts, the first part being a noun indicating the genus to which the animal belonged, and the second part, usually an adjective, descriptive of the particular species. Thus he called the common dog *Canis familiaris;* the fox, *Canis vulpes;* the wolf, *Canis lupus.* Concise diagnoses and definitions in Latin accompanied each named species, so that anyone anywhere could distinguish them apart. Whenever a new species was discovered by Linnæus, he assigned it to a known genus and family or else created for it a new genus, or possibly a new family, thus definitely placing it in his system. While he greatly increased our facilities for diagnosing and classifying species, he made little progress in the discovery of the broader relations of the great groups. Six classes of animals were distinguished by him: Mammalia, Aves, Amphibia, Pisces, Insecta, Vermes. This is hardly as adequate as the classification of Aristotle. Probably Linnæus' failure to see more deeply into the fundamental grouping of organisms was due to his slavish adherence to the idea of special creation. For him all species had been created essentially in their present form, except that certain hybrid types had arisen through crossing. While he did much to advance the practical methods of taxonomy, Linnæus is commonly viewed as a retarding agent because of his reactionary views on evolution. Furthermore, he set a style in Zoölogy that has had a wide vogue. The great majority of naturalists became species hunters. The one who named the most species was supposed to be the greatest man. So keen did the race for species become that old species were split up into several new ones in order to furnish material for more names. Thus taxonomic Zoölogy has come into bad repute among the experimental zoölogists. This attitude is, however, only partially justified, for modern taxonomists of the better type do not aim chiefly at species making but, rather, at a discovery of the true relationships of both older and newly discovered species.

4. *Progress in Comparative Anatomy*

We have seen that the early human anatomists, realizing that there was a close similarity of structure between man and the higher vertebrates, made use of the principle of homology without realizing its evolutionary significance. Out of this unpromising beginning arose a true science. Vast stores of anatomical facts were accumulated and needed only the genius of great organizers to give them significance and coherency. A group of able comparative anatomists attempted this task of making a system out of comparative anatomy. Among the leaders in this effort were the French zoölogists, *Lamarck, Geoffroy St. Hilaire, Cuvier,* and the Germans, *Meckel* and *Goethe.* During the latter part of the eighteenth century and the first part of the nineteenth the combined efforts of these men led to the formulation of certain definite guiding principles, or laws, and especially the law of the

Correlation of Parts and that of the Homology of Organs. The first means that there is always a relationship of interdependence among various structures, so that changes in one part involve corresponding changes in others; the second was a greater principle and one that underlies the whole subject of comparative anatomy.

5. *The Principles of Homology and Analogy*

An analysis of the situation showed that a distinction must be made between structural and functional resemblances. A part is homologous with another if it is similar in structure, in embryonic origin, in position relative to other parts; it may have also a similar function, but this is not necessary, for homologous structures often have the most diverse functions. On the other hand, similar or equivalent functions may be performed by organs that anatomically are quite unlike. One of the most important and difficult tasks of the comparative anatomists was that of distinguishing, in certain crucial cases, between homologous and merely analogous organs. The former are considered as evidences of relationship; the latter are believed to have no bearing on relationships, but

FIG. 5.   Georges Cuvier.

are interesting primarily as adaptations. *Cuvier* (1769–1832) was probably the ablest of the early comparative anatomists and may be called the founder of that science. In addition to his knowledge of modern forms he was also conversant with fossil organisms, to which he applied the same anatomical principles as he did to living forms. It seems strange that this step did not lead him directly toward the idea of descent with modification (the essence of evolution); but he was a convinced believer in special creation and a favorite with both Church and Court. He explained the differences between the faunas and floras of the various geologic strata and their dissimilarity to those of the present by means of his Cataclysmic Theory: that there had been numerous creations, each of which had been completely destroyed and its place taken by another. Noah's flood was only the last cataclysm. Thus did the great anatomist cast the burden of his influence on the wrong side of the balance. He fought against the concept of evolution in debates against both Lamarck and St. Hilaire, and because of his great ability and influence succeeded in suppressing the growing evolutionary theory so that it was held, in abeyance until revived by Charles Darwin about a generation later.

Today, in spite of hindrances and delays, Comparative Anatomy has come into its own as, perhaps, the chief handmaiden of Evolution and the soundest tool of the taxonomist.

6. *The Discovery of the Microscope and Its Effect upon Zoölogical Progress*

Classification and comparative anatomy depend largely upon the gross structure of animals, and much progress was made in these sciences by observing relations with the naked eye or with the aid of simple hand lenses. It was only when the need of a finer analysis of the constituents of organs and tissues became necessary that the microscope came to be employed. The problem of the finer structure of living tissues was one full of hope and stimulus to the early microscopists. They doubtless believed, as so many moderns still believe, that if they could magnify things highly enough, they would reveal the ultimate structure of living matter and

Fig. 6. Marcello Malpighi.

thus unravel the secret of what life is. So difficult was the technical task of making adequate microscopes that some of the earlier microscopists became more interested in instrument making than in the biological end in view. Some of the earlier and better known of the microscopists were the Englishmen, *Hooke* and *Grew,* the famous Italian, *Malpighi,* and the Dutchmen, *Leeuwenhoek* and *Swammerdam.* Of these Malpighi

FIG. 7.   Antony van Leeuwenhoek.

(1628–1694) was probably the greatest. He wrote a famous treatise on the minute structure of the silkworm and made some important contributions to histology and embryology. Leeuwenhoek is especially known for his discovery of male germ cells, spermatozoa, which he pictured without fully realizing what he saw.

The invention and development of the microscope gave a great impetus to the study of minute anatomy and rapid progress was made along several different lines.   We now await with eagerness further great improvements in microscopes and their accessories, wondering what new things they may reveal.

7. *The Discovery of Cells*

Among the earliest results of the application of the microscope to biological materials was the discovery that all tissues are made up of small units which came to receive the name CELLS, because Hooke, the first discoverer of them, thought that they were like empty boxes or rooms surrounded by walls.   This discovery was made as early as 1665, but it was not until over a century later that the significance of the discovery of the cellular structure of tissues was appreciated.

The Cell Principle.—Many workers, bending long hours over their microscopes, saw and figured minute organisms swimming about in pond water; others found that eggs were cells; still others that muscle fibers, skin units, and the structural units of other tissues were cells.   Although *Lamarck* as early as 1809 had stated in his usual somewhat vague fashion the idea that all living tissues are cellular and that growth and development are concerned with cells, it was not until 1838 and 1839 that two Germans, *Schleiden* and *Schwann,* arrived at one of the most important generalizations of Biology. Next to the Principle of Evolution the Cell Principle has had the widest influence in the development of biological science. In brief, the principle is: That all organisms are composed of cells, all of the activities of tissues are cellular activities, that growth and development, heredity and its mechanism, even evolution itself—all are affairs of cells. When the vast import of

Fig. 8. Matthias Jacob Schleiden.

this principle came to be understood, little wonder that the majority of zoölogists for many years after decided that the study of cells rather than the study of the organism as a whole was the more promising line of endeavor. Thus grew up the clans of laboratory zoölogists, many of whom came to look upon a knowledge of microscopic technique as the chief essential for biological training and neglected to become acquainted with life in the great out-of-doors.

8. *The Rise and Progress of Embryology*

Even before the Cell Theory had acquired its present for-

Fig. 9. Theodor Schwann.

mulation, considerable progress had been made in comparative embryology.   Even Aristotle had made out with the naked eye some of the salient features of embryonic development.   It is to *K. E. von Baer,* however, that we owe the scientific beginnings of embryology.   His classic treatise on the development of the chick appeared in 1832.   He is the founder of the "germ layer theory" of development, by which is meant that the whole organism is developed from the elaboration of certain embryonic cell layers, which, by foldings, irregularities of growth, and thickenings produce all of the structures of the body.

Preformation and Epigenesis.—One of the most persistent and time-honored controversies of zoölogical science arose out of a study of embryology.   It was known that every organism is to be traced back to a one-cell stage, the egg.   The question naturally arose as to whether the egg contains within itself a representative of each organ of the

Fig. 10.   Karl Ernst von Baer.

adult, or whether the egg was undifferentiated at the beginning and only acquires differentiated structures during the course of development as the result of functional activities.   The PREFORMATION IDEA is in its earliest form totally unacceptable.   The egg was believed by the extreme preformationists, such as *Bonnet,* to be merely a very much shrunken and condensed organism that needed only to feed and expand in order to unfold into an adult.   The EPIGENESIS IDEA as proposed by *Wolff* was that an egg, such as that of a hen, was at the beginning a homogeneous mass of living substance and that organs gradually differentiate out of it *de novo.* No one today holds to either of these views to the exclusion of the other, but it is the modern orthodox opinion that development is the result of a certain inherited, therefore predetermined, germinal constitution influenced at every step by environmental and functional factors. The main controversy at present seems to center about the problem of the relative potency of heredity and environment in the determination of individual development.

Experimental Embryology.—So long as embryology remained purely observational it did not throw much light upon the mechanics of development. Fortunately, however, embryology and its cousin-science, cytology, rapidly became experimental, and the results have been most illuminating. This phase of embryology and cytology has come to be known as the Physiology of Development (*Entwicklungsmechanik* of the Germans). The problems that confront experimental embryology are of extreme difficulty. We know that the egg must contain within itself the potentiality to become an adult, but we do not yet know the nature of this potentiality. Some hold that every adult difference is represented by a minute organic particle in the chromatin of the nucleus; others hold that the egg cell is merely a fairly simple reaction-system and that the environment determines the course and the consequences of development. Experimental methods of analysis involve the alteration of various environmental relations, one at a time, and the results are then compared with those seen under normal conditions. Comparative studies of results obtained in related and in unrelated groups are made, and generalizations as to how much of development is due to hereditary factors and how much to environmental factors have been deduced; but the main problems of experimental embryology remain still unsolved.

9. *The Rise and Progress of Genetics*

One of the direct results of the adoption of the experimental method of studying development was the birth of the modern science of Genetics. The first great step was taken by *Gregor Mendel* (1822–1884), a man who appeared a generation before the world was ready to receive his message. He studied the processes of development and heredity at first hand. He was not interested in any theories of evolution nor in any controversies as to preformation and epigenesis. All he wanted to know was something exact and definite about the rules according to which offspring repeat the characters of their parents. Using simple, easily controlled materials (common garden peas) he worked out the celebrated Laws of Heredity that bear his name. Today Mendelian Heredity forms the heart and core of modern genetics, which in turn is, perhaps, the liveliest phase of modern Zoölogy. What a profound effect a knowledge of Mendel's findings would have had upon the evolutionary conceptions of Charles Darwin! Darwin, however, never knew of Mendel's work; in fact, no one seems to have known anything about Mendel until 1900, sixteen years after his death, when his work was redis-covered. Now his name has become a household word al-most as familiar as that of Darwin.

10. *Progress in Evolution*

We have seen that the be-ginnings of the evolution idea go back beyond the dawn of scientific Zoölogy, appearing in the speculations of Greek natural philosophers as to the origins and transformations of living things and culminat-ing in the relatively elaborate evolutionary conception of Aristotle.

FIG. 11.   Gregor Johann Mendel.

After Aristotle the evolu-tion idea made no progress for many centuries. Even after zo-ologists had developed a considerable knowledge of classification and comparative anatomy, a fair comprehension of the cell principle, and some experience in embryology, they continued to hold to the special creation doctrine. Species were looked upon as fixed or constant, each created in the form in which it is now found. One after another, however, zoölogists became dis-satisfied with a static conception of the world and came to adopt the idea of a changing world, an evolving world. Although a number of philosophers had expressed evolutionary convictions, it remained for *Buffon* (1707–1778) to put evolution on a natural-istic basis; hence he is called the founder of the modern applied form of evolution. His ideas, however, were far from clear and he finally retracted them altogether under pressure of the Church authorities. *Erasmus Darwin* (1731–1802) published in his classic volume, *Zoönomia* (1794), a complete theory of evolution, which was a partial anticipation of the principal views of Lamarck. His concepts were largely deductive and unsupported by any adequate body of facts. *Lamarck* (1744–1829) was perhaps the most important figure between Aristotle and Charles Darwin. His theory of *The Inheritance of Acquired Characters* as an explanation of the cause of adaptation is still held by a growing minority of modern zoölogists. The essential features of his theory are: first, that all structures of an individual are modified by use or disuse and by changing environment; second, that changes in the body thus produced are passed on by heredity to offspring. Whether or not Lamarck was right is still unsettled. This is one of the oldest and most acrimonious of biological controversies.

Fig. 12. Jean-Baptiste Lamarck.

Lamarck was strongly opposed by his eminent contemporary, *Cuvier,* who, though his own discoveries furnished strong evidence of evolution, continued steadfastly to the end of his life a special creationist. In a famous debate in the French Academy in 1830, Cuvier and *Geoffroy St. Hilaire,* a leading zoölogist and champion of Lamarck, argued the question at great length. Cuvier was adjudged the decisive winner. This decision was a serious blow to the evolution theory and served to check further development along evolutionary lines for nearly thirty years.

Charles Darwin (1809–1882).—The most striking figure in zoölogical history is Charles Darwin. Barely twenty-one years of age at the time of the great Lamarckian debate just referred to, he had not yet seriously entertained the evolution concept, but after reading *Malthus' On Population* and *Lyell's Principles of Geology,* and especially as a result of his journey around the world in the ship, *Beagle,* during which he accumulated a great mass of data, he became convinced of the truth of the evolution idea and set about

FIG. 13.　Charles Darwin.

proving it. This he did by means of a vast array of facts which support and agree with the theory. He also offered as an explanation of the cause of evolution his famous theory of *Natural Selection*, or survival of the fittest, a theory held at the present time to be of secondary importance, though valid within certain limits.

Darwin's first large publication was his famous *Origin of Species* (1859). This book stirred up an immense amount of controversy. It was bitterly opposed by churchmen in general and ardently supported by scientists. *Huxley* (1825–1895) was the leading advocate of Darwinism and is credited with a complete victory over the supporters of special creation. For many years there was no further serious opposition to the general principle of evolution, but there is no general agreement even yet as to the causes and methods of evolution. These are hard problems that will yield only to long and

FIG. 14. Thomas Henry Huxley.

arduous investigation. That we do not know exactly the causes of evolution is no valid reason for doubting so well established a principle. As well doubt the fact of individual development, or that of heredity, because we do not know exactly their causes or mechanisms.

Summary.—The history of Zoölogy has been traced from its crude beginnings, through its many vicissitudes, its ups and downs. It has had an evolution much like that of an organism or a group of organisms. It has become split up into a number of subordinate special sciences, like the species of a genus. Some of these subsciences have proved more fruitful and more important than others and have added prestige to the group as a whole; others have only begun to gain a foothold. Each part has some connection with all others, just as each species in a given ecological complex is more or less dependent upon others and all are parts of a great delicately balanced system. We cannot follow all the branches at once but must in the future isolate them, one after the other, for special treatment.

CHAPTER III

THE ORIGIN OF LIFE

A. Abiogenesis

The first natural philosophers believed that life arose spontaneously out of such nonliving materials as water and air, or from the interaction of earth, air, fire, and water. This process of generation was believed to be frequently repeated and to be a matter of everyday occurrence. Lowly creatures of all sorts were thought of as arising *de novo* out of previously nonliving materials, without any particular cause, *i.e.*, spontaneously. Human beings were known to develop within the uterus of the mother, but the beginning of a new human being was supposed to be largely spontaneous or to depend upon an act of the gods. The idea of ABIOGENESIS (SPONTANEOUS GENERATION) has been held persistently and is still believed by a few to hold good for the lowest organisms; but the vast majority of modern scientists have entirely abandoned this view.

The history of the origin and abandonment of the idea of the spontaneous origin of living organisms is of so great significance that we shall give it in some detail.

Among the Greeks we find that **Thales** believed that Mother Ocean was the parent of all life. **Anaximines** thought that air imparted life to all things. **Aristotle,** even though he knew that at least some animals arise from eggs produced by parents, asserted that "sometimes animals are formed in putrefying soil, sometimes in plants, and sometimes in the fluids of other animals."

In later times we find the poet **Virgil** describing in the *Georgics* what he evidently believed to be a practical method of obtaining bees by spontaneous generation:—

"First, a space of ground of small dimensions is chosen; this they cover with the tiling of a narrow roof and with confining walls, and add four openings with a slanting light turned toward the four points of the compass. Then a bullock, just arching his horns upon his forehead of two years old, is sought out; whilst he struggles fiercely, they close up both his nostrils and his mouth; and when they have beaten him to death, his battered carcass is macerated

31

within the hide which remains unbroken. Then they leave him in the pent-up chamber, and lay under his sides fragments of boughs, thyme, and fresh cassia. This is done when first the zephyrs stir the waves, before the meadows blush with new colors, before the twittering swallow suspends her nest upon the rafters. Meanwhile, the animal juices, warmed in the softened bones, ferment: and living things of wonderful aspect, first devoid of feet, and in a little while buzzing with wings, swarm together, and more and more take to the thin air, till they burst away like a shower poured down from summer clouds; or like an arrow from the impelling string, when the swift Parthians first begin to fight."

The reader will doubtless surmise that Virgil was less observant than poetic and described the emergence of bee-like carrion flies and not the spontaneous generation of bees.

Ovid extends the notion of spontaneous generation much farther in the following passage, which purports to expound the doctrine of the Pythagorean philosophers:—

> "By this sure experiment we know
> That living creatures from corruption grow:
> Hide in a hollow pit a slaughtered steer,
> Bees from his putrid bowels will appear,
> Who like their parents, haunt the fields and
> Bring their honey harvest home, and hope another spring.
> The warlike steed is multiplied we find,
> To wasps and hornets of the warrior kind,
> Cut from a crab his crooked claws and hide
> The rest in earth, a scorpion thence will glide,
> And shoot his sting; his tail in circles toss't
> Refers the limbs his backward father lost;
> And worms that stretch on leaves their filmy loom
> Crawl from their bags and butterflies become.
> The slime begets the frog's loquacious race;
> Short of their feet at first, in little space
> With arms and legs endued, long leaps they take,
> Raised on their hinder parts and swim the lake,
> And waves repel; for nature gives their kind,
> To that intent, a length of legs behind."

That spontaneous generation was not merely an example of poetic license is emphasized by the fact that *Van Helmont,* a famous physicist and chemist of the sixteenth century, describes in a circumstantial way how mice could be spontaneously engendered by putting some dirty linen into a receptacle together with some grains of wheat or a piece of cheese. The same writer gives us the following amusing recipe for engendering scorpions— "Scoop out a hole in a brick. Put into it some sweet basil, crushed. Lay a second brick upon the first so that the hole may be perfectly covered. Expose the two bricks to the sun, and at the end of a few days the smell of the sweet basil, acting as a ferment, will change the earth into real scorpions.''

Cardan, in 1524, declared that fishes were spontaneously engendered in water and that many animals are the product of fermentation. Other alleged authorities claimed to have seen with their own eyes the origins of certain animals out of various plant or inorganic materials. In rural communities everywhere today it is rather generally believed that frogs sometimes come down in rain and that mosquitoes arise spontaneously in stagnant water. Every one has doubtless been told that a black horsehair, if left for some time in a watering trough, will transform itself into a wriggling threadworm. Everybody believed, until *Redi* proved the contrary, that maggots were spontaneously generated in putrid meat. Redi in 1680 performed a classic experiment which showed the fallacy of this popular conception.

Redi's Experiments.—He had frequently observed the stages of decay in meat and had noted that, long before maggots appeared in it, flies hovered around and sometimes alighted upon it. Could the maggots be the progeny of the flies, he wondered. If the flies were prevented from reaching the meat by placing paper on the glass containers the meat putrefied as usual, but no maggots appeared. Instead of paper he then put a fine gauze over the meat which allowed the odors of decay to pass out. Flies, attracted by the odors of decay, buzzed and crawled about, laying eggs at some distance from the meat upon the gauze. The result was that many maggots hatched out upon the gauze but none upon the meat. This proved once for all that maggots are not spontaneously generated on meat. So conclusive was this experiment that it practically broke down belief in spontaneous generation in general.

Discovery of Bacteria.—The belief, however, took a new lease of life when, in 1683, *Leeuwenhoek* discovered bacteria. These lowliest forms of life were so small and simple in organization that it did not appear so unreasonable for them to be spontaneously generated as it was for frogs, fish, maggots, and other much larger forms. Gradually the belief gained headway that bacteria were the product of fermentation and decay of organic matter. Thus *Needham* in 1749 firmly believed that he was able to observe the spontaneous generation of bacteria upon a grain of barley kept in water in a carefully covered watch glass. We now know that the watch glass was not really so covered as to keep out the spores of

FIG. 15.   Louis Pasteur.   (From Peabody and Hunt.)

bacteria that are ever present in the air. Many other experiments with increasingly fine technique were performed to test the possibility of the spontaneous generation of bacteria.   Even within recent years **Bastian** (1905) in a large treatise on *The Nature and Origin of Living Matter* maintained that he had actually seen the origin *de novo* of bacteria in infusions which, he claimed, had been heated to a point that must have killed all life and which were afterwards kept sealed up so as to prevent the possible ingress of the spores of bacteria.

Louis Pasteur.—We owe it to Pasteur that the belief in spontaneous generation of bacteria was finally abandoned by scientific men. He devised for this experiment a type of flask, shown in Figure 16. The neck of the flask containing putrescible material was drawn out and bent into the shape of a V. This could be left open while the contents of the flask were thoroughly boiled, and even after it cooled, without any contamination from the outside air being permitted. All the air that entered the body of the flask had to pass through the tortuous passage and through the fluid of condensation contained at the bottom of the V. Under these conditions bacteria never appeared in the body of the flask.

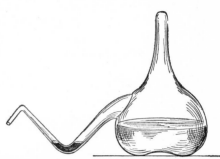

Fig. 16.—Flask used by Pasteur in his experiments upon the spontaneous generation of life. Note that the top has been sealed after the contents have been poured in and that the bent neck is effectually protected from contamination by germs by means of the accumulated water of condensation. (From McFarland.)

Tyndall, with more elaborate apparatus (Fig. 17) and more detailed precautions against contamination, fully confirmed Pasteur's conclusions.

Bacteriological studies of *Cohn* and others have shown that bacteria under conditions of desiccation pass into a resting, or spore, stage and are capable of being carried about suspended in the air, ready to germinate under appropriate conditions. When, as in Bastian's experiments, bacteria appear in media that have been boiled for short periods and then bacteriologically sealed up, the only possible conclusion is that the spores have been heat-resistant to a degree higher than usual and have not been killed by the supposedly killing heat.

Conclusion.—It may now be stated with confidence that, with the world in the stage of development in which we find it today, spontaneous generation of life is unknown and that the only way in which life is known to arise is through the reproductive capacity of living organisms already in existence. Harvey's dictum *omne vivum ex ovo* (all life from the egg), which had for a long time been accepted as valid for higher organisms, may be modified so as to include all organisms and be stated: *omne vivum ex vivo* (all life from preëxisting life). This may be called the principle of Biogenesis, one of the best established and most fundamental laws of life.

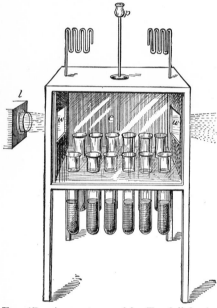

FIG. 17. Apparatus used by Tyndall for investigating the spontaneous generation of life. The front is of glass, as are the side windows, w, w. The optical test for the purity of the contained atmosphere is made by passing a powerful beam of light from the lamp, l, through the side windows. When the atmosphere of the chamber, e, contains no suspended particles, the tubes in the bottom are filled through the pipette, p. (From McFarland, after Tyndall.)

B. THEORIES OF THE BEGINNING OF LIFE

If all life came from previously existing life *ad infinitum*, there could be no beginning of life; but we do not believe in any such absurdity. Life must have begun upon the earth at some time. Even if conditions today are such as to preclude the possibility of the origin of living matter *de novo* from lifeless materials, it does not follow that conditions have always been so unfavorable. Whether we accept the Nebular Hypothesis of *Laplace* or the Planetesimal Hypothesis of *Chamberlin* and *Moulton* as the better explanation of the origin of the solar system, there was a time in the young world when the surface was too hot for life, as we know life, to exist. According to Chamberlin's view, there was a time when everything was favorable for the origin of life. At that time the atmosphere was heavy with planetesimal dust, which acted as a

blanket against the intense radiance of heat and light from without
and from inequalities of radiance from within. There was probably no free oxygen in the atmosphere. Pools of water existed on
the rough land surfaces and there were lakes and seas. This water
was of prime importance as the mother fluid of life. It is capable
of dissolving many materials and in it as a medium vast numbers of chemical reactions can take place. Carbon must have
existed in great abundance in the form of carbonic acid dissolved
in water. Out of the carbon, hydrogen, and oxygen in such a mixture could have arisen a great many kinds of plastic organic compounds. The building stones were there. Just how they were
fabricated is quite unknown. Probably thousands of compounds
appeared which were somewhat labile and had some of the properties of living matter, but only one or a very few compounds
possessed the requisite properties for self-defense against a hard
and inimical environment or for self-perpetuation under conditions
that proved fatal to many a promising start. These surviving
minute masses of living material, we believe, became more and
more perfectly adapted to the environment, improving here and
there and finding some spots in the environment especially favorable. In time, life became thoroughly established, probably after
untold ages of struggle during which its existence was threatened
over and over again. Many promising starts were doubtless wiped
out and there may have existed living things so unlike what we
now call organisms that we would not recognize them as truly
living. So we allow ourselves to speculate. When we have no
facts upon which to rely, we are forced to use our imaginations.
The problem of the origin of life is still unsolved. But we are not
pessimistic enough to believe that its solution will always be
impossible.

Certain scientists have attempted to side-step the issue as to the
original coming into existence of life by suggesting that the germs
of living creatures first reached the earth in the cracks of meteor-
ites or in the fine cosmic dust that sifts down from the skies.
Helmholtz and *Lord Kelvin* point out that some spores and seeds
are capable of withstanding prolonged exposure to low temperatures and some of them can keep alive at very high temperatures.
The spark of life can smolder along even in the almost complete
absence of moisture and of oxygen. These facts are taken by
Kelvin as favoring the possibility that long journeys through

space—say from one planet to another—might be taken by particles of living matter, and thus life might be passed through space from one celestial body to another. But even if we fall back upon such a theory of the origin of life upon our own planet, we still are confronted with the same old problem as to how life first started somewhere.

It would hardly be fair to conclude the present discussion of the origin of life upon the earth without presenting at least an outline of some of the leading theories thus far advanced.

Pflüger's Theory.—Starting in with the assumption that the earth was once in a superheated, incandescent condition, Pflüger conceives of the origin out of this heated mass of a chemical combination of carbon and nitrogen atoms to form the radical, CYANOGEN (CN). This radical, in process of formation, takes up a great deal of heat energy and is therefore a source of great energy for the proteins of which it is believed to form an essential part. The adding of cyanogen to organic compounds previously lacking this radical is looked upon as equivalent to imparting life to previously lifeless substances, for it is believed to be the source of the internal energy of the protein molecule. "Thus it may be said that the problem of the origin of living substances culminates in the question: How did cyanogen arise?"

"Nothing," says Pflüger, "is clearer than the possibility of the formation of cyanogen compounds when the earth was wholly or partially in a fiery or heated state." In a sense, this implies the origin of life out of fire.

Moore's Theory.—In contrast with Pflüger's idea that life arose from heat is Moore's idea that life arose from cooling. According to this theory, the gradual process of cooling off of a hot earth allowed of the formation one after the other of the various kinds of chemical compounds, beginning with the simplest and most stable and ending with the most complex and unstable. Thus oxides appeared as soon as the temperature dropped sufficiently low to permit of oxidation; then carbonates were formed; then came the inorganic colloids, more complex and less stable. Finally, with the earth sufficiently cooled to permit of their origin and maintenance, the organic colloids appeared. These substances are characterized by their highly complex molecular structure, their instability, their slowness of reaction, and their sensitivity. Many different kinds of organic colloids were formed and these from time to time united in various proportions to form colloidal aggregates, some of which became organized into the first cells, which, among other properties, possessed the ability to reproduce.

These theories, though they may seem to us like mere gropings in the dark, are in reality the earnest attempts of man to lift the veil of the unknown. No matter how hopeless the solution of a problem may seem, there are always men who joy in making a bold attempt.

CHAPTER IV

THE NATURE AND MANIFESTATIONS OF LIFE

Definitions of Life.—Most of us think we know what life is, but if asked to define the term "life," we flounder about and get ourselves into great difficulties. Even the dictionaries and encyclopedias, which are supposed to give definitions of everything, are powerless to give us definitions of life that really define. One of them states that "Life is the state of living"; another that "Life is the sum total of vital functions"; still another that "Life is metabolism."

Just as there is no satisfactory definition of "life" so there is no term exactly antithetical to "life." The antithesis of light is darkness; the antithesis of heat is cold; but the antithesis of life is not death, for death merely implies a cessation of life. Whereas the noun *life* has no antithesis, perhaps the adjectives *living* and *lifeless* are sufficiently antithetic for our purpose, and we may thus be aided in defining life by contrasting the living with the lifeless.

Life, we may say, is some quality or property present in living things that is absent in lifeless things, and therefore a definition of life could be made up by listing the properties peculiar to living matter.

Living versus Lifeless Matter.—The one outstanding fact that we may seize upon as an aid in our search for differences between the living and the lifeless is that all living creatures, animals and plants alike, contain a fundamental substance not found in lifeless things which we have agreed to call PROTOPLASM. We do not know exactly how to define the term, "protoplasm." If we simply call it "the living substance," we are merely back where we started; if we call it, as Huxley did, "the Physical Basis of Life," we are not much better off. As a matter of fact we have no more exact definition of protoplasm than we have of life itself. Protoplasm is so infinitely varied in its expressions that no definition will cover all of its manifestations.

No less an authority than *Professor E. B. Wilson* has recently expressed the following opinion:—

"When we speak of protoplasm as the physical basis of life, we mean simply the sum total of all the substances that play an active part in the cell life; and we cannot, I think, exclude from the list such substances as the inorganic salts which we commonly think of as 'lifeless.' At first sight this may seem a rather barren conclusion; but the fact is quite otherwise. No conception of modern biology offers greater promise of future progress than that the cell, regarded as a whole, is a colloidal system, and that what we call life is, in the words of Czapek, a complex of innumerable chemical reactions in the substance of this system."

If life is no more than a set of chemical reactions, in what respects does it differ from the nonliving? We may, I believe, answer this query by saying that the difference lies in the quality of the chemical activities and in the organization of these activities. Living substance differs from lifeless substance in a variety of ways. If we are able to list all of the properties peculiar to living matter and not found in lifeless matter, we may be able to infer from this something as to the nature of life.

A. THE PROPERTIES OF LIVING MATTER (PROTOPLASM)

1. *Chemical Composition*

One fact about the chemical composition of protoplasm bulks large: there is no unique element in it and it contains only a limited number of the commonest, most abundant elements, such as Carbon, Hydrogen, Oxygen, Nitrogen, Sulphur, Phosphorus, Chlorine, Sodium, Potassium, Calcium, Magnesium, and Iron, and occasionally Iodine, Silicon, Copper, and a few others. We can discover this much only when we kill the living substance and subject it to the rending processes of analysis. When we have discovered the ingredients of living substance, we see nothing in them that accounts for life. We might as well try to understand a cathedral in terms of the elements that enter into the stones and mortar out of which it is built. Moreover, we now realize that protoplasm is an elaborate mixture of different compounds in a state of colloidal solution and that each material is arranged in a definite way with respect to each of the others. The essential feature is that the mixture is organized into definite units. While we must never forget that living substance is a definitely organized system, we do no violence to the scientific attitude in recognizing that there are in protoplasms certain distinctly different compounds of which the most important are: proteins, carbohydrates, fats (lipins and extractives), and inorganic salts.

a. Proteins.—One of the ingredients of the protoplasmic mixture which is never absent from living substance is protein. This is a general name applied to a vast number of different compounds. There are specific proteins for each species of animal and each animal has many unique proteins. In fact, the differences between individuals are, in last analysis, largely dependent upon the differences inherent in their special proteins. The proteins, as such, might almost be identified as the essential living substances of organisms, but the proteins cannot live alone. In order that they may remain alive, feed, grow, and multiply, they must be intimately associated with various other compounds such as carbohydrates, fats, and salts in solution. Not all protoplasm contains these ingredients, however, so we are forced to conclude that the proteins constitute the essential basis of living matter. These innumerable proteins, however infinitely varied they may be in their chemical composition and in the types of structure which they are able to produce, are, from the standpoint of their chemical make-up, similar. Just as a vast number of different kinds of houses or other structures can be made up out of bricks, stone, mortar, and lumber, so the same ingredients, Carbon, Hydrogen, Oxygen, Nitrogen, and Phosphorus, can be put together in an infinite variety of ways to produce different protein molecules. Certain relatively simple organic compounds known as AMINO ACIDS are called the building stones of proteins. A certain number and arrangement of these stones gives one protein, another number and arrangement gives another. The possible variety thus attainable is almost unlimited. It does not seem advisable in a beginning course in Zoölogy to go too deeply into the chemistry of protoplasm. One should, however, carry away the impression that a complete understanding of all vital processes, in fact any appreciation of what life is, must rest, in last analysis, upon a detailed understanding of the chemical composition of protoplasm and of the chemical and physical processes that go on in it. One of the most important properties of the proteins is their INSTABILITY. They are constantly undergoing chemical

decomposition, but they are also as constantly building themselves up again.   This balanced process of waste and repair is
commonly called METABOLISM, a property of protoplasm which
will soon be dealt with.

b. Carbohydrates.—Carbohydrate substances are composed of
different combinations of the elements carbon, hydrogen, and
oxygen, in which the hydrogen and oxygen are usually present in
the proportion found in water (H_2O).   They are simpler in chemical structure than the proteins, but have a wide range of complexity among themselves.   Some of the simplest of the carbohydrates are the so-called simple sugars such as glucose and
fructose, and among the more complex are the starches and
cellulose, the latter forming the solid part of wood.

c. Fats.—Fats contain the same elements as do the carbohydrates, but their proportions and arrangements are entirely different.   In general, we may say that they contain less oxygen
and are therefore more oxidizable than are carbohydrates, a
property that accounts for their richness in potential energy.
Among the common organic fats are butter, meat fats, and the
oils of various plants.

These three classes of compounds, proteins, carbohydrates, and
fats, are not found in nature except in association with protoplasm.
Nevertheless, chemists have succeeded in producing artificially
carbohydrates, fats, and some of the amino-acid ingredients of
proteins.

d. Other Ingredients.—Various inorganic salts and water are
essential ingredients of protoplasm, and possibly there is still another type of necessary ingredient which we have heard much
about of late years, namely, VITAMINS.   We do not as yet know
the chemical structure or mode of action of these substances, but
we have reason to suspect that they act as catalyzers, or enzymes.
Finally, we may mention a group of substances generally known
as HORMONES, whose action seems to be associated chiefly in
maintaining organic balance.

2. *The Physical Properties of Protoplasm*

Protoplasm, when in the living condition, whether that of plants
or animals, presents the appearance of a semifluid or viscous material, nearly transparent and often colorless.   Under high magnification it reveals itself as a complex mixture of various kinds of

granules, fibers, vacuoles, and solid bodies, imbedded in a more or less homogeneous ground substance, or matrix. All of these ingredients are integral parts of the living substance and they are disposed in a definite, ordered fashion.

From the purely physical standpoint protoplasm of any sort is a COLLOIDAL MIXTURE, a mixture sometimes so intimate as to constitute an EMULSION. These terms need definition. A COLLOID is a substance with a gluelike consistency, lacking crystalline structure and incapable of going into true solution in the ordinary solvents. When mixed with a solvent such as water, the molecules do not separate nor break up into ions, but remain in bundles or aggregates known as COLLOIDAL PARTICLES that may attain a considerable size and are merely suspended in the liquid medium.

When these colloidal particles are densely packed together the material becomes stiff, or sets into a condition known as the GEL state; but when the particles are well separated the mixture resembles a solution and is said to be in the SOL state. Thus solid gelatin, a colloid in the gel state, when heated with water becomes first a mucilaginous fluid and then a thin watery fluid as the particles are forced farther and farther apart. Colloids readily pass back and forth from sol to gel states. In some cases the change is equally easy in both directions, but in other cases the change in one direction is easy and in the other difficult. Thus it is easy to gel the white of egg, but difficult to get it back to the sol state. It is now thought that certain rhythmic changes, such as the movements of pseudopodia in Amœba, of cilia in Paramecium, of muscle in contracting and relaxing, and many other active movements of protoplasm are based upon reversible changes in colloidal state.

Most protoplasmic colloids belong to a category known as EMULSOIDS. In this state the suspended particles are relatively stable, less easily coagulated by salts than are simple colloids, are commonly viscous, tend to form surface membranes, and exhibit a high capacity for reversible changes of state of a rhythmic sort. All these properties will be recognized as among the most characteristic features of living matter, yet they are purely physical phenomena characteristic of certain kinds of matter in the colloidal state. An understanding of the physics and chemistry of colloids adequately explains most of the active movements of protoplasm.

3. *Metabolism*

Metabolism goes on in all living substance, and some of the lower organisms furnish a relatively simple picture of the process. Paramecium, a very common aquatic microscopic animal, which will be studied in detail in the laboratory, is a metabolic machine. It swims about in stagnant water by means of minute whiplike locomotor organs called cilia, and it uses these same cilia to whip masses of bacteria into its mouth. If a Paramecium is kept for some time in pure water, it keeps on swimming about actively and gradually wastes away its substance. One can notice empty vacuoles opening up in its body substance, and after a time it is a mere skeletal framework, which grows smaller and then dies. Feed such a Paramecium before death ensues and it will once more build up its materials and even grow larger than before, and this, in spite of continuous dissipation of energy in locomotion.

A Paramecium has been compared to a coal fire. The coal is like the living substance; it is a material within which, long ages ago, has been imprisoned energy from the sun. This potential energy can be released by the process of combustion, a chemical process involving a union of the carbon and hydrogen of the coal with the oxygen of the air. Heat and light are the result of released energy, and certain by-products of combustion, carbonic oxide (CO_2), water (H_2O), and other gases containing much less latent energy, are left after combustion is complete. This transformation of stored, or potential, energy into kinetic, or free, energy is the secret of the active movements of organisms as well as of the power producing capacity of coal.

The fuel materials of the Paramecium are the proteins, the carbohydrates, and the fats in the protoplasmic mixture. Oxygen is the essential combusting agent, and water, carbonic oxide, urea, and other compounds are the by-products of combustion. If no more fuel is added in the form of food, the fire of life simply burns down and goes out—as in the starved Paramecium; but if new fuel be added before the fire goes out entirely, the flame may burn up brightly again even if only a spark of life be left. The new fuel comes into the body in the form of living organisms—bacteria— which are themselves composed of elaborate protoplasmic mixtures; but this material cannot be burned directly. It must first be broken down by digestion into its building stones before it can be built up again into the characteristic proteins, carbohydrates, fats, that the Paramecium machine elaborates and uses as fuel.

4. *Growth*

All healthy organisms—at least until they grow old—tend to increase in size. This we call growth. Ordinarily the building up of new living substance goes on somewhat more rapidly than does the waste or combustion of the old living substance. This inevitably results in an increase in mass. We then distinguish two phases of the metabolic process: one is a building-up process, ANABOLISM; the other, a breaking-down process, KATABOLISM. When—as usually happens in young, healthy organisms—anabolism exceeds katabolism, growth results. Growth, however, cannot go on indefinitely, for there is a certain maximum size limit for each species of animal. In some of the microörganisms the size limit is very quickly reached; while in the whale or the elephant the size limit is very greatly increased. Just what are the factors responsible for the limitations of size in different species we do not know: this is one of the great unsolved problems. When the size limit is reached, the organism may be said to have arrived at a period of maturity. This period of maturity is essentially a period of equilibrium between the opposed processes of anabolism and katabolism, and may be very greatly prolonged. During this period of maturity we find that the organism tends to reproduce—to give off from itself other organisms more or less like itself. This power to reproduce is one of the chief characteristics of living things.

5. *Reproduction*

While all living organisms reproduce, there is a vast number of ways in which they go about it. In some of the lower organisms the production of offspring is relatively simple. A parent individual merely divides, more or less evenly, into two similar pieces, each of which is a child of the parent organism. But in this mode of reproduction the parent all goes over into offspring. As some one has well said, the offspring of such forms are orphans, for they come into existence as the result of the using up of the entire body of the parent. This simplest of reproductive processes is known as BINARY FISSION. In other organisms a representative part of the parent is sufficient material out of which to form an offspring, and this does not involve the loss of the parent's identity.

Various ways of doing this are known, one of the commonest of which is BUDDING. In Hydra, for example, a bud of the parent's body wall grows out, produces a new mouth, and sooner or later cuts itself loose. Sometimes, as in certain protozoa, the whole organism may fragment into large numbers of small representative masses known as SPORES. Among the higher organisms, however, the characteristic mode of reproduction is by means of germ cells. Germ cells are of two kinds, either eggs or spermatozoa. They may be thought of as samples of the characteristic protoplasm of the parent organism, capable of producing organisms similar to the parent. Usually an egg and a spermatozoön have to unite to produce a new individual. When this occurs, it is called SEXUAL, or GAMETIC, REPRODUCTION. Not infrequently we find cases where the egg is capable of developing without the aid of the spermatozoön: this is called PARTHENOGENESIS.

6. *Adaptation*

Another of the properties of protoplasm is its ability to undergo adaptive changes appropriate to its life needs and to the changing environment. This is one of the most striking features of living things and is usually called adaptability. The adaptations may be either structural or functional or both. Much of the adaptiveness of organisms is dependent upon a property of protoplasm, which by some authors is listed as a separate type of peculiarity —the capacity to respond to stimuli. This is sometimes called IRRITABILITY. It seems to us, however, that responsiveness is but one of the phases of adaptiveness. In another chapter we shall discuss these large questions in greater detail.

7. *Organization*

Living things are usually spoken of as organisms. The implication is that the parts are so integrated that the whole thing is a unit—an individual. The problem of individuality is one of the difficult problems of our science and will be dealt with later. In this place we must be content with the statement that individuality is due to the fact that some one part of the organism which is most intensely alive presides over the less active parts and keeps them all in organized subordination. There is throughout an organism, then, this interdependence of parts, together with a centralized control, that makes of it an individual rather than a mere inchoate mass.

It is in the possession of these seven properties—peculiar chemical composition, physical properties, metabolism, growth, reproduction, adaptiveness, and organization—that living matter differs from lifeless. Are these properties individually unique for protoplasm, or may the various lifeless materials exhibit one or more of these properties? Certain writers have entertained themselves and their readers by pointing out instances of the supposed ability of various lifeless materials to perform acts approximately equivalent to those claimed to be purely vital in character. For example, the candle flame, remaining constant in its form and structure while taking in and giving out new substance all the time, is said to be essentially a replica of metabolism. Again, it is pointed out that crystals in a solution grow in size and even bud off new crystals; while colloid particles of lifeless matter are said to grow to a maximum size and then to divide into two half-sized particles. Still again, it is pointed out that some of the most characteristic ingredients of protoplasm have been synthesized in the chemical laboratory. In spite of these points of somewhat remote contact with inorganic things, living beings do actually stand sharply apart from lifeless, and there are no transitional stages. No one has ever found a being half living and half lifeless any more than one has been able to observe the spontaneous generation of even the simplest organisms. Any attempts to break down the line of demarcation between the living and the lifeless are at the present time quite futile and are interesting chiefly as examples of ingenuity; for the line between the living and the lifeless is sharply drawn. This statement seems to open up the whole question of whether or not life is to be explained on the basis of the laws of physics and chemistry, a question discussed rather fully in a subsequent chapter.

B. MECHANISTIC AND VITALISTIC POINTS OF VIEW

The majority of biologists at the present time have adopted the Mechanistic Theory as a working hypothesis, but are none too sanguine as to the adequacy of this theory to give a complete explanation of all vital phenomena. They feel that any theory that has been so fruitful an incentive to research is worthy of retention as a working hypothesis so long as it continues to yield results; yet one cannot but agree with the position taken by a prominent American zoölogist, "that the mechanistic hypothesis or machine theory of living beings is not fully established, that it *may* not be adequate or even true; yet I can only believe that until every other possibility has really been exhausted, scientific biologists should hold fast to the working program that has created the science of biology. The vitalistic hypothesis may be held, and is still held, as a matter of faith; but we cannot call it science without misuse of the word."

The whole question is well summed up in a recent discussion by *Professor Woodruff:*—

"The vitalistic conception that life phenomena are in part at least the resultant of manifestations of matter and energy which transcend and differ intrinsically in kind from those displayed in the inorganic world—a denial, as it were, in the organism of the full sufficiency of known fundamental laws of matter and energy— has arisen many times in the development of biological thought, either as a reaction against premature conclusions of the nascent sciences or from an overwhelming appreciation of the complexity of life phenomena. Vitalism goes back as far as the history of science is recorded, but it attained its most concrete formulation as a doctrine during the early part of the eighteenth century, in opposition to the obviously inadequate explanations which chemistry and physics could offer for the phenomena of irritability of living matter then prominently before the professional biologist. The vitalists at that period abandoned almost completely all attempts to explain life processes on a physicochemical basis and assumed that an all-controlling, unknown, and unknowable, mystical, hypermechanical force was responsible for all living processes. It is apparent, of course, that such an assumption in such a form is a negation of the scientific method and at once removes the problem from the realm of scientific investigation. No biologist at the present day subscribes to vitalism in this form; some uphold vitalism (if it must still be called vitalism) in its modern aspect, while all will undoubtedly admit that we are at the present time utterly unable to give an adequate explanation of the fundamental life processes in terms of physics and chemistry. Whether we shall ever be able to do so is unprofitable to speculate about, though certainly the twentieth century finds relatively few scientists who really expect a scientific explanation of life ever to be attained or expect that protoplasm will ever be artificially synthesized."

CHAPTER V

THE CELL PRINCIPLE

Second only to the Evolution Principle in far-reaching applicability and in unifying effect is the so-called "Cell Theory." These two great principles, together with the Organismal Theory, lie at the very foundations of biology. With these great guiding principles biology becomes a science; without them there is no meaning to nature. So well established has the Cell Theory become that we would now be justified in calling it the Cell Principle or the Cell Law.

In the historical chapter of this book the story of the discovery of the microscope and the resultant revelations as to cells has already been told. We have seen that the first clear and definite formulation of the Cell Theory was made by *Schleiden* and *Schwann* in 1839. Of the two, Theodore Schwann had by far the more penetrative intellect and saw much more clearly the far-reaching applications of the theory. In its extreme form the Cell Theory claims that all plants and animals are made up of cells; that all biological phenomena are, in last analysis, cellular phenomena. Thus variation, heredity, reproduction, are due to properties of cells. Furthermore, the individual is no more nor less than a society of cells, each in some degree dependent upon others. A protozoan organism is viewed as a single cell, equivalent to one of the cells of a metazoan organism, but merely more versatile in its activities and capacities. This extreme form of the Cell Theory has come in for much criticism, as we shall bring out later on in our discussion of the Organismal Theory. In spite of its limitations along these lines, the Cell Principle deserves to rank high among the Laws of Life.

A. The Cell Concept in the Making

The first conceptions of the essential features of a cell were crude and erroneous. *Hooke* and *Grew,* who first studied cells under the relatively low powers of their primitive microscopes, noted a sort of honeycomb texture in the tissues which they examined. Hence they applied the name "cell" to the unit of composition, doubtless influenced by the fact that the term had been used for the sections of honeycomb. Thus we see that the original concept of the cell emphasized the walls and practically ignored the important substances within them. More adequate technique revealed within the inclosure a nucleus, but this structure was thought to be part of the wall. The semifluid substance filling the cavity, which we now know as the essential living substance, protoplasm, was at that time thought to be only a by-product of the cell. Even Schleiden, one of the founders of the Cell Theory, spoke of it as a kind of gum.

It is to *Felix Dujardin* (1801–1860) that we owe the first recognition of the importance of the cell contents. He studied this material, tested its solubility and chemical properties, and decided that it was a special cellular material which he named SARCODE. Dujardin did not, however, appreciate the full significance of his discovery, believing that this sarcode was found only among lower organisms. Further study, however, soon showed that this was a mistake. *Hugo von Mohl,* in 1846, during his studies of plant tissues, found a similar cell content and called it PROTOPLASM, a name used in a more limited sense at an earlier time by *Purkinje.* Von Mohl was responsible for bringing the term "protoplasm" into general use and hastened the development of the growing conception that protoplasm was common to all living tissues and was much more essential than the cell wall. It is to *Max Schultze* (1825–1874), more than to any other biologist, that we owe the establishment of the present conception of the essential protoplasmic organization of the cell. The organized mass of protoplasm *is* the cell. The walls and the various contained materials other than protoplasm are merely the manufactured products of cell activity.

Cell Products.—It soon came to be recognized that many tissues, such as bone and cartilage, are only partially cellular. In such tissues the cells are situated relatively far apart, separated by a mass of nonliving material known as a MATRIX. This matrix, though not itself living, is produced by and excreted from the protoplasm and is therefore a cell product. Similarly, cellulose in plants, the hard shells of mollusks, arthropods, and many protozoa, are cell products.

The Cell Both a Structural and a Functional Unit.—The founders of the Cell Theory were purely morphologists and thought only in terms of structure. The concept of the cell as the morphological unit out of which all organisms are composed soon began to change. The rise and growth of the science of physiology and, within the last few decades, the rapid development of the science of genetics, have focused attention upon cell activities as over against mere matters of structure. Slowly there has come to the front the idea that the cell is the physiological unit, that the activities of an organism may be conceived of as the sum of the individual cell activities. Each cell is supposed to be a physiological unit performing a particular kind of work, and the resultant of these combined labors constitutes the life of the organism. We now realize that there is an interdependence among these cells, that cells can live and function normally only when in their proper relations to the other cells of the organism.

The Cell a Unit of Development and Heredity.—As the science of embryology progressed it soon came to be recognized as a general law that organisms, no matter how complex or massive they may be in the adult condition, have their origin in a single cell, the egg. This is not a matter of theory, for the entire developmental process may be watched step by step. The method of development is seen to be essentially that of the multiplication of cells by cell division, the forming of layers of cells, the production of folds and processes in cell layers as the result of regional inequalities in rates of growth, the migration of certain cells from one place to another, and the influence of one type of cell upon others. The whole infinitely complex process may be shown to be, in last analysis, a matter of cellular activity. The question as to whether the cells do it all or whether there is something at work more potent than mere combined cell activity, is a problem for future consideration.

The result of embryonic development is the production of a new individual more or less similar to the parent. The reason for this likeness is that each of them, parent and offspring alike, starts out from an egg, goes through parallel embryonic stages, and comes to a stop at the same level of organization. The basis of specific resemblance is obviously to be found in the common start made by the two; for both parent and offspring come from germ cells that have the same or a similar protoplasmic organization, the same rate of cell division, and the same growth peculiarities. Even when we consider that an individual is the product of the union of two cells, an egg of the mother and a spermatozoön of the father, we see that its origin is cellular. Modern genetics has shown that the mechanism of heredity involves the assembling in the germ cell of hereditary materials of two strains and the assorting and redistribution of these cellular elements in very precise ways. Although we do not yet understand either the exact causes of or the driving forces operating this heredity machine, we realize that in last analysis it is a cellular mechanism.

For these and other reasons, the extreme advocates of the Cell Doctrine have come to be imbued with the conviction that it is the most important unifying fact of biology and that we must approach the solution of all our problems from the cellular standpoint.

B. THE FAR-REACHING INFLUENCE OF THE CELL THEORY

The Cell Theory was the first of the great biological generalizations to be commonly adopted and it is to this great unifying principle that we owe, more than to any other, the first great advance of Zoölogy along truly scientific lines. This was the first idea broad enough in its scope to bring all of the facts of biology under its sway. All life came to be thought of as cellular. It is interesting to recall that the great master principle, Evolution, had only a very sparse following until after the publication of Darwin's *Origin of Species* in 1859, just twenty years after Schleiden and Schwann formally launched the Cell Theory. There is little doubt but that the gradual maturing of the Cell Principle paved the way for the acceptance at the hands of biologists of other fundamental generalizations; for the idea of the oneness of living organisms resulting from their cellular constitution suggested the idea that all cellular organisms probably had a common origin.

Cytology.—Out of the study of cells as units of organization there grew the study of the finer structure of the cell and its parts and the mechanisms of cell multiplication and heredity, a specialized branch of biology now in a mature state and known as Cytology. Today Cytology concerns itself particularly with germ cells, but should not, and in reality does not, exclude from its scope the significant features of cells other than germinal.

General Physiology.—The study of cellular activities has developed along other lines into what we know as General Physiology, essentially cellular physiology as distinguished from the physiology of organs or systems. General physiology concerns itself with the structures and properties of cell membranes, their permeability to substances in solution, the phenomena of surface tension, the electrical state of the surface as compared with the interior, the transmission of stimuli from cell to cell or from one part of the cell to another. In other words, the subject of general, or cell, physiology has come to be almost synonymous with biophysics and biochemistry.

In this introductory chapter on the Cell Principle we cannot more than indicate the scope and the importance of the conception. In subsequent chapters we shall see how the principle comes to be applied to special problems.

Tuesday

CHAPTER VI

MORPHOLOGY AND PHYSIOLOGY OF THE CELL

A. General Properties of Cells

Why We Study Structure and Function Together.—In most of the accounts of the cell found in textbooks the plan of dealing first with the cell as a static system of structures, and subsequently giving a separate treatment of cell physiology more or less unrelated to the previous account of cell structure, appears to us not only bad pedagogy but open to objection on logical grounds. Structure is meaningless without function, and *vice versa*. In last analysis, function conditions structure and structure in turn conditions function. The two are merely parts of the same thing, opposite sides of the coin.

The Cell an Organized Individual.—Perhaps the most important fact about cells is not so much that they are units of organization as that each is an organized individual itself. Life does not inhere in the chemical composition of the protoplasm nor in the presence of particular substances or particular structures, but in the relations of these parts to one another and their integration into a unity of structure and function which we call organization. The cell is, above all else, an organism. In an individual composed of many cells we know that the organism transcends the units of its structure; similarly, in a unicellular individual a deep-seated unity presides over the individual elements that make up its structure. We shall come back to this conception later, but it is one that must be borne in mind from the first if we are to gain a true insight into what a cell is.

The Size and General Shape of Cells.—The size of cells varies greatly. The smallest cells known are so minute as to be barely visible under the highest powers of the microscope. Most cells, in fact, are microscopic in their dimensions, for one cannot with the naked eye distinguish the individual cells of any tissue. It is only in the case of some isolated cells such as the larger Protozoa— if these are truly cells—or the egg cells of various organisms, that the cell can be seen with the naked eye. Thus the "yolk" of a hen's egg is a single cell of considerable dimensions; while that of an ostrich egg is proportionately larger. A single nerve cell, al-

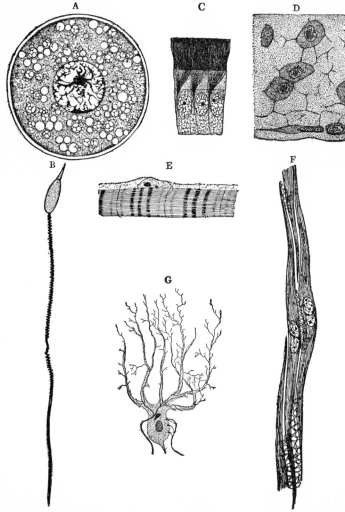

Fig. 18. Various kinds of cells. **A,** female germ cell, ovum of a cat. **B,** male germ cell, spermatozoön of a snake, *Coluber.* **C,** ciliated epithelium from the digestive tract of a mollusk, *Cyclas.* **D,** cartilage of a squid. **E,** striated muscle fiber from an insect larva, *Corydalis cornutus.* **F,** smooth muscle fibers from the bladder of a calf. **G,** a nerve cell from the cerebellum of man. (From Hegner after Dahlgren and Kepner.)

though of no great mass, may have an extraordinary length, in some cases being several feet long. While there is this extreme variation in size of different kinds of cells, the cells of any given tissue of a particular organism are nearly uniform in size. The function of any particular kind of cell seems to have much to do with determining its size limits. If a cell is to function as a storehouse of nutriment for sustaining an embryo up to the time when it can be independent, it must be relatively large and massive. If a cell is to function as a sort of animated telegraph wire, connecting one remote part of an organism with another, it needs to be very much elongated. Muscle cells need to be elongated when at rest so that when they contract they may shorten up. Lining, or epithelial, cells need to be pavement-like or tilelike, so as to form firm, smooth surfaces (Fig. 18).

While the shapes of cells are many and varied, the typical shape of a cell uninfluenced by inequalities of environment, pressures, specialized functions, and relations, is spherical, because a fluid system, on account of the tension of the surface membrane, tends to assume the most compact form with the least possible surface for a given mass—the sphere. It is mainly in free cells such as eggs and some of the Protozoa that we find the true spherical form retained. The demands of the Protozoa for locomotor organs, or for a shape with stream lines adapted to swift motion through a resistant medium, cause these active types of cells to modify their spherical form in an amazing variety of ways. Only when such cells go into a "resting" condition do they assume the typical spherical form. Many cells have a more or less stiff surface covering— pellicle or cortex—that serves to hold the body in a permanent, though flexible, shape; while other cells, such as leucocytes and amœbæ, are constantly thrusting out long fingerlike processes (pseudopodia) which serve as feet for walking and hands for grasping and mouths for engulfing food.

Tissues are aggregates of similar cells performing similar functions. Such cells, packed close together as they are, are subject to the laws of mechanics, and just as inert units would do under similar conditions, they assume the form of polyhedrons of various types, depending on their functions and the physiological demands of the case. They may become elongated rectahedrons; they may be flat and tilelike; they may be elliptical, spindleshaped, discoid, or stellate—each according to its surroundings and the rôle it has to play in the organism. In spite of this almost limitless variety of size and shape, however, all cells have an organization dependent upon the possession of certain components necessary for cell life.

B. The Detailed Structure of Cells

1. *Nucleus and Cytosome*

Some of the simplest plant cells consist of merely a mass of homogeneous protoplasm, with a cell membrane but no other

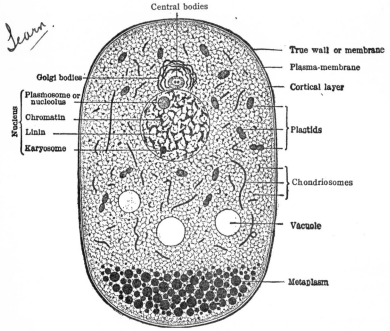

Fig. 19.   General diagram of a cell.   (From Woodruff, after Wilson.)

differentiated parts. All animal cells, however, are more complex than this. In addition to the cell body, known as the CYTOSOME, there is always a second internally placed body, known as the NUCLEUS. Both cytosome and nucleus are composed of living protoplasm, but they differ from each other both physically and chemically. We commonly speak of the cytosomic protoplasm as CYTOPLASM and of the nuclear protoplasm as NUCLEOPLASM.

Both cytosome and nucleus are commonly quite complex in structure, each composed of a number of characteristic differentiated structures. Figure 19 shows in diagrammatic fashion a sort of composite cell containing most of the types of formed components found in both plant and animal cells. No single kind of cell is possessed of all the structures shown in this illustration.

Since cytosome and nucleus are the two primary parts of a cell, all other details of cell structure may be described as formed components of one or the other. We shall first describe the formed components of the cytosome and then those of the nucleus.

2. *The Formed Components of the Cytosome*

The variety of formed components of the cytosome is so great that in this brief survey it is necessary to confine attention to a few of those whose occurrence is most general. Following *Professor E. B. Wilson,* we may consider these as belonging to eight categories:—central bodies, cytoplasmic granules, fibrillæ, plastids, chondriosomes, Golgi-bodies, vacuoles, and cell membrane.

a. Central Bodies.—The term central body is applied to that structure which lies at the focus of the astral rays during mitotic cell division. It is usually rather small and relatively inactive during the so-called resting, or vegetative, phases of cell life, but awakens to intense activity during the actively dividing phases. In the resting state the central body consists typically of a sphere of more or less hyaline protoplasm in the center of which lies a minute granule, or more commonly a twin pair of these, known as the CENTRIOLE. While the central body usually lies close to the nucleus it may be either considerably removed from it or else be located within the nucleus. In the chapter on cell division the central body will receive further attention.

b. Cytoplasmic Granules.—There is a confusing array of many different sorts of granular cytoplasmic components all suspended in the clear, hyaline ground substance, or HYALOPLASM. In size these granules range from those so small as to be nearly at the extreme limit of microscopic visibility to those of relatively large size, such as yolk granules. A rather complicated terminology has been devised to aid in the classification of cytoplasmic granules, but it must suffice here to mention only a few of the main types, such as microsomes, mitochondria, secretory, storage, and pigment granules.

c. Fibrillæ.—These are among the most striking and significant of cytoplasmic structures. Muscle fibrillæ, or myofibrils, have a precise and characteristic arrangement and appearance and are doubtless responsible for muscular contractility. In nerve cells there is usually a definite network or basketwork of fibrillæ, neurofibrils, that come together at one pole of the cell and pass out into the cell process, or axis-cylinder. Many types of gland cells and certain kinds of epithelial cells also possess conspicuous fibrillar components.

d. Plastids.—These are far more common in plant cells but are found also in a few types of animal cells, notably in some flagellate protozoa. Among plants the most important type of plastid is the chloroplast, the green body that gives color to leaves and other structures and that is responsible for the synthesis of starch out of the raw materials, water and carbon dioxide.

e. Chondriosomes.—These bodies occur in nearly all kinds of cells. Usually they are granular, rodlike, or filamentous in form at any given moment, but in living cells they appear to be constantly changing position and form. These most plastic of all cell components are believed by some cytologists to be formative bodies out of which the various other, more stable, cell structures, such as plastids, fibrils, and various specific types of granules, are produced.

f. Golgi-bodies.—These elements are quite distinct both morphologically and physiologically from chondriosomes, though they are sometimes confused with them. They occur in two main forms, localized and diffuse. When differentially stained, they appear as loops or networks occupying definite positions. Very little is known as to their function.

g. Vacuoles.—These are spherical cavities filled with fluid substances of various kinds, each bounded by a delicate film. Under this head come various types of cell organs to be studied later, such as the food vacuoles and contractile vacuoles of Amœba and Paramecium. In some cells the vacuoles are so conspicuous that the whole cytoplasm has a foamy, or alveolar, appearance. Vacuoles are especially prominent in plant cells and in the Protozoa among animals, but are not usually well developed in the cells of higher animals.

h. Cell Membrane.—All cells, even those apparently naked cells such as Amœba and leucocytes, have at least a PLASMA MEMBRANE, or limiting surface membrane. This is considered as the true cell membrane and must not be confused with the cell wall which lies outside the cytosome, sometimes separated from it by a considerable space. The CELL WALL is usually regarded as a protoplasmic product and is not believed to be truly living even though in some cases it seems to be capable of growth.

The plasma membrane is the surface film of the cytosome, comparable with the film that forms at the surface of certain colloidal systems such as that on the surface of scalded milk. This membrane possesses considerable toughness and elasticity and serves to protect the cytosome from dissolution and from chemical and mechanical injury, while at the same time it is sensitive and responds readily to stimuli by changes of form and permeability. It has the capacity of SEMIPERMEABILITY, permitting the passage of solvents and some solutions while preventing the passage of colloidal materials and of other substances in solution. This property is of the utmost importance in the life of the cell, in as much as protoplasm is essentially a colloidal system that would readily be disrupted were it not protected from coming into direct contact with water and other materials in the surrounding medium. Yet it is imperative that various substances involved in the metabolic activity of the cell should have free ingress or egress through the cell membrane. No more important structure of cells exists than the plasma membrane, for it is responsible for maintaining the individuality of the cell and presides over the chemical traffic of the protoplasm that constitute the essence of its life.

The forces in operation in the passage of fluids through membranes are the physical forces of DIFFUSION and OSMOTIC PRESSURE. If two substances in solution be brought together without any barriers between them, the molecules of both tend to distribute themselves throughout the fluid until they are evenly distributed to all of its parts. If free diffusion be interfered with by the interposition between two solutions of a semipermeable membrane, water tends to pass from the fluid with the lower concentration of soluble substance to that of higher concentration, and this will take place even against the resistance of gravity or other hindrances. This sort of diffusion takes place with considerable energy or pressure through a force known as osmotic pressure, one of the important factors of the physicochemical activities of living organisms. A cell membrane may become tense and stretched if, through osmotic pressure, more water goes into the cell than comes out; it may become wrinkled and slack if the opposite relation of income and outgo prevail. Normally the cell contents are osmotically nicely balanced with the surrounding fluids, so that exchanges through the membrane are equivalent. When a solution is in osmotic equilibrium with another, it is spoken of as ISOTONIC or ISOMOTIC with it. If two solutions are out of equilibrium, so that one would lose water to the other through a membrane, the one that loses water is known as HYPOTONIC and the one that gains water as HYPERTONIC. Most of the exchanges within the bodies of animals, involving the passage of materials from cell to cell, are osmotic in character and are regulated by cell membranes.

3. Components of the Nucleus

While the typical form of nuclei is spherical or nearly so, there are many other forms. Some are horseshoe shaped, others resemble chains of beads, still others are more or less branching or even reticular. In some cells, notably the bacteria, the nuclear material is diffusely scattered throughout the cytoplasm in the form of numerous granules. In other cells there may be two or several nuclei. Whatever the form of the more massive types of nuclei, all are more or less complex in organization and, as in the cytosome, there are several well defined categories of components, among which the following are nearly universal:—nuclear membrane, nuclear framework, nucleoli, and nuclear sap.

a. Nuclear Membrane.—This delicate but well defined surface film plays the rôle of arbiter over the chemical exchanges between the nucleus and the cytosome and, like the plasma membrane, is semipermeable. Microdissection has demonstrated that it possesses considerable toughness and elasticity. At times however, especially during mitotic cell division, the nuclear membrane breaks down and the nucleoplasm and cytoplasm become very intimately commingled. After mitosis the membrane is reconstituted. In some cases this membrane seems to be formed exclusively of nuclear material; in other cases it is formed partly from the cytoplasm.

b. Nuclear Framework.—This part of the nucleus contains the most distinctively nuclear materials, for it is made up of a complex spongy network of CHROMATIN (basichromatin) and LININ (oxychromatin). The exact interrelationship existing between these two materials is not yet fully clear. It is sometimes difficult to distinguish sharply between them. In the growing, or vegetative, phases of cell life, the chromatin proper appears to exist in the form of numerous granules of varying sizes strung upon a linin network. When, in division stages, chromosomes are formed, both chromatin and linin contribute to their substance. In several later chapters chromosomes will receive much attention on account of the fact that these bodies play a very important rôle in heredity.

c. Nucleoli.—This term has been applied to quite a variety of entirely different nuclear bodies and some confusion exists as to just what sorts of structures should be called nucleoli. It seems well to include under this head the so-called true nucleoli, or PLAS-MOSOMES, and chromatin nucleoli, or KARYOSOMES. The plasmosomes are entirely distinct from chromosomes, but karyosomes may be identical with chromosomes, sometimes being merely chromosomes that in the resting phases of cell division remain in a condensed state. Both kinds of nucleoli may be present at once in the same cell, but they are readily distinguishable by their different staining reactions. While the function of the karyosomes seems quite clear, since they are chromosomal in character, that of the plasmosomes is still quite problematical. There is some evidence, however, that these bodies may have something to do with the secretory processes of the cell.

d. Nuclear Sap.—While it has been generally supposed that the nuclear sap is no more than a structureless fluid, there are observations indicating that it may have a firmer consistency than that of an ordinary watery solution. The actual character of the nuclear sap is very imperfectly understood and needs investigation.

4. *Cellular Polarity*   ~~omitted~~

Enough has been written to emphasize the fact that the cell, though in most cases small in size, is far from simple in its organization. No two kinds of cells are alike in their constitution, some possessing one complex of cytoplasmic and nuclear components, others another complex. Within a single organism the nuclei of all cells may be essentially alike, but there is an almost endless variety of differences in the organization of the cytosome in different kinds of tissue cells. In any one kind of tissue cell, however, the cytoplasmic constitution is fairly uniform. There is nothing indefinite about the constitution of cells, whether relatively simple or relatively complex. Each cell is a definite life unit, with a precise arrangement and interrelation of all components, large or small.

A cell is a true microcosm in which innumerable minor units are ordered in all their changes so that unity and harmony prevails. This ordered arrangement of parts within the cell has been long noted by biologists and has been described in terms of polarity and symmetry.

A typical cell, such as an egg cell, has one pole at which the protoplasm is most active, where the rate of metabolism is highest, and an opposite pole where the metabolic activity is lowest. The more active pole is usually called the ANIMAL POLE and the less active pole, the VEGETAL POLE. Between the two poles there is a gradient of metabolic activity extending down the meridians. The cell is then an organized metabolic system. Besides the polarity of the cell there is to be recognized another gradient from the center to the surface. A resultant of these two gradients determines the differentiations at the various levels of the cell. As this gradient conception is to be more fully explained in a subsequent chapter we need not elaborate it further in this place.

C. The Problem of the Ultimate Physical Structure of the Cytoplasm

One of the very interesting chapters in the history of zoölogical progress centers about the attempt of both earlier and later workers to discover the essential or ultimate physical make-up of the living substance, especially of that part of it situated in the more homogeneous regions of the cytoplasm. The earlier workers attacked this problem somewhat naïvely, with the hopeful idea before them that if they could discover the construction of the machine, they would soon be led to an understanding of how the machine works, and would then be in a position to solve the perplexing problem: what is life? These hopes have been realized only very partially. As microscopic technique has been improved and refinement after refinement has been added to the optical equipment of the students of cell structure, more and more accurate pictures of protoplasmic structure have come to view. Various theories have followed one another as to the finer structure of the protoplasm:—

a. The Granular Theory.—According to the granular theory the protoplasmic mass is made up of tiny units or granules that are sometimes massed into solids and sometimes arranged in linear series so as to form fibrils.

b. The Fibrillar Theory.—Emphasis is here laid upon the fibrous nature of cytoplasm, looking upon the mass as a more or less dense feltwork of fibers.

c. The Reticular Theory. —This theory emphasizes the fibrous make-up, but adds the conception that the fibers are knotted together into an intimate network like a series of hammocks knotted together, one on top of another (Fig. 20).

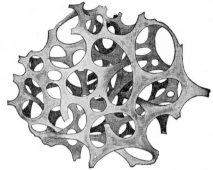

d. The Alveolar Theory. —The granules and fibers of the earlier theories are viewed in the alveolar theory

FIG. 20. Diagram to illustrate the *reticular* theory of protoplasm. (From Dahlgren and Kepner.)

as artifacts—appearances caused by the rough handling of protoplasm by chemical agents in process of fixation. According to *Bütschli,* the leading advocate of the alveolar view, protoplasm is a sort of foamy emulsion of two substances intimately mixed,

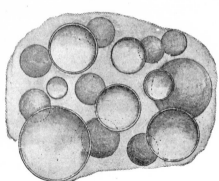

much like an emulsion of oil and water. In the latter case we have fine spheres of oil in a matrix of water, each oil droplet surrounded by a film of water. In protoplasm it appears that there is a sort of ground substance, probably collodial in character, with spheres of more liquid material suspended in it (Fig. 21). Living protoplasm, when seen free from the cell, often has

FIG. 21. Diagram to illustrate the *alveolar* theory of protoplasm. (From Dahlgren and Kepner.)

the alveolar appearance, but this is only the gross, not the finer, structural organization. *omit*

e. The Colloidal Theory.—~~Professor~~ *E. B. Wilson* has recently stated that the "so-called 'alveolar' structure is not a primary characteristic of this protoplasm. It is of secondary origin, arising by the appearance in the homogeneous ground substance of extremely minute scattered bodies which by growth and crowding together finally produce the emulsion-like structure. In the middle stages of this process the protoplasm gives an interesting picture. When viewed under relatively low magnification, *e.g.*, 300–500 diameters, only the larger bodies are seen; but as step by step we increase the magnification, step by step we see smaller and smaller bodies coming into view, at every stage graduating down to the limits of vision. This remains true even with the highest available powers. The microscopical picture offered by such protoplasm is thus somewhat like the telescopic picture of the sky. At each step in the improvement of the telescope new and fainter stars come into view. At each step the astronomer has felt sure that still more powerful telescopes would bring into view stars hitherto unseen. The cytologist is equally sure that if the present limits of direct microscopical vision could be extended, we should see disperse bodies still more minute; . . . below the horizon of our present high power microscopes there exists an invisible realm, peopled by a multitude of dispersed particles, a realm quite as complex as the visible one with which the cytologist is directly occupied."

We have reason to believe that the ultimate particles suspended in the aqueous matrix are masses somewhat larger than molecular size, consisting of aggregates of molecules, sometimes not very large in numbers. At this point, as Professor Wilson remarks, "we have reached the borderland where the cytologist and the colloidal chemist are almost within hailing distance of each other."

Conclusion.—We may well conclude this chapter with an important summary of his own conclusions, taken from an earlier paper by Professor Wilson:—

"My own long-continued studies on various forms of protoplasms have likewise led to the conclusion that no universal formula for protoplasmic structure can be given. . . . It is impossible to resist the evidence that fibular and granular as well as alveolar structure are of wide occurrence; and while each may be characteristic of certain kinds of cells or of certain physiological conditions, none is common to all forms of protoplasm. If this position be well grounded, we must admit that the attempt to find in visible protoplasmic structure any adequate insight into the fundamental modes of physiological activity has thus far proved fruitless. We must rather seek the source of these activities in the ultramicroscopical organization, accepting the probability that apparently homogeneous protoplasm is a complex mixture of substances which may assume various forms of visible structure according to its modes of activity."

Thus we are once more disappointed in our attempts to solve the puzzle as to the nature of life. The study of protoplasmic structure, even when carried as far as our best optical equipment permits, falls far short of revealing to our eyes the life-machine at work.

CHAPTER VII

CELL DIVISION

A. THE PROBLEM OF THE ORIGIN OF CELLS

FOR a considerable number of years after 1839, when the Cell Theory was formulated by Schleiden and Schwann, the problem as to how cells arise was still unsolved. The leading experts in cell study knew that some cells were produced by division of previous cells, but they also believed that cells sometimes arose by "free cell formation" as the result of a process resembling the origin of crystals in a solution. They believed that a cell might grow out of a nutritive substance by gathering to itself the necessary ingredients. Few examples of dividing cells had been observed, and it was believed that cells usually arose spontaneously in the manner described. This view of cell origin naturally prevailed so long as belief in the spontaneous generation of life held sway. If, they thought, organisms of some complexity could arise spontaneously out of nutritive media, cells should be able to arise even more readily in the nutritive media furnished by organisms. When, however, the ideas of spontaneous generation of life broke down under experimental demonstration, it at once became evident that cells, the units of life, must likewise arise from previously existing cells. Thus Harvey's dictum, *omne vivum ex ovo* (all life from the egg), was extended so as to fit the cell situation when **Virchow** in 1855 proposed the equally famous dictum, *omnia cellula e cellula* (all cells from cells), a dictum which is now considered a universal biological law.

B. DISCOVERY OF CELL DIVISION AND PROGRESS IN OUR KNOWLEDGE OF ITS MECHANISM

From the very first there was great curiosity about the mechanism of cell division, but little progress was made toward the discovery of its essential details for about a quarter of a century after Virchow stated the law of cell origin. Biologists were busy exploring the world of cells, bringing forth further evidence of the universal applicability of the Cell Theory. Microscopic technique, furthermore, had not reached the state of maturity necessary for the successful preparation of thin sections of tissues properly stained to show the details of cell division; nor had lenses of sufficiently high quality for visioning such fine details been devised. Progress in the study of cell division went along slowly because the investigators had to invent improved methods of preparing tissues for study and improved microscopes and modes of illumination.

A first crude attempt at a description of the events of cell division was made by *Remak* in 1855. His scheme was essentially as follows: The nucleolus first divides; then the nucleus follows suit, each part of the nucleus containing a new nucleolus; finally the cytoplasm divides into two equivalent parts, each with its nucleus, by means of a surface constriction which gradually cuts the cell into two cells. Though this process, which is equivalent to the mode of cell division known today as AMITOSIS, may, and probably does, occur in some tissues under some conditions, it is now known to be relatively rare. Further investigations under improved conditions soon showed that the usual method of cell division is far more complex than Remak supposed—in fact, one of the most complicated and difficult to interpret among elementary cellular phenomena. This complicated method of cell division came to be spoken of as INDIRECT CELL DIVISION as contrasted with Remak's scheme of direct cell division. Certain technical terms, however, have come to be applied to both methods. For the complicated or indirect method the names KARYOKINESIS (meaning nuclear activity) and MITOSIS (referring to the fact that at certain phases of the process the chromatin assumes the form of threads) have come into common use; while the direct method is called AMITOSIS (signifying the absence of any threadlike or fibrous condition of the chromatin). The terms mitosis and amitosis are now thoroughly intrenched.

In giving an account of mitosis one feels himself in the position of a showman who is able to present a series of pictures but can present no story that serves to explain the sequence of events or the underlying causes of the observed changes. If we could do so, we would take great pleasure in detailing for our readers the narrative of the events of mitosis with a running account of the physiological significance of each step and the exact value of each part in the division mechanism. It is unfortunate that at present we cannot do this. The problem of the mechanism of mitosis is entirely unsolved. Later on we shall discuss some suggestions as to the nature of the mechanism, but we shall have to describe in a purely morphological fashion the more important scenes in the moving picture of mitosis. The process of mitosis is one of the most universal of biological processes, common to plants and animals, to the lowest and highest phyla of both kingdoms. No more fundamental vital process is likely to come to our attention. The process is one of those phenomena which may be thought of as expressing the essence of vital activity. If we could gain an adequate understanding in terms of physics and chemistry of mitosis, I suspect that we would not be far from a solution of the mystery of life.

C. The Events of Mitosis

While mitosis, wherever we find it, has certain universal features, considerable differences exist as to details, on the one hand, between that of animals and plants, and, on the other hand, among animals themselves. The account here given is that of the division of typical animal cells during cleavage, the period of cell multiplication in early embryonic development. This account will not apply to higher plants, for there we find no centrosome nor aster; neither will it apply without considerable reservation to cell divisions as seen in the Protozoa. The process of mitosis is a continuous one, really a cycle; for, starting out at any point in the series of events, we find ourselves coming back to the same point with the completion of each cell division   Even a continuous process, however, may be arbitrarily subdivided into periods, just as a drama may be subdivided into acts and scenes according to certain climaxes that serve as time markers of progress. Four periods in the process of mitosis have been distinguished and have been termed PHASES. These phases are: (1) the PROPHASES, including all of the events beginning with the first steps in division of the central body and culminating in the stage where the chromosomes lie in equilibrium in the equatorial plate; (2) the META- PHASE, the stage in which the chromosomes are longitudinally split and begin to separate into two half chromosomes; (3) the ANAPHASES, the steps during which the half chromosomes travel toward the opposite poles of the spindle; and (4) the TELOPHASES, during which the cytoplasm of the cell divides to form the two daughter cells, and the two chromosome groups are reorganized into the so-called resting nuclei, the equivalents of the original

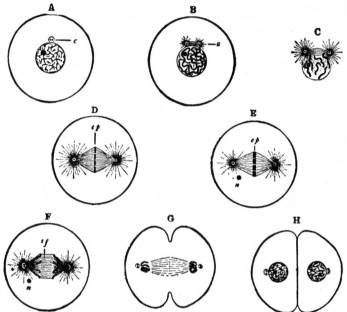

FIG. 22. Diagrams of typical stages in mitosis. **A,** resting cell with chromatin presenting a net-like arrangement within the nuclear membrane; *c,* central body divided; **B,** prophase (early): central body, asters (*a*), and spindle; most of the chromatin material seems to assume the form of a long thread (spireme); **C,** prophase (later) involving the disappearance of the nuclear membrane, and the separation of the chromatin of the spireme stage into discrete bodies (chromosomes); **D,** prophase (final) with chromosomes arranged in the equatorial plate (*ep*); **E,** metaphase; each chromosome splitting lengthwise; **F,** anaphase: the daughter sets of chromosomes moving toward the asters; *if,* 'inter-zonal fibers'; **G, H,** early and later telophase involving the gradual loss of visibility of chromosomes as they spin out into the resting net-like arrangement of the chromatin; division of the cytoplasm; *n,* nucleolus. (From Woodruff, after Wilson.)

nucleus we started out with. And thus we have rounded out the cycle. The classic semidiagrammatic illustration from **Wilson** tells the story in condensed form (Fig. 22).

We have now outlined what is essentially a drama in four acts, badly constructed from the artistic standpoint, for the climax, the most important event of the whole plot, takes place in the second act at the metaphase, and the remaining acts are perhaps in the nature of an anticlimax. Relating the story of mitosis is like trying to keep track of several characters of a drama at once, for we have to note what goes on in the nucleus, especially the chromatin, what goes on in the central body, and what goes on in the cytoplasm. The story, on that account, will be a little disjointed, but the accompanying figures give "stills" at various stages so that we can see how each character has progressed. In the detailed account that follows, the illustrations represent the phases of mitosis of one species of clam, and are accurately drawn.

1. *The Prophases*

Between two periods of cell division the cell is in the so-called "resting stage." It is resting only in so far as division is concerned, for this is the period when metabolic activity is at its height and the cell grows from a half-sized to a full-sized unit. During this period the nucleus is spherical (Fig. 19) and the chromatin is arranged in the form of a fine network composed of scattered granules strung upon the threads of LININ. Some parts of the chromatin may remain relatively large and massive during the resting phase. These larger masses are probably chromosomes that are relatively inactive during that period. At this time the centriole is seen as a pair of granules located in the middle of the central body.

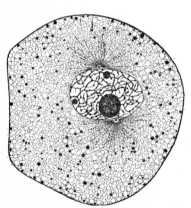

FIG. 23. Beginning of fourth cleavage division of oösperm of *Unio*. Central bodies appearing on sides of nucleus. (From Dahlgren and Kepner.)

The first indication that a cell is about to divide is to be seen in the migration apart of the centrioles. As they do so they seem to spin between themselves a small spindle of fibers. Each central body also becomes crowned with a halo of radiating lines, which seem to have no solid consistency but are mere indications of lines of force emanating from the central body out into the cytoplasm (Fig. 23). While this has been going on, the chromatin in the nucleus has changed in appearance. It seems to have undergone a process of condensation, probably passing from a sol to a gel state, and appearing as a set of long thin threads coiled intricately into a close skein called a SPIREME (Fig. 24), in which the folds go back and forth but do not touch or cross. Later the threads condense further, becoming shorter and thicker so as to form an open skein or LOOSE SPIREME. By this time the two central bodies are far apart and the spindle clearly defined, with well-marked radiations from both central bodies. The whole mechanism of spindle and asters lies against the nuclear membrane and is known as the AMPHIASTER, or the ACHROMATIC FIGURE, because it is not composed at all of chromatin. Soon after this the chromatin spireme separates into a definite number of loops or rods to form the CHROMOSOMES, which seem to be scattered at random through the nucleus. Up to this time the events inside of the nucleus and those associated with the amphiaster, outside the

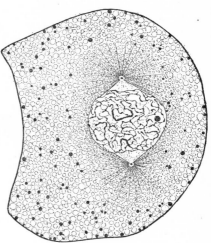

FIG. 24. Later stage than Fig. 23. Irregular spireme, central bodies moving apart and nuclear membrane beginning to fail where touched by the forming spindle fibrils. (From Dahlgren and Kepner.)

nucleus, seem to have been going on without reference to each other, but now the plot thickens. The nuclear membrane breaks down, possibly through the action of the forces resident in the central bodies; the spindle takes up its position where the nucleus had been, with the central bodies at opposite sides of the nucleus; and the chromosomes mingle among the spindle fibers, apparently attaching themselves thereto (Fig. 25). Slowly the chromosomes take up an orderly relation to the central bodies, migrating toward the equator and coming to lie in an equatorial plate equidistant from the two centrosomes. What impels them to take up this accurately balanced position we do not know, but will suggest certain possibilities later. The EQUATORIAL-PLATE stage marks the close of the prophases and ushers in the metaphase, the climax of the drama.

2. *The Metaphase*

This phase is evidently one of equilibrium, for the chromosomes frequently rest there for a time as though balanced between two opposing forces (Fig. 26). During this period of standstill the

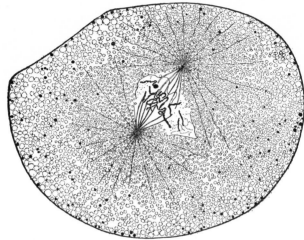

FIG. 25.   Later stage of this mitosis.   Nuclear membrane nearly gone.   Spireme breaking to form chromosomes.   Spindle fibrils growing toward each other.   Nucleolus almost gone.   (From Dahlgren and Kepner.)

chromosomes, if they have not already done so precociously, split lengthwise into two equal halves. The exact equivalence of the two pieces of each chromosome is a matter of considerable consequence, for it is upon the accuracy of this division that we base our conceptions of the mechanism of heredity   If chromosomes are highly individualized bodies, each carrying definite specific particles of substance that determine the characters of the individual, it is of prime importance that they should be divided in such a way as to maintain the integrity of their diversified composition and to insure its equal distribution to cell descendants. The mitotic mechanism appears to be ideally constructed to give these results. This fact lends added significance to the detailed study of mitosis. Some writers define the metaphase as no more than the period of splitting of chromosomes. This definition breaks down in the case of many species in which the splitting takes place before the equatorial plate stage. Moreover, the use of the word "splitting" for chromosome division carries false implications; as well use the word for cell division itself. The lengthwise division of chromosomes is a genuine reproductive process involving the growth and division of each of a long series of heredity units, genes, a series of which, like a chain of beads, makes up each chromosome. The arrangement of genes into

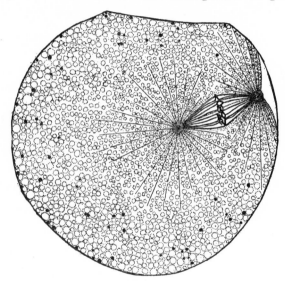

Fig. 26. Same process at time of formation of equatorial plate of chromosomes. (From Dahlgren and Kepner.)

chains is apparently a matter of quite secondary importance as compared with the highly specific character of the genes themselves. It is the twinning of genes, their division into equivalent halves, that constitutes the most important feature of chromosome behavior in mitosis.

3. *The Anaphases*

Soon after chromosome division is complete, the daughter chromosomes separate and drift apart from the equator of the spindle toward opposite poles (Fig. 27). Some go more rapidly than others; some lag behind after the rest have reached their destinations; but sooner or later they form two closely-packed groups about the two poles of the spindle. All of the steps in the process of distributing daughter chromosomes to their new locations, the centers of the prospective daughter cells, are anaphases.

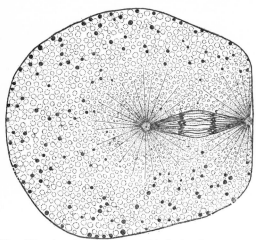

There is no exact point at which we can say definitely that the anaphases end and the telophases begin. The two processes are continuous. Usually it is during the late anaphases that the cell membrane begins to show the first signs of constricting to divide the cytoplasm. A slight furrow arises in the plane of the former equatorial

FIG. 27. A cell of the same kind showing separation of the chromosomes. (From Dahlgren and Kepner.)

plate and grows gradually deeper and deeper until it passes across the equator, which is marked by the presence of a plate of small granules indicating the site of the chromosomes when they were at the equatorial plate.

4. *The Telophases*

This is the period of reconstitution of the normal vegetative condition of all the cell organs: nucleus, cytosome, central body (Fig. 28). The half cell becomes a whole cell with a complete membrane surrounding it; the nucleus becomes spherical and acquires a nuclear membrane; the chromosomes gradually reverse the order of their former changes, becoming less and less dense until they return to the condition of an apparent reticulum of granules strung on linin fibers. The achromatic figure is slow to disappear; even after the cells are completely cut apart, portions of the spindle fibers are to be seen in their original locations. The astral rays, however, disappear promptly and completely, leaving the central body of each cell in the original compact form in which we first saw it. Thus the little mitotic machine has retired into small scope and remains inconspicuous until the approach of the next period of division.

The process of cell division, a simple reproductive event, may now be considered as completed. Now ensues the other phase of the cellular life cycle, that of growth. Growth has been in abeyance during the period of division, so that each daughter cell is but a half-sized cell. It now proceeds to feed and to grow till it reaches the maximum size limit of cells of its kind. Then it must divide again in order that growth may continue.

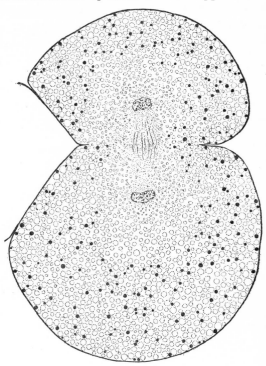

FIG. 28. Division of nucleus almost completed. Cell beginning to divide. (From Dahlgren and Kepner.)

The above account of mitosis is a generalized one based on the usual conditions seen in animals. There are, however, many exceptional forms of mitosis, a few of which will now be dealt with.

D. VARIOUS TYPES OF MITOSIS

The commonest departures from the typical condition described above have to do with the absence of central bodies. The higher plants present a naked spindle with neither centrioles nor asters. The maturation spindles of vertebrate eggs seem to be very much like those of the flowering plants. Thus the first maturation spindle of the mammalian ovum is clearly without asters and its central body seems to be no more than the point of convergence of the spindle fibers. Another important variation from the norm is seen in species of Protozoa, *e.g.*, Euglypha, in which the whole spindle forms inside of the nuclear membrane and the entire process of division is confined to the nucleus.

E. NUMBERS AND SIGNIFICANCE OF CHROMOSOMES

Mitosis seems to be primarily a mechanism for multiplying and accurately distributing chromosomes. There is ample evidence that the chromosomes are the bearers of hereditary materials called determiners or GENES. Hence the mitotic mechanism, including the chromosomes, may be thought of as the "heredity machine." There is now little doubt but that the chromosomes are qualitatively different and that each stands for a definite set of factors in heredity. It is of some interest to note that there is a constant number of chromosomes for each species, the number ranging from as low as two for the nematode worm, *Ascaris megalocephala univalens*, to sixty-four for the crustacean, *Artemia*, and even higher numbers in various animals and plants. The now famous fruit fly *Drosophila melanogaster*, whose chromosomes are better known than those of any other animals, has 8 chromosomes; while man, according to leading authorities, has 48. In the chapter on *Genetics* we shall deal at greater length with the rôle of chromosomes in heredity.

F. THE PROBLEM OF THE MECHANICS OF MITOSIS

It has already been intimated that our knowledge of the events of mitosis is at present almost entirely confined to a description of appearances. In other words, we know something about the morphology of mitosis, something about the importance of its rôle in development and heredity, but nothing very definite about the physiology of the process. What are the forces at work that make the central body divide and the two products migrate apart? What substances give rise to the spindle fibers? What causes the chromosomes to undergo progressive condensation and to migrate first toward the equator of the spindle, to divide lengthwise, then to leave the equatorial plate and migrate toward the poles? What causes the constriction of the cell membrane? These and many other questions of a physiological character remain as yet unanswered, but we are not without certain interesting and in some cases valuable suggestions that may lead ultimately to a satisfactory solution of this extremely difficult problem.

Numerous observations have forced the conviction that mitosis is far from being a unitary process. The facts that nuclei often divide without any division of the cytosome, that spindles form without asters, that chromosomes divide prior to the formation of the spindle, indicate that the whole complex process of mitosis may be merely a coördination of a group of autonomous processes, each of which may be relatively simple in itself and capable of an equally simple explanation. If this be true, it would be futile to attempt to explain on physicochemical grounds the whole mitotic complex as a single mechanism. If we can explain the mechanism of one part at a time we may arrive at an adequate explanation of the whole.

Numerous theories have been devised to account for the nature of the asters and spindles, the reason for the constriction of the plasma membrane in the equatorial region, the nature of the spindle fibers and how they effect the migration of the chromosomes to opposite poles, why the cell elongates prior to cleavage. Some of these theories may with profit be briefly outlined.

a. Electromagnetic Theories of the Mitotic Figure.—There is a striking resemblance between the picture of mitosis in the metaphase and that presented when iron filings scattered evenly on a piece of paper are subjected to the forces emanating from the poles of an electromagnet. A spindle-like series of rays extends between the two magnetic poles and aster-like radiations extend out from the poles for some distance. According to one theory, we may view the changes in the cell and its ultimate division as the result of changes in the chemical constitution of various parts of the cell, resulting in electrical changes necessitating changes of shape and position of parts in order to restore equilibrium. The close resemblance of the mitotic figure to a field of polarized electrical forces may be merely illusory, but is at least very attractive.

b. Theories of Diffusion Streams and Surface Tension.—According to these views, of which there is a considerable variety, the astral rays represent lines of diffusion currents or lines of protoplasmic flow. Currents have actually been observed in favorable material, and it is known that the direction of flow is centripetal, that is, from the periphery toward the center of the

asters. This involves an accumulation of materials in the central
bodies and the consequent growth of the latter as mitosis pro-
gresses. With the migration of more solid materials from the
surface and from the equator of the cell toward the two central
bodies, there is a resultant change in surface tension. This might
account for the elongation of the cell in the axis of the spindle and
for the constriction of the cytoplasm at its weakest point, between the two central bodies.

   c. Theories of the Relation of Viscosity Changes to Mitosis.—
These theories are intimately related to those just discussed and
seem to supplement them. It has been pointed out by various
observers that marked changes in viscosity of the protoplasm
occur during the course of mitosis. There appear to be two periods
of maximal viscosity, one during the prophases, the other just
before the final step of cleavage. Relatively low viscosity prevails between these two points. Microdissection has revealed
the fact that the astral rays are most viscous in the center and
progressively less viscous toward the periphery. These and other
observations have led to the conclusion that the aster is a sphere
of solidification which extends its diameter as mitosis proceeds.
The growth of two large solid regions tends to elongate the cell
and to leave only one relatively fluid region, that between the two
central bodies. Constriction occurs in this region because of
changes of surface tension and in response to the tendency for
the somewhat fluid outer portions of the cell to regain the spherical form.

   At the present time there is no complete or adequate explanation of the mechanics of mitosis, but there is no reason for dis-
couragement, for these problems are among the ultimate problems
of life and we must be satisfied with progress in the direction of
their complete solution, but must not expect such a solution very
soon.

CHAPTER VIII

THE UNITY OF THE ORGANISM

"They (the cells) are no more the producers of the vital phenomena than the shells scattered along the sea-beach are the instruments by which the gravitative force of the moon acts upon the ocean. Like these, the cells mark only where the vital tides have been, and how they have acted."

—T. H. Huxley.

A. Organismal versus Elemental Theories

"In its earliest infancy," says W. E. Ritter, "the science of living beings presented two theories apparently diametrically or irreconcilably opposed to each other. Stating the case in familiar terminology, according to the one the organism is explained by the substance or elements of which it is composed, while according to the other the substance or elements are explained by the organism." The first of these conceptions may be called the Elemental Theory and the second, the Organismal Theory.

The older students of Zoölogy were interested in the organism as a whole, in its activities, habits, responses, and the rôle played in the economy of nature. This is the point of view which we to-day call Natural History. The naturalist is one who studies organisms in nature with especial reference to the relation between the organism and its living and lifeless environment. This conception of natural history will be seen to coincide very closely with that of ecology, for everything that concerns the interplay of organism and environment is ecological. The naturalist and the ecologist are primarily interested in the organism as a whole, while the laboratory zoölogist is inclined to lose the naturalistic point of view and to become overly imbued with the elementalist idea.

B. Progress toward the Elemental Conception

The laboratory method of zoölogical study has led progressively to a more pronounced emphasis upon the parts of the organism and a neglect of the organism as a whole. The shifting of interest began with the analysis of an organism into systems and organs.

This, in turn, was followed by the microscopic study of the tissues (histology) and consequent emphasis upon the cellular composition of all living tissues. More intensive study of cells revealed that other units of organization were present, and attention became focused upon the chromosomes as all important elements. The chromosomes in turn are found to be composed of chromomeres, and the chromomeres are interpreted as bundles of genes or determiners. These genes appear to be hereditary materials capable of being transmitted as independent units. This whole process of analysis of the organism into its ultimate components has led to the view that an organism is a sort of bundle of unit characters and that the individual is no more nor less than the sum of its parts, or, in other words, a sort of mosaic or elaborate patchwork of more or less independently inherited characters. Thus the analytical procedures of genetics have drawn away our attention from the organism as a whole and have focused it upon the parts of the organism, the genes or factors. This is the logical tendency of the "elemental theory," which seems to have reached its climax in the analysis of the mechanism of heredity.

The extreme form of the Cell Theory is also an elemental conception. As we have already pointed out, the advocates of the Cell Theory hold that, in last analysis, all life is a cellular phenomenon; structure, function, development, heredity, and even individuality, are held to be fully accounted for as the result of the form and activities of cells. Even the organism as a whole owes its unity or individuality to the properties of the cells of which it is composed.

C. The Organismal Conception

It is because of this extreme emphasis upon the parts and the neglect of the fundamental principle of the UNITY OF THE ORGANISM that we find it necessary in this place to bring the latter conception into its proper perspective. The Cell Theory is unquestionably an important and far-reaching generalization and it has been most fruitful as a working hypothesis, but it does not adequately account for many of the most strikingly vital of biological phenomena.

For nearly half a century following the announcement of the Cell Theory by Schleiden and Schwann and the founding, a few years later, of the science of histology at the hands of Bichot, the organismal conception lay almost wholly dormant, but, beginning about 1890, it has been resuscitated and aroused to new vigor especially at the hands of the American biologists, C. O. Whitman, E. B. Wilson, F. R. Lillie, J. Loeb, C. M. Child and, most recently, W. E. Ritter. The leader in this movement was Professor Whitman, who, in his essay, *The Inadequacy of the Cell-Theory of Development*, says: "Comparative embryology reminds us at every turn that the organism dominates cell-formation, using for the same purpose one, several, or many cells, massing its materials and directing its movements and shaping its organs, as if cells did not exist, or as if they existed only in complete subordination to its will, if I may so speak." In another place he says: "The fact that physiological unity is not broken by cell-boundaries is confirmed in so many ways that it must be accepted as one of the fundamental truths of biology."

In his essay, *The Mosaic Theory of Development*, Professor E. B. Wilson says: "The only real unity is that of the entire organism, and as long as its cells remain in continuity they are to be regarded, not as morphological individuals, but as specialized centers of action into which the living body resolves itself, and by means of which the physiological division of labor is effected."

In an important paper on the development of Chætopterus, a marine worm, Professor F. R. Lillie discusses the subject *Properties of the Whole* (Principle of Unity) as follows: "If any radical conclusion from the immense amount of investigation of the elementary phenomena of development be justified this is: That the cells are subordinate to the organism, which produces them, and makes them large or small, of a slow or rapid rate of division, causes them to divide, now in this direction, now in that, and in all respects so disposes them that the latent being comes to full expression. . . . The organism is primary, not secondary; it is an individual, not by virtue of the coöperation of countless lesser individualities."

These opinions show clearly how strong has been the reaction against the elemental conception of life; yet even at the present time we find the elementalist point of view alive and vigorous in the work of some of the leading geneticists of the period. Doubtless both points of view embody a part of the truth, but neither is the whole truth. If we can succeed in amalgamating these diverse

points of view, we are more than likely to have a workable biological philosophy.

D. Individuality in Organisms

Accepting as a valid postulate that the entire organism is a real
unity and not merely an assemblage of minor unities, we may ask
what constitutes unity of organization—what are the agencies
responsible for this unity? The organism is an INDIVIDUAL. Let
us define an individual by answering, in the words of *Professor
Child,* the question: In what does individuality consist? "In the
first place, the organic individual is alive and therefore consists of
the complex of substances termed in general protoplasm; secondly,
it is more or less definitely limited in size; thirdly, it possesses a
more or less definite morphology, a visible form and structure,
which is associated in some way with dynamic and primarily chemical activity; fourthly, a greater or less degree of order, coördination, correlation, or harmony, as it is variously called, is perceptible
in the character of its form and structure and in the dynamic activities of its constituent parts. In short, the organic individual
appears to be a unity of some sort, its individuality consists primarily in this unity, and the process of individuation is the process
of integration of a mere aggregation into a unity, for this unity is
not simply the unity of a chance aggregation, but one of a very
particular kind and highly constant character for each kind of
individual."

Our task is now to determine the nature of the unity which underlies individuality. Many workers have essayed to picture for
us the underlying basis of individuality, but none has, I believe,
so successfully done this as Professor Child, who has given us a
dynamic conception of the organic individual that is at once highly
illuminating and consistent with an immense array of facts in
nature. The essential features of Child's theory is that: "The
foundation of unity and order in the organic individual is the transmission of dynamic change, 'stimulus,' 'excitation,' from one point
to another in the protoplasm." In the course of such transmission
the original dynamic change falls off in intensity in a steady way
until at a given distance from the source of the stimulus it fades
out and becomes ineffective. Thus a region of the body with a
high metabolic rate, a region where life exists at an intense level,
imparts a wave of excitation to other parts of the system, each

part passing on to the next, in diminished intensity, the dynamic change. This means that the region of highest metabolic rate becomes the dynamic head of the organism, the center of its organization. All of the parts occupy a position of subordination to the head, or the APICAL REGION, as it is more technically called. We have a parallel to this sort of organization in the business world. Every great commercial organization has one head, or director, who gives coherency or unity to the whole organism, because from him emanate the orders which pass to the subheads and from them down the line to the lowest worker. A great business organism is successful only so long as it retains its responsiveness to the central authority and thus remains a unit, an individual.

In like manner, individuality in organisms depend on unified control. If any part of the organism becomes insubordinate or ceases to be reached by the stimuli emanating from the apical region, this part ceases physiologically to be a true part of that organism and will sooner or later become independent, acquiring an individuality of its own. This, in passing, is Child's theory of the physiological basis of asexual or agametic reproduction and is to be dealt with elsewhere.

E. AXIATE ORGANIZATION THE BASIS OF INDIVIDUALITY

Organisms that have a well-defined individuality are invariably organized about one or a few broad architectural lines or axes. Let us take a human being as a familiar example of a definite axiate organism and view for a few moments his broad lines of structure. We can readily recognize the PRIMARY AXIS, or AXIS OF POLARITY, as an imaginary line running from the anterior or head end to the posterior or tail end of this axis. In general we recognize that the most active and the most sensitive organs are aggregated at or near the anterior end of this axis. The anterior end is the APICAL END or the controlling end of the axis. A secondary axiate arrangement is the AXIS OF SYMMETRY, which may be thought of as being the resultant of two elements (DORSOVENTRAL and BILATERAL AXES). Although we realize the importance of the symmetry relations as elements in the maintenance of organic individuality, it will be simpler to confine our attention at this time strictly to the primary axis.

In a higher organism that has a well developed brain and nerve cord it is easy to understand how the apical parts of the organism can coördinate and keep in control all other parts of the organism. The brain is the apical point of both primary and secondary axes

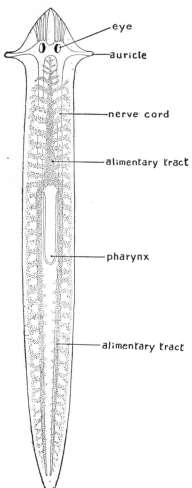

and, since the brain is the most active tissue, dynamic changes in the brain are readily transmitted over the nerve paths to other parts of the organism, and subordinate parts are kept in line through their dynamic connections with controlling parts. Man, of course, is the culmination of individuation, the finest example of the control of the whole individual by the dominant region, the brain, but the same type of thing is found all the way down the scale of animals until we come to the simplest forms, even those without nervous tissues.

F. The Axial Gradient Theory Experimentally Tested

Physiological evidence as to the nature and mode of operation of the factors that make for individuation—a useful word meaning the production or maintenance of an individual—may best be set forth in connection with the familiar flatworm, Planaria.

Fig. 29. *Planaria dorotocephala*, showing especially its axiate organization. (After Child.)

Planaria dorotocephala (Fig. 29) is a typical flatworm belonging to the Phylum Platyhelminthes. In Chapter XVI this group will be dealt with in detail. Our interest at present is to be confined to a very brief statement of the axiate organization and the evidences for it. Planaria is almost diagrammatically an axiate organism, with (a) a well defined axis of polarity extending from anterior to posterior, and (b) an equally well defined axis of symmetry running from the mid-ventral region dorsally and laterally and expressing itself in dorsoventral flattening and in bilateral symmetry. While we have equally good physiological evidences for the minor axis, we shall confine our demonstration at this time to the major gradient, the axis of polarity. Morphologically, it is obvious enough that the apical or anterior part of the axis (the head) is more highly differentiated than the rest of the body, which, except for the presence of the pharynx about halfway back, shows no obvious gradations in degrees of differentiation. The head has a pair of cephalic ganglia (the brain) which have associated with them a pair of primitive eyes, a pair of lateral auricles whose function is probably tactile, and a series of terminal sensory end organs which probably subserve a general chemical-sensory function. Running backward from the paired ganglia are two nerve cords, separated some distance from each other and fused with the ventral ectoderm. The whole organism appears to be designed as a true organism should be, with controlling region situated in an advanced part of the body and well connected up by means of communication paths with subordinate regions. This is as far as a purely morphological analysis will take us.

By experimental procedures, however, we can discover further evidences of axiate organization that are not visible to the eye. If, for example, we remove both the head and the tail end—the latter is known to be a prospective second zoöid and is therefore not an integral part of the individual—we can prove that the middle part of the body is not all of the same character, but that a gradient of metabolic activity runs from anterior to posterior ends. If, after head and tail are removed, we cut up a hundred worms each into four pieces, and separate anterior pieces, second pieces, third pieces, and posterior pieces, into four groups, we can test them chemically as to their rates of metabolism. It has been shown that the anterior pieces use up more oxygen and give off more carbon dioxide than the rest, that second pieces come next, third pieces next, and posterior pieces last. The same relations hold good if eight pieces are taken. There is therefore a true gradient in the rate of fundamental chemical activity running from anterior to posterior, each anterior level having a higher rate than any level posterior to it. It has also been shown that the bioelectric current runs (internally) from the anterior toward the posterior, from the point of higher metabolic rate to lower.

The SUSCEPTIBILITY METHOD of testing the gradient brings out the same plan of organization. If one puts planarians in a solution of an anæsthetic, whose known effect is that of lowering the rate of oxidation, those parts needing oxygen most—that is, the parts with the highest rate of metabolism—will show the first signs of injury and there will be a wave of injury running down the gradient. If we use a concentration of anæsthetic sufficient to kill and disintegrate tissues, but weak enough to kill only slowly, we find a progressive wave of death changes proceeding slowly down the axis from anterior to posterior levels.

In general, it may be said that the chemical character of the axiate plan of organization has been demonstrated in many different ways and the results are all consistent with each other and with the conception that the nature of the organizational control is dynamic and depends upon the relationship of dominance of regions of highest metabolic rate over all regions of lower metabolic rate. If each region of the axis dominates all regions subordinate to it and all regions are subordinate to one point of highest rate, the apical end or head, we have the necessary mechanism for holding together all the parts of an individual under unit control. In other words, we have in this dynamic system the mechanism of organization, of the maintenance of individuality.

G. SUMMARY

This important conception will necessarily need further explanation, but it seems better to leave it for the present, postponing further elaboration for later chapters. For our purposes it is important to have emphasized at this point in the course an important biological principle, usually called The Organismal Theory, which is of general significance for the whole subject and must rank as one of the three great zoölogical principles, the others being the Cell Theory and the Evolution Theory. The Cell Theory and the Organismal Theory seem to be more or less opposed to each other, the former emphasizing the individual parts that make up an organism, the latter laying stress upon the fundamental unity of the whole organism. Both are generalizations of wide application and together they apply to the whole biological field, in so far at least as we are dealing with organisms of today. Evolution is essentially the historical view and involves inquiries into the past. It deals with problems of the origin and development of the present organic world.

These three great principles run as main threads through the fabric of the science of Zoölogy, and from here on for some time to come we shall study the implications of these concepts as exemplified in the various groups of animals as they exist today.

We are now ready to make a general survey of the animal kingdom, or at least of the groups that represent the principal levels of organization. As we proceed with our examination of these groups, and especially as we enter upon a more or less intensive study of certain types that are chosen as representatives of the groups, the main principles of biology will be exemplified and many minor principles will be introduced. In this way we shall do two things at once: learn something about a representative array of real animals, and carry on as we go a further study of the underlying principles of the subject.

CHAPTER IX

THE ANIMAL KINGDOM

A. The Naturalist's Point of View

Perhaps the best preparation for the study of Zoölogy is to capture the spirit of the subject by taking the attitude of the naturalist toward it. The true naturalist is one who sees Nature broadly and is able to soften the focus of his mind's eye so as to catch an impressionistic vision of the whole. For a time let us forget the infinite details of structure and function and view with the synoptic eye of the naturalist a representative patch or two of Nature's endless patchwork.

1. *The Tide Pool Complex*

One finds in the tide pools of the Pacific Coast, such as those near Monterey, California, examples of Nature in some of her most lavish and kaleidoscopic aspects. If one has the opportunity to spend an hour or so in an examination of these pools, especially if the tide be more than commonly low, he will come away with the feeling that he has spent his time in a veritable animate museum. Almost all of the main groups of animals are represented in any pool of moderate size, and the numbers of individuals of many of the more conspicuous types exceed all expectation.

Perhaps the most obvious of all the peculiar forms are the echinoderms. The bottom is literally paved with purple and wine colored sea urchins, ranging in size from a quarter of an inch to six inches in diameter. The rocky walls and floors of the pools are decorated with the colorful forms of starfishes of several species, blood red, orange, yellow, cream, purple, gray, brown, and green. The twenty-rayed starfish, with soft, tentacle-like arms, adds a touch of weirdness to the scene.

Enormous numbers of mollusks, representing a great variety of orders and families, rival the echinoderms for supremacy as the dominant tide pool inhabitants. One can count in a few minutes scores of species of gastropods (sea snails). Conspicuous among these are the well known abalone, the large Cryptochiton (the sea hare), and several kinds of nudibranchs; but more varied and numerous are the many species of limpets, chitons, and ordinary snails. Although not commonly an inhabitant of the smaller pools, the octopus is occasionally caught in them and thus isolated for a few hours from his usual haunts.

Almost equally in evidence are the crustaceans. Crabs of various sorts scramble over to rocks or swim about in the water. Barnacles, degenerate relatives of the crabs, form rugged incrustations upon the rocks, their knifelike shells a menace to waders. Shrimps, isopods, and amphipods dart from shelter to shelter.

Marine worms of many sorts lend variety to the scene. Some crawl about with the wriggling wormlike motion that characterizes their kind; others swim with graceful undulations through the water; still others—and these are the most interesting and attractive in appearance and the least wormlike in aspect—are the fixed, or sessile, tube dwellers, whose pink and orange plumes (branchiæ) wave gracefully about on their stems like rows of delicate flowers. One can hardly believe that these are animals at all until at a touch of the finger, the flower-like plumes are suddenly withdrawn into the shelter of the tube, only to blossom forth again when all is quiet.

The cœlenterates, too, are well represented. Giant sea anemones spread their broad tentacled faces as traps for the unwary, while innumerable smaller sea anemones spread their multicolored tentacles like gardens of flowers. An occasional spectral jellyfish floats jerkily by, propelling himself with rhythmic contractions of his umbrella-like body. All sorts of colonial hydroids, aided by incrusting sponges and bryozoans (moss animals) help to soften the contours of the rocks and form a miniature forest shelter for the hosts of microscopic animals—chiefly larvæ and protozoans—that make of the sea water a veritable "sea-soup" upon which many of the somewhat larger forms subsist.

Almost overlooked at first because they are so perfectly camouflaged, but far from being the least important elements in the intricate complex, are the tide pool fishes that take toll of most of the edible small fry.

In addition to all of these strange and interesting creatures— and we have named only a few of the most conspicuous of the tide pool organisms—are the seaweeds: kelps, sea lettuce, Fucus. These play the indispensable rôle of furnishing food for the herbivorous animals and of keeping the waters supplied with fresh oxygen, to say nothing of the fact that they give shelter to many of the more timid and retiring animals that haunt their fronds and their roots.

While such an intricate complex of conflicting and struggling organisms may seem to the uninitiated observer to be nothing but confusion, the ecologist sees in it a settled order, a balanced community, holding its equilibrium from age to age.

2. *The Inhabitants of Two Square Feet of Soil*

As a companion study to the marine picture outlined above, let us look for a few moments at a little plot of dry land. An investigator of the United States Department of Agriculture, interested in the problem of the food of birds, set out to discover just what animals and plants inhabit two square feet of soil to a depth of a bird's ability to scratch. In this little patch of meadow soil he found 1254 animal objects and 3113 plant objects. These consisted of a great variety of kinds of living creatures. One kind of soil inhabitant that few persons have ever seen or even suspected the existence of is the group known as nematode worms, tiny little threadworms whose sheer numbers open our eyes to unexpected vistas of the limitless myriads of living things.

In a monograph on these animals, **N. A. Cobb,** a leading student of the group, says:—

"Not the least interesting thing about nematodes is the astounding variety of their habits. They occur in arid deserts, on the bottoms of lakes and rivers, in the waters of hot springs and in polar seas where the temperature is constantly below the freezing point of fresh water. They were thawed out alive from Antarctic ice in the far south by the Shackleton expedition. . . . A thimbleful of mud from the bottom of river or ocean may contain hundreds of specimens. The nematodes of a 10-acre field, if arrayed in single file, would form a procession long enough to reach around the world. A lump of soil no larger than the end of one's thumb may contain hundreds, even thousands, of nematodes, and yet present few points that would distinguish it from a lump of soil destitute of these organisms. . . . In short, if all other matter in the universe were swept away, our world would still be dimly recognizable, and if, as disembodied spirits, we could then investigate it, we should find its mountains, hills, vales, rivers, lakes, and oceans represented by a film of nematodes. The locations of the towns would be decipherable, since for every massing of human beings there would be corresponding massing of certain nematodes. Trees would stand in ghostly rows representing our streets and highways."

3. *The Superabundance of Life*

Innumerable as are the animals in every nook and cranny of the world, there seems to be no limit to the urge of life to multiply and to increase itself. Always more and more creatures of every sort are being born and there is a constant oversupply, a prodigality of wastefulness, which means a constant struggle for existence. Perhaps we may see with Darwin the value of overproduction in that it gives Nature a chance to select the best and throw out the poorest; thus may the standard be maintained or even improved. The world is now so running over with life that only those types or those individuals that can succeed in meeting the conditions of competition persist and leave offspring Thus we can understand, with Darwin, why all living things seem to be so well adapted to the conditions of life; for how could a poorly adapted form have come through these ages of struggle till now?

4. *General Remarks*

We have now with the sweeping naturalist's eye looked, with vision not too sharply focused for details, over the world of teeming life. We have noted its amazing variety and almost inconceivable abundance. We see that the earth's surface is not only a lithosphere and an aquasphere, but a biosphere as well; for there is an almost unbroken layer of life covering the surface of the globe. One cannot long be satisfied, however, with this impressionistic view of life. The human instinct to group, to classify, gains the upper hand, and we yield to it here to the extent of presenting, as a preliminary to the more intensive study of some selected groups and types, a general systematic survey of the broad divisions and interrelation of the animal kingdom.

B. The Method of Classification

When we look over the animal kingdom as a whole, we begin to notice that there are certain assemblages that hang together because they possess in common one or a number of unique structural characteristics. Thus, it is not difficult to sort out of the miscellany of the world's animals a great group of backboned animals which we call vertebrates. We recognize that the vertebrates are composed of a mixed assortment of forms which we have come to designate as fishes, amphibians, reptiles, birds, and mammals. There are, however, several groups of animals, such as the lancelets, tunicates, and enteropneustans, that are not fully vertebrates but have certain combinations of characters that only they and the vertebrates possess. This suggests that they are the distant relatives of the vertebrates, derived from a remote common ancestor. Feeling that all of these groups are bound together by ties of blood relationship, we have brought them all into a large assemblage, or phylum, called the Chordata. A phylum is a major division of a kingdom or of a subkingdom. If highly diversified, as is the phylum Chordata, it may be divided into subphyla; but usually the next division after a phylum is a class. Classes are divided into orders (sometimes subclasses being an intermediate grouping). Orders are divided into families; families, into genera (singular, genus); genera, into species; and species, into varieties. In the larger more highly diversified phyla other intermediate groupings are sometimes necessary, such as series, legions, and cohorts. The more we come to know about a group of animals, the more we see the need of specialized modes of grouping. Experts in various groups come to be familiar with all of the available forms belonging to their particular field and are likely to see the need of subdivisions of various kinds that a superficial survey fails to reveal. Thus, with increasing specialization comes the tendency for more elaborate systems of classification and a multiplicity of new names and divisions. Fortunately, perhaps, for our present purposes, we do not need to go into classification further than to outline its broader aspects.

As a concrete illustration of the ranking of the various recognized categories of the animal kingdom let us trace out the classification of a red squirrel:—

SUBKINGDOM—*Metazoa* (multicellular organisms)
  PHYLUM—*Chordata* (the chordates)
    SUBPHYLUM—*Craniata* (the vertebrates)
      CLASS—*Mammalia* (the mammals)
        SUBCLASS—*Eutheria* (viviparous mammals)

DIVISION—*Monodelphia* (placental mammals)
SECTION—*Unguiculata* (clawed mammals)
ORDER—*Rodentia* (the rodents)
SUBORDER—*Sciuromorpha* (squirrel-like rodents)
FAMILY—*Sciuridæ* (flying squirrels, marmots, squirrels, chipmunks, etc.)
SUBFAMILY—*Sciurinæ* (marmots, squirrels, chipmunks)
GENUS—*Sciurus* (tree squirrels)
SUBGENUS—*Tamiasciurus* (red squirrels)
SPECIES—*hudsonicus* (Hudsonian red squirrel)
SUBSPECIES—*loquax* (Southern Hudsonian red squirrel)

The majority of animals would have as elaborate a classification as this, and some have an even more imposing taxonomic setting. We need not fear, however, that it will be necessary to characterize all of our animal friends in this fashion. We do not care to place so difficult a hurdle before the uninitiated, for many of the veterans would come a cropper if required to give from memory a classification like that just presented.

C. THE MAJOR DIVISIONS OF THE ANIMAL KINGDOM

For our present purposes we need only name and characterize the phyla and their broadest subdivisions.

Subkingdom A, Protozoa

Those who see in the Protozoa nothing more significant than that they appear to be one-celled animals, commonly rank this immense group of small animals as a phylum on a par with any one of the dozen or more other phyla of the animal kingdom. There is a growing conviction, however, that the Protozoa represent a vast system parallel to and in many ways equivalent to the rest of the animal kingdom. Some of our protozoölogists, such as Dobell, Calkins, Kofoid, see in the Protozoa almost all of the biological situations found in Metazoa. Subsequent facts brought out in the chapter on the Protozoa will, we think, justify us in giving to this group subkingdom value. Four classes of Protozoa are distinguished:—

Sarcadina

CLASS I. RHIZOPODA. Protozoa with pseudopodia, which are changeable protoplasmic processes. ⟨Example, **Amœba.**

CLASS II. MASTIGOPHORA. Protozoa with one or more whiplike vibratile processes, used for locomotion and in the capture of food. Example, **Euglena.**

CLASS III. INFUSORIA. Protozoa with numerous small hairlike vibratile processes (cilia) used for locomotion and feeding; with fixed opening for food ingestion and for the extrusion of solid wastes. Example, **Paramecium.**

CLASS IV. SPOROZOA. Parasitic Protozoa; usually without special organs of locomotion and without mouth; reproduction by spores. Example, **Monocystis.**

If the Protozoa be given the rank of a subkingdom, it would be appropriate to elevate the classes to phylum value. This, in fact, has been done by some of the most ardent advocates of the equality of the Protozoa with the Metazoa.

Subkingdom B, Metazoa

Under this subdivision would come all animal organisms that are not Protozoa, with the exception of a few anomalous types commonly spoken of as Mesozoa, that seem to fall midway between the two subkingdoms. There is no unanimity among zoölogists as to the number of phyla of Metazoa. *Calkins,* a protozoölogist, recognizes seventeen phyla and even then omits several smaller groups recognized as phyla by other authorities. According to his classification Crustacea, Arachnida, Insecta are each given phylum value and Myriapoda are left out in the cold. Similarly, Tunicata are taken out of the Chordata and given phylum value, while Balanoglossus and its relatives are left out of consideration.

A more conservative classification of the Metazoa gives us ten major phyla and ten groups of animals of uncertain affinities, which cannot safely be placed in any of the ten well defined phyla, but may represent as many small phyla of their own. In this book we shall confine our discussion to the ten major phyla.

PHYLUM I. PORIFERA (the sponges). Diploblastic, asymmetrical or radially symmetrical animals, with loose organization and ill-defined individuality. The body is perforated by numerous pores and is supported by a skeleton of calcareous or silicious spicules or of spongin. Example, **Grantia.**

Class 1. *Calcarea.*

Class 2. *Hexactinellida.*

Class 3. *Demospongia.*

These classes are distinguished chiefly by the form and composition of the skeletal spicules and by other considerations of a technical character.

PHYLUM II. CŒLENTERATA. These are diploblastic, radially symmetrical animals, with a single gastrovascular cavity, tentacles, stinging cells (nematocysts), no anus. The life history typically involves an alternation of generations between a hydroid type and a medusa type. The group includes **polyps, jellyfishes, sea anemones,** and **corals.**

Class 1. *Hydrozoa.* Without stomodæum or mesenteries, eggs and sperms discharged to the exterior, hydroid and medusoid forms in life cycle, though only medusoid forms (with a velum) of some species are known. The group includes **Hydra,** colonial **Hydrozoa,** and **a few small jellyfishes.**

Class 2. *Scyphozoa.* Cœlenterates without conspicuous hydroid stage in the life cycle. The medusa stage is large and elaborate and has no velum; margin of umbrella notched. **Larger jellyfishes.**

Class 3. *Anthozoa.* Cœlenterates without medusa stage in life cycle, stomodæum and mesenteries well developed. **Sea anemones** and **corals.**

PHYLUM III. CTENOPHORA (the comb-jellies). This is a relatively small phylum of jellyfish-like sea animals that are triploblastic; with partly radial, partly bilateral symmetry; and with eight bands of vibratile swimming plates composed of rows of fused cilia radially arranged. **Sea walnuts, comb jellies.**

PHYLUM IV. PLATYHELMINTHES (the flatworms). These are triploblastic, creeping, animals, with body much flattened dorsoventrally and with pronounced bilateral symmetry; there is a single gastrovascular cavity with no anus; in extreme parasitic forms there is no digestive tract.

Class 1. *Turbellaria.* Free-living flatworms with ciliated epidermis. Example, **Planaria.**

Class 2. *Trematoda.* Parasitic flatworms without cilia in the adult condition, attaching themselves to host by means of suckers. Example, the **liver flukes.**

Class 3. *Cestodes.* Parasitic flatworms consisting of a head, or attachment individual, connected with a linear ribbonlike series of minor individuals (proglottids) that are produced by transverse fission from one original individual. **Tapeworms.**

PHYLUM V. NEMATHELMINTHES (roundworms, threadworms). Triploblastic, bilaterally symmetrical worms; with long slender body; a body cavity, sometimes considered a cœlom; digestive tract with both mouth and anus. Example, **Ascaris.**

PHYLUM VI. ECHINODERMATA. This group has no common name. Triploblastic, radially symmetrical forms, with well developed cœlom, usually with five radially repeated divisions, or antimeres; a calcareous dermal skeleton and usually dermal spines; a water-vascular system operating a system of locomotor structures, the "tube-feet." The group includes starfishes, brittle stars, sea urchins, sea cucumbers and stone lilies.

Class 1. *Asteroidea.* Free-living starshaped forms with wide arms not sharply marked off from the central disk; distinct ambulacral grooves. **Starfishes.**

Class 2. *Ophiuroidea.* Free-living, long-armed forms, the slender arms marked off sharply from the central disk, and no open ambulacral grooves. **Brittle stars, serpent stars, basket stars.**

Class 3. *Echinoidea.* Free-living, frequently sedentary forms without arms; a solid test composed of closely united plates; movable spines. **Sea urchins, heart urchins, sand dollars.**

Class 4. *Holothuroidea.* Free-living, more or less elongated echinoderms with soft body and very muscular body wall; skeleton represented by microscopic plates; a crown of specialized tube-feet around the mouth, acting as tentacles in feeding. **Sea cucumbers.**

Class 5. *Crinoidea.* Fixed (sessile) echinoderms fastened to a stalk by aboral surface, with oral surface turned upwards; five arms, usually much branched; skeleton very solid and heavy; stalk frequently jointed. Some species are secondarily free-living. **Feather stars, stone lilies, sea lilies.**

PHYLUM VII. ANNELIDA (The segmented worms). Triploblastic, bilaterally symmetrical elongated worms, characterized by well defined internal and external metameric segmentation; well defined cœlom (except in leeches); skin bristles, or setæ, usually present.

Class 1. Archiannelida. Primitive marine worms without parapodia or setæ. Example, **Polygordius.**

Class 2. Chætopoda. Annelids with setæ and segmented cœlom; marine, fresh-water, and terrestrial habitat. Examples, **Nereis** and **earthworm.**

Class 3. Hirudinea. Somewhat flattened annelids with blood-sucking habits, and provided with anterior and posterior suckers. **Leeches.**

PHYLUM VIII. MOLLUSCA (Mollusks). Triploblastic, nonmetameric, bilateral or asymmetrical, animals; with cœlom secondarily obliterated; usually with a muscular foot; an external secreted shell usually present. **Snails, clam,** etc.

Class 1. Amphineura. Mollusks with definite bilateral symmetry; a series of several shells on the back, and several pairs of gills. The **Chitons.**

Class 2. Gastropoda. Mollusks with distinct head and with body more or less spirally coiled; shell in one piece, sometimes spirally coiled. **Snails.**

Class 3. Pelecypoda. Mollusks with obvious bilateral symmetry; headless; shell consisting of paired valves; a bilobed mantle. **Mussels, clams.**

Class 4. Cephalopoda. Mollusks with head and foot fused into an elaborate tentacled secondary head; bilaterally symmetrical externally; suckers on the tentacles. **Squids, cuttlefishes, octopi.**

Class 5. Scaphopoda. Mollusks with elongated form; with tuskshaped shell; headless; bilaterally symmetrical; foot trilobed. Example, **Dentalium.**

PHYLUM IX. ARTHROPODA (Arthropods). Triploblastic, bilaterally symmetrical, metameric animals, with segmentation well defined externally but largely obliterated internally; cœlom much reduced; paired, jointed appendages; chitinous exoskeleton; regional specialization of somites.

Class 1. *Crustacea.* Gill-breathing arthropods with two pairs of antennæ. **Crayfish, shrimps, crabs,** etc.

Class 2. *Onychophora.* Primitive arthropods, with annelid-like nephridia and insectlike tracheæ. **Peripatus.**

Class 3. *Myriapoda.* Tracheate arthropods with one pair of antennæ and numerous legs. **Centipedes.**

Class 4. *Insecta.* Tracheate arthropods with three pairs of legs and one pair of antennæ. **Insects.**

Class 5. *Arachnida.* Arthropods with gill books, lung books, or tracheæ; no antennæ. **Spiders, scorpions, mites, Limulus,** etc.

PHYLUM X. CHORDATA (Chordates). Animals possessing at some stage a notochord, pharyngeal clefts, and a central nervous system arising from the middorsal ectoderm.

Subphylum 1. *Hemichordata.* Animals with some chordate affinities, but not fully accepted as chordates. Some are worm-like, others sessile. **Balangolossus, Cephalodiscus.**

Subphylum 2. *Urochordata.* Chordates with notochord confined to temporary tail of larva. Adults are usually degenerate, sessile, headless types. **Tunicates, salpians, appendicularians.**

Subphylum 3. *Cephalochordata.* Small sand burrowing, somewhat fishlike chordates, with permanent notochord extending from end to end and numerous pharyngeal clefts. **Amphioxus.**

Subphylum 4. *Craniata* (Vertebrates).

Class 1. *Cyclostomata.* Eellike aquatic vertebrates without jaws, paired fins, or scales; a permanent notochord. **Hagfishes** and **lampreys.**

Class 2. *Elasmobranchii.* Cold-blooded, fishlike vertebrates; with jaws, gills, paired fins, cartilaginous skeleton, placoid scales, and no air bladder. **Sharks, skates, rays.**

Class 3. *Pisces* (True fishes). Aquatic, cold-blooded vertebrates; with jaws and paired fins; scales; a two chambered heart; air bladder, sometimes used as lung. **Perch, trout,** etc.

Class 4. Amphibia. Cold-blooded vertebrates with gills during larval life, lungs in adult; scales usually absent; heart three chambered. **Newts, salamanders, frogs.**

Class 5. Reptilia (Reptiles). Cold-blooded vertebrates; without functional gills at any time; covered with scales; three chambered heart. **Turtles, crocodiles, lizards, snakes.**

Class 6. Aves (Birds). Warm-blooded vertebrates, with wings, feathers, a four chambered heart.

Class 7. Mammalia (Mammals). Warm-blooded vertebrates, at some stage covered with hair; young suckled by mammary glands; a muscular diaphragm separating thorax and abdomen.

D. Discussion of the Probable Interrelationships of the Animal Phyla

The problem of the phylogenetic (ancestral) relationships of the various animal phyla to one another received a great deal of attention from morphologists of the older schools, but during the last few decades the experimental method has come so to dominate biological science that the somewhat speculative phylogenetic aspects of the science have grown into disrepute. Of late, however, interest in phylogeny has been revived in various parts of the world, especially in connection with one of our great seaside laboratories, where a group of American zoölogists have collaborated in working out a new theory of phyletic relationships that has come to be known as the theory of the DIPHYLETIC TREE, a diagrammatic expression of which is shown in Figure 30 on the following page.

This theory is coming to be rather widely accepted as the best supported guess as to the broader lines of animal relationship, but must not be accepted as more than tentative at the present time. Uncertain as it is in some of its details, it has great pedagogical value in that it helps to unify and correlate our knowledge of animal morphology, and especially of those very general characteristics of organisms that form the bases of classification of animals into their larger groupings.

To give an adequate presentation of the evidences upon which the theory is based would not only require more pages than we can spare, but would involve us in a technical discussion of many

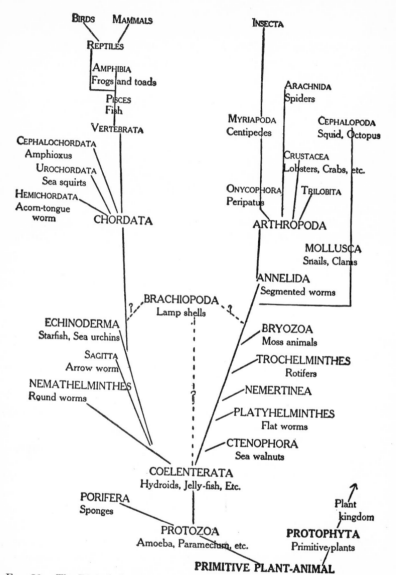

Fig. 30.   The Diphyletic Tree.   (After Allee, courtesy University of Chicago Press.)

matters that would be quite unintelligible to beginning students. Since, however, we propose to present the representatives of the various phyla in the order suggested by the diphyletic system of descent, it seems necessary to attempt a brief and simplified justification of the diphyletic tree.

1. *The Simpler Forms*

a. The Primitive Plant-animals.—At the bottom of the tree we find an anomalous group of lowly organisms, unicellular in character and possessed of a combination of plant and animal characters. In this group we would place the slime molds and such forms as Euglena, Volvox, and others that are claimed by both botanists and zoölogists.

b. The Protozoa.—From the plant-animals it is believed that two main branches arose, the PROTOPHYTA (unicellular plants) and PROTOZOA (unicellular animals). From these two main trunks arose the Animal and the Plant Kingdoms. Since this is a course in Zoölogy, we shall confine our attention to the Animal Kingdom. At the bottom of the main animal trunk are the Protozoa, many representatives of which are still surviving in the primitive form so far as their unicellular character is concerned. The ancestral Protozoa are believed to have undergone divergence into two distinct subkingdoms, modern PROTOZOA and METAZOA. The Protozoa have retained the one-celled structure characteristic of the earliest forms of life and have proceeded to specialize parts of the single cell for various functions. The Metazoa have adopted the scheme of multicellularity, involving specialization of groups of cells for a great variety of functions. Hence the Protozoa might be called CELL ANIMALS and the Metazoa TISSUE ANIMALS.

c. The Porifera (Sponges).—This group is multicellular with a relatively slight degree of cellular differentiation and a poorly defined axiate organization. They are viewed as an unprogressive side line of evolution that has led to no other groups than to the sponges themselves, the least animated of present-day animals. Because they seem to have no affinities to any other Metazoa, the Porifera may be considered as a third independent offshoot of the primitive protozoan stock correlative with the Protozoa and the Metazoa. They might be called PARAZOA.

d. The Cœlenterata.—Constituting the first really progressive metazoan stock and generally recognized as belonging at the base of the main trunk of metazoan evolution, and thus the ancestral to all higher groups, are the Cœlenterata. The cœlenterates are the only DIPLOBLASTIC forms now living and are also the only forms that exhibit no bilateral symmetry, but are primitively radially symmetrical.

2. *The Basis for the Diphyletic System*

Above the cœlenterate level the diphyletic system begins, for all the other phyla, with a few doubtful exceptions, may be arranged in the form of two main branches each subdividing into a number of minor branches. The right-hand branch in our diagram (Fig. 30) contains the majority of metazoan phyla and is called for convenience the ANNELID-ARTHROPOD BRANCH; the left branch includes only a few phyla and is called the ECHINODERM-CHORDATE BRANCH. The series of forms making up the two great branches have many fundamental features in common among the members of the same branch, and many differences between the members of different branches. Some of the *criteria upon which the diphyletic arrangement rests* may be briefly outlined as follows:—

a. **Determinate and Indeterminate Cleavage.**—The members of the Annelid-arthropod series exhibit typically a mode of cleavage (the early divisions of the egg leading to embryo formation) known as DETERMINATE. In this type of cleavage the blastomeres, or early embryonic cells, are very definitely arranged in a stereotyped pattern and each early cell has a fixed prospective rôle in the formation of a particular part of the body. The members of the Echinoderm-chordate series, on the other hand, exhibit typically a mode of cleavage known as INDETERMINATE, in which the cleavage pattern lacks definiteness and the early blastomeres retain their unspecialized character and whose fate in tissue formation is still undetermined. There are several important exceptions to this rule that will readily occur to any zoölogist, but there are explanations for these that cannot be presented without too serious a digression.

b. **Methods of Mesoderm Formation.**—In the members of the Annelid-arthropod series the mesoderm (third germ layer) arises from one particular cleavage cell designated by students of cell lineage as "4D." This cell gives rise by division to two pole cells from which two solid mesodermic bands, a right and a left, proliferate. In the Echinoderm-arthropod series the mesoderm arises in an entirely different fashion, as an outgrowth of an already well-defined embryonic tissue, the primitive gut, or archenteron.

c. Methods of Cœlom Formation.—In the Annelid-arthropod series the cœlom, or true body cavity, arises by a secondary hollowing out of the originally solid mesodermal bands, the cells merely spreading apart so as to produce a cavity or series of paired cavities. In the Echinoderm-chordate series the cœlom is formed by means of paired out-pouchings of the archenteron, or primitive gut. In these the cavity is present from the first and was once continuous with the archenteric cavity.

d. Mouth Formation.—In the Annelid-arthropod series the blastopore, or primitive mouth, of the blastula (the two-layered embryonic stage) gives rise directly to the true mouth of later stages and an anus is secondarily opened up at the opposite end. In the Echinoderm-chordate series the primitive mouth of the blastula becomes the anus of later stages and a new mouth is opened up by secondary processes.

All of these criteria represent morphologic characters of a very deep-seated and fundamental sort, about the most fundamental that could well be found. Taken together they afford a firmer foundation for phylogenetic theory than we have had heretofore.

3. *General Statement about the Annelid-arthropod Assemblage*

We are not to think of the members of this series as in any sense a linear phylogenetic series, each higher type being a descendant of the type next lower in the series. Rather, it seems more likely that they all represent side branches from some as yet unknown ancestral stem that gave rise at different levels to the ancestors of the present-day phyla. A hypothetical "trochozoan" common ancestor has been suggested, a type resembling in some respects the trochophore larvæ of the various phyla and in other respects the adult ctenophores of today. Among the upper phyla of this series there is evidence of much more direct descent. Connecting link types, both living and fossil, help to bridge the gaps between the annelids and the arthropods and between the various arthropod classes.

4. *General Statement about the Echinoderm-chordate Assemblage*

The left-hand branch of the tree contains relatively few phyla, but must not be neglected, for this is the branch that has given rise to the vertebrates, including man. The series includes the roundworms, the arrow worms, the echinoderms, the various subphyla of chordates, and the true vertebrates. There is some question as to the correctness of this placing of the roundworms. At best they must be viewed as an early aberrant side branch that has been relatively unprogressive in structure, but extraordinarily successful in exploiting the earth. The affinities between the echinoderms and the chordates, and between the latter and the vertebrates, are unmistakable. It is thought that the main stem ancestral type must have resembled in many respects the larvæ of certain types of echinoderms and chordates. There is, for example, a striking resemblance between the larva of the primitive chordate, Balanoglossus, and those of such echinoderms as the starfishes and sea cucumbers. In several other important respects the echinoderms and the chordates show resemblances, but these are of too technical a nature to be presented at this time. For similar reasons it would be inadvisable to discuss the anomalous position of the Brachiopoda or to justify the placing of the Nemathelminthes at the bottom of the left-hand branch.

While it is not expected that the beginning student will at this early stage of the course fully understand the last few paragraphs, he will at least have grasped the general idea of the diphyletic tree and will appreciate the order of presentation of the types of the various phyla, an order that is suggested by the relationships discussed above.

PART II

ANIMAL TYPES (INVERTEBRATES)

CHAPTER X

THE SUBKINGDOM PROTOZOA

A. Protozoa Defined and Characterized

Protozoa have been defined as organisms consisting of one cell, while Metazoa are organisms consisting of many cells. It is implied that we mean the same thing by the word "cell" in both cases. The whole protozoan individual is supposed to be essentially equivalent to any single cell of a metazoan organism except that the latter may be specialized in many ways for particular functions, while the former has retained the primitive versatility of ancestral cells and is therefore able to perform all the necessary vital functions. Out of this conception of the Protozoa the conviction has grown that they are essentially extremely simple animals without special organs for special functions, and that the undifferentiated protoplasm performs all functions. This interpretation of the Protozoa is the logical result of a too slavish adherence to the Cell Theory: the idea that a cell is a cell wherever one finds it and that a protozoan is merely an independent cell. This conception of the Protozoa is misleading and needs to be contrasted sharply with the organismal view of this group.

First and foremost, a protozoan is an organism. That it is an organism without divisions into separate cells is an important consideration, but it is not paramount. *Clifford Dobell,* the eminent English protozoölogist, expresses the most radical antagonism to the interpretation of Protozoa as one-celled animals when he says that the protozoan body "does not correspond to a minute fragment of a metazoan body, one of its myriads of cells, but to the whole body." Dobell's distinction between the Protozoa and the Metazoa is expressed in the idea that the latter are cellular, the former noncellular.

According to this conception the metazoan is an organism which has made use of the scheme of dividing up its nucleus and cytoplasm into a large number of units (cells) the more effectively to accomplish differentiation into organs and tissues specialized for particular functions. The protozoan is likewise a complete organism which has been able to attain various degrees of complexity of organization and specialization of function without resort to the cellular scheme. Protozoa have in many cases great complexity of organization. Organs of all sorts are to be found within the limits of the protozoan body, but they are not composed of tissues or cells in the sense of the Cell Theory.

On the other side of this controversy it must be said that a protozoan usually has but one nucleus; that this nucleus contains chromatin; that distinct chromosomes may often be distinguished; that nuclei divide by a process very similar to mitotic cell division; and that the whole protozoan body is divided much as a single cell is divided. Moreover, whole protozoans are differentiated into gametes, equivalent to egg cells or sperm cells in the Metazoa, and the sperm individuals fuse with the egg individuals in a fashion that is unmistakably equivalent to fertilization. Not only this, but prior to their union the prospective gametes appear to undergo reduction divisions similar to those exhibited by eggs and sperm cells during maturation. This and much more evidence points strongly to the conclusion that protozoans are cells and that the whole individual protozoan is in a sense equivalent to a germ cell or any other cell of a metazoan organism. Dobell's radical suggestion that Protozoa be regarded as noncellular organisms is, therefore, not likely to gain general acceptance. Yet he has done good service in pointing out that a too slavish adherence to the implications of the Cell Theory has caused the Protozoa to be wrongly interpreted. With Professor Ritter, we may conclude that in connection with the Protozoa "the concept *cell* must be held in strict subordination to the concept *organism*, in this as well as in other portions of the living world." The protozoan is unquestionably a cell, but it is more than that: it is a complete organism.

B. The False Idea of the Simplicity of Protozoa

Because a protozoan is a single cell, an impression has come to prevail that it is on that account relatively simple. "Hardly anything," says **Ritter,** "could be more misleading than the almost universal practice in elementary teaching of introducing beginners to the protozoa by showing, very superficially, an Amoeba and emphasizing its simplicity, and then keeping it in the foreground of the learner's thought as an exemplification of the doctrine that the Protozoa are 'extremely simple' animals, that they are undifferentiated into organs and tissues—that in fact they are hardly 'true animals at all.'" No better method of correcting this misapprehension is available than to compare a highly differentiated

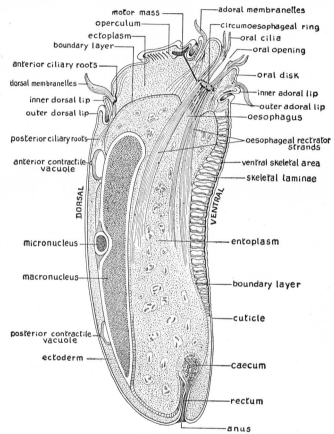

FIG. 31. *Diplodinium ecaudatum.* An example of a complex protozoan. (After Sharp.)

protozoan with one of the simpler metazoans. For this purpose let us compare *Diplodinium ecaudatum* (Fig. 31)—a ciliate protozoan which inhabits the intestine of cattle—with a fresh-water Hydra (Fig. 32). Both figures are longitudinal sections showing the amount of differentiation present. Which is the more complex, and which the simpler organism? One basis for comparison of the degree of differentiation present is to count the labeled regions in the two. There are 33 labeled structures, all of them different, in the protozoan, Diplodinium, and only 16 different labeled struc-tures in the metazoan, Hydra.

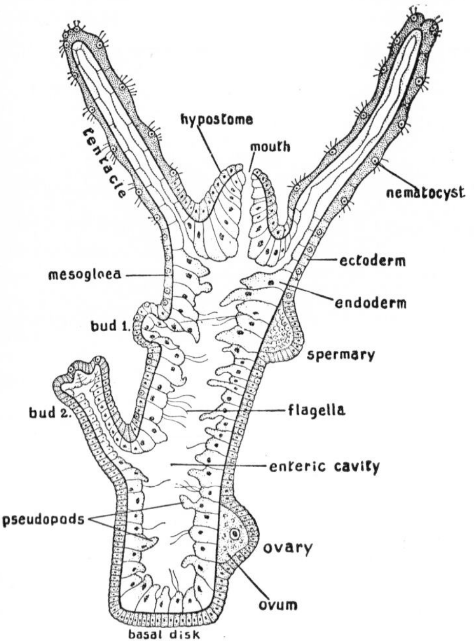

Objections have been made to this mode of comparison on the ground that, were Hydra magnified to the same degree as Diplo-dinium, many more dif-ferentiated structures would be revealed, and that if these were all labeled, Hydra would then appear the more complex of the two. In spite of these considera-tions Ritter seems to the writer to be more or less justified in his claim that Diplodinium, a microscopic protozoan organism, is more highly

FIG. 32. *Hydra.* An example of a simple meta-zoan. (Redrawn after Parker and Parker.)

differentiated than the much larger metazoan, Hydra. It has a skeleton, a digestive tract with mouth and anus, locomotor organs, excretory organs, contractile organs performing a muscular function, sensory, and conductile organs. This organism gives one a good idea of what may be attained in complexity of organization without employing the scheme of multicellularity and of cellular specializa-tion. The animal has a definite organization, with organs of higher rates of metabolism situated at the anterior end and those of lower rates of metabolism at the posterior end. We find regions of the cytoplasm clearly differentiated into organs or systems. Even a nervous system is present consisting of receptors and effectors, the latter associated with muscular organs. We call these structures ORGANS (more technically, ORGANELLES), and advisedly so, for we cannot exclude them from such a title unless we arbitrarily define organs so as to include only structures composed of cells.

Only the small size of Diplodinium prevents the general recognition that it is a relatively highly differentiated organism. Too readily we assume its lowly status because it is a protozoan. There are simple Protozoa and there are complex Protozoa—just as there are both simple and complex Metazoa—and there is about as wide a divergence between simplest and most complex within the bounds of one subkingdom as within those of the other. In neither group are there forms that very closely approach real simplicity of organization approximating a homogeneous or structureless condition. A baseless assumption that some Protozoa are essentially undifferentiated masses of protoplasm has found its way into the more speculative phases of biological literature. A good illustration of the fallacy is found in **Haeckel's** *The Evolution of Man,* where he says: "The earliest unicellular organisms can only have been evolved from the simplest organisms we know, the *monera.* These are the simplest living things we can conceive. Their whole body is nothing but a particle of plasm, a granule of albuminous matter." As a matter of fact this *monera* is a pure fiction. There are no Protozoa that even approximate the condition of an undifferentiated, unorganized particle of plasm.

We shall next make a detailed examination of *Amœba proteus* as a type of the less complex Protozoa and of *Paramecium caudatum* as an example of the more complex Protozoa. From these two studies we may gain a general knowledge of the biology of the group.

CHAPTER XI

AMŒBA

(SUBKINGDOM PROTOZOA)

No microscopic organism has come to be an object of so general popular interest as Amœba. Even writers of fiction speak glibly of the course of evolution "from Amœba to man." One popular writer refers to Amœba as "the Adam and Eve of animate life." The impression prevails that Amœba is the lowest possible expression of life, a mere primordial mass of substance endowed with a spark of life. Not only is Amœba supposed to occupy the lowest rung of the phylogenetic ladder, but the assertion is not infrequently made that it is the actual ancestor of higher forms of life. The absurdity of claiming a relationship of ancestry and posterity between two contemporaneous groups need scarcely be pointed out, but this is the same fallacy as that involved in statements that man is the descendant of the present anthropoid apes or monkeys. Amœba is supposed to be a lowly form of life that has lived and multiplied throughout the millions of years since life began without having very materially advanced. The pedigree of Amœba is doubtless as long as that of man and involves hundreds of times as many generations, yet Amœba remains in a relatively primitive and uncomplicated state. It may possibly have had a period of greater complexity of organization and then regressed secondarily to a simpler condition. About the real ancestral history of Amœba we know nothing.

A. General Characters of Amœba Proteus

There are many kinds (species) of Amœba, some simpler, some more complex than *Amœba proteus*. Hence the species which we are going to study in detail is a sort of representative Amœba. This little organism, sometimes called the "proteus animalcule," when in the full-grown state is about .25 mm. ($\frac{1}{100}$ of an inch) in diameter, a relatively large one-celled organism. It lives in fresh-

114

water ponds and in damp places. *Leidy,* who published a classic study of Amœba and its relatives, found his best specimens in some abandoned tanning pits. *Amœba proteus* was doubtless named after Proteus, a mythological sea god of the ancients, who was constantly changing his shape. Its ever shifting form is a characteristic of Amœba: its irregular outlines are always changing. It is often described as a shapeless mass of protoplasm, colorless except for the presence of darker food particles inclosed within its substance. Careful examination and study of its behavior indicate, however, that it is a true organism and that it is less simple than some would have us believe. *Hyman* has shown experimentally that Amœba has a definite though shifting axiate organization. There is always, in an active individual, one end that keeps ahead in locomotion and an opposite end that drags behind. Lobe-like PSEUDOPODIA are thrust out in the direction of locomotion and the latest pseudopod represents for the time being the controlling region, or the apical end, of Amœba. A newer pseudopod then usurps control and the older ones retire to subordinate rank and withdraw. Amœba then has an organization, but one that is not fixed for long periods, a shifting organization which is to be contrasted sharply with that of Paramecium.

B. General Anatomy of Amœba Proteus

It is customary to distinguish in the body of Amœba two main structural regions: an outer clear, translucent layer of apparently homogeneous protoplasm, the ECTOPLASM, and an inner, central mass of heterogeneous consistency, the ENDOPLASM (Fig. 33, C). Somewhere in the endoplasm lies a NUCLEUS, and, moving about more or less, a CONTRACTILE VACUOLE which disappears and reappears at intervals. Numerous vacuoles containing particles of food in various stages of digestion lie scattered about the endoplasm. Occasionally one of these FOOD VACUOLES, containing débris consisting of sand grains or indigestible food materials, approaches the exterior, breaks through the ectoplasm, and discharges its contents (Fig. 33, A). Each of these regions and organs demands more detailed examination.

The ECTOPLASM (*ec*) is not a true cell membrane, but possesses at least the functional equivalent of a membrane on its outer surface; in fact, a distinct pellicle has been demonstrated by microdissection methods in *Amœba verrucosa*. The whole ectoplasm has a semi-

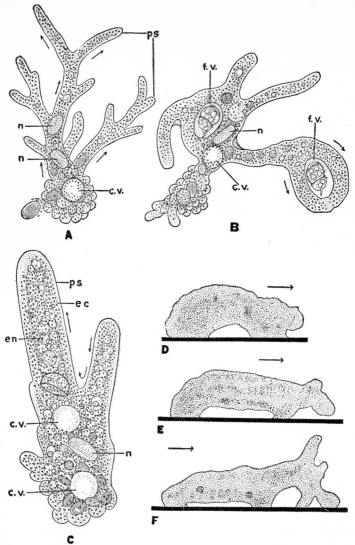

FIG. 33. *Amœba proteus.* **A, B, C,** various forms assumed by this species. *c.v.* contractile vacuoles; *ec*, ectoplasm; *en*, endoplasm; *f.v.*, food vacuoles containing other organisms in process of digestion; *n*, nucleus; *ps*, pseudopodium. Arrows indicate the direction of the movement of the pseudopodia. **D, E, F,** show three successive views of a single Amœba walking; arrows show direction of progress. In **D** a new pseudopod is extending; in **E** this is about to attach itself to the substratum and a second pseudopod is forming; in **F** both first and second pseudopods have attached themselves, and two new pseudopods are forming. (**A, B, C,** after Leidy; **D, E, F,** after Dellinger.)

solid or gelatinous consistency and is able to change shape only quite slowly.

The ENDOPLASM (en) is much more fluid in its consistency. One can readily see vesicles shifting about as though suspended in a fluid medium. The two body regions are not sharply marked off from each other but seem to blend one into the other.

The NUCLEUS (n) is so nearly colorless and so likely to be surrounded by other, more visible granules and vacuoles that it is difficult to distinguish in living specimens. In stained and mounted specimens, however, it is seen to have the form of a somewhat flattened sphere whose position with reference to the other structures of the body is quite variable. It has a definite nuclear membrane and contains a large number of small deeply staining, spherical particles that have all the properties of CHROMATIN. The nucleus has been shown experimentally to be the metabolic center of the body. If a large Amœba be cut into two pieces, one with the nucleus and the other without, the nucleated piece lives on normally, grows, and multiplies; while the enucleated piece ceases to feed or to grow and soon wastes away and dies. The nucleus plays also a very important rôle in reproduction, as will be brought out in a subsequent paragraph.

The CONTRACTILE VACUOLE (c.v.) can be seen under the microscope as a clear round space, slightly pinkish in tint and larger than other vesicular bodies in the endoplasm, which arises as a small spot and then grows larger and larger until, like a bubble from a bubble pipe, it bursts and disappears. This body, judging by its optical properties, is a vesicle filled with watery fluid which is collected from the surrounding protoplasm and then discharged through a perforation in the ectoplasm. Careful studies of the phases of growth and discharge of this structure have shown that the vacuole first lies near the nucleus, but as it grows it leaves the latter and moves toward the surface, coming to rest against the ectoplasm near the posterior end of the body. It presses against the ectoplasm, flattening it out until only a thin film separates it from the exterior. This film finally breaks suddenly and the liquid wastes of the vacuole are discharged. The function of the contractile vacuole is not fully determined, but the consensus of opinion is that it serves as a means of regulating the proportion of water in the body of the organism. Feeding processes seem to require the taking in of a good deal more water than can be used, and excess water must be eliminated. Recent work on Paramecium seems to indicate that the contractile vacuole excretes little, if any, nitrogenous wastes. In view of this it is an open question whether in Amœba the contractile vacuole plays any other than a water regulating rôle.

C. Physiology of Amœba

1. *The Nutritive Processes*

Amœba illustrates the processes of feeding, digestion, assimilation, energy production, and excretion, reduced to very simple terms. Thus we may study the whole metabolic cycle carried on within the confines of a small one-celled body. Amœba, like any other animal, depends for its nutriment upon smaller animals and plants. Though so small and so lowly, it is a miniature pond ogre, going about seeking whom it may devour. Its prey consists chiefly of smaller Protozoa and small aquatic plants, such as desmids and diatoms. Even small Metazoa, such as rotifers, are caught, subdued, and swallowed whole by a large Amœba. An Amœba has the ability to discriminate between inorganic particles, such as sand, and objects suitable for food, and seems to show a preference for certain large species of diatoms, one of which is quite a meal for a protozoan.

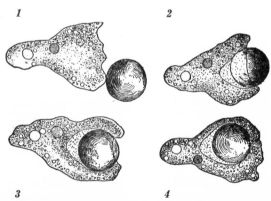

FIG. 34.   Amœba ingesting a *Euglena* cyst. *1, 2, 3, 4,* successive stages in the process.   (From Jennings.)

a. How Amœba Feeds.—The taking of food into the body is called INGESTION and the mouth is the usual organ of ingestion. Amœba, curiously enough, has no mouth. Any point on the surface that comes into contact with food may become, for the time being, a mouth. The method of ingestion is that of engulfing (Fig. 33, B and Fig. 34). An Amœba in its forward progress comes in contact with a food mass. The part immediately in contact with the food stops flowing forward and the parts of the body above, below, and on the sides, flow forward, forming a pocket about the food. The edges of the pocket bend in, meet, and fuse so as completely to surround the ingested object. More or less water is

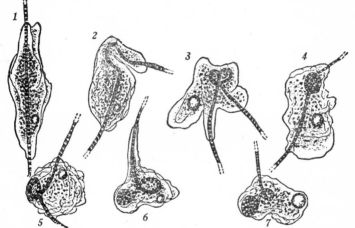

Fig. 35. *Amœba verrucosa* devouring a filament of *Oscillaria*. (From Rhumbler.)

taken in at the same time and thus is formed a FOOD VACUOLE (Fig. 33, B and Fig. 34, 4). One favorite kind of Amœba food is a filamentous green alga (Oscillaria), a primitive and very abundant water plant. Filaments many times the length of Amœba are engulfed (Fig. 35). Starting in either at one end or the middle, the ingested part is progressively coiled up inside until the protoplasm has flowed around the whole piece. Sometimes the prospective meal of an Amœba proves somewhat refractory, moving away when the process of engulfment begins, or struggling to release itself; but the devourer is not easily discouraged, following up and repeating its attempts until ultimately successful, or until the prey moves entirely out of range. Discrimination between inedible and edible substances implies sensibilities of a highly specific sort. Though there are no organs of smell or of taste, the surface protoplasm has the capacity to receive and to react to chemical and physical stimuli. In order properly to stimulate the engulfing reflex, a substance must have a certain amount of solidity and also certain chemical properties. Neither digestible substances in solution nor nonnutritious solid particles are effective in stimulating the events of ingestion.

b. How Amœba Digests Its Food.—A food vacuole is in reality one of the stomachs of an Amœba in which its food is digested. It is more than a stomach; it is a whole digestive tract in miniature. The surrounding protoplasm secretes digestive juices and pours them into the vacuole. Food is rendered liquid and diffuses out of the vacuole into the surrounding protoplasm and the indigestible débris is carried to the surface and egested or cast out by being simply left behind when the Amœba moves on (Fig. 33, A); at least that is how it appears. A sort of baglike mass of heavy materials seems to gravitate toward the posterior end of a forward moving Amœba and when it becomes too heavy it seems to be merely dropped out through the ectoplasm, and the lightened organism moves on.

The processes of ASSIMILATION and DISSIMILATION are the same in Amœba as elsewhere: the dissolved food materials, such as sugars and peptones, are built up into living protoplasm and the living protoplasm is constantly breaking down by oxidative processes, releasing heat and energy for locomotion and other physiological activities. There is some evidence that the by-products of dissimilation are the same as in larger animals, namely, water, urea, and CO_2.

c. How Amœba Breathes.—There is no question but that Amœba respires: it takes oxygen from the surrounding water and combines it with protoplasmic matter. Carbon dioxide and other wastes are given off by the contractile vacuoles. If an Amœba is placed in water from which oxygen has been removed, its activities gradually cease. No more food is ingested and it goes into a dormant condition from which it may be aroused by adding oxygen to the water. Amœbæ live commonly in rather foul water in which the amount of oxygen in solution is relatively low, and where, owing to the prevalence of decaying vegetation, the concentration of CO_2 is relatively high. Removal of oxygen from the water is therefore not immediately felt and it may take a number of hours to make an Amœba show marked signs of asphyxiation.

start for Thurs.

2. *The Locomotor Processes*

Amœba actually walks on its false feet (pseudopodia), although this fact was not discovered until after years of study by various competent investigators. The discovery of how Amœba walks is a miniature historical romance. When these little animals were first discovered, the observers noted, just as you can note when looking at any Amœba under a microscope, that the ectoplasm bulges out at some point and the endoplasm flows out into the process. Thus the whole organism seems to flow forward in the direction of the advancing pseudopod. Sometimes two pseudopods start out in different directions and the Amœba seems to have a hard time to decide between two directions of advance. There is an apparent contest between the two pseudopods until one gives up and flows back, while the other flows more rapidly forward. It has long been a great problem to explain on mechanical grounds the formation of pseudopodia and the way in which they draw after them the rest of the body. The whole point of this problem lies in the fact that here we have a very simple case of spontaneous movement in protoplasm or of mechanical work done by protoplasm. If we could solve the mechanism of pseudopodial movement, we should have the key to other, more complex expressions of protoplasmic mechanics, such as ciliary activity or muscular contraction.

Three main theories have been advanced to account in physicochemical terms for pseudopodial locomotion. A brief outline of each is presented herewith.

a. The Adhesion Theory.—According to this view, Amœba moves for the same reason that a drop of water or any other inorganic fluid placed on a piece of glass sometimes spreads irregularly instead of maintaining a circular outline. The explanation given is that the glass has an uneven surface, is not perfectly clean, but is slightly greasy in spots. Where the glass is clean, adhesion takes place more perfectly and the drop spreads out more rapidly, while it adheres less well to grease or other substances. Applying the adhesion theory to Amœba, it was supposed that the surface on which it moves is irregular as to its adhesive properties and that the pseudopods flow in the paths of greater adhesion. The weakness of this theory is that pseudopods are very frequently thrust out free, not in contact with any surface. Hence contact of any sort is not a necessity, and the adhesion theory proves unsatisfactory.

b. The Surface Tension Theory.—Surface tension is a physical property of fluids which involves a tensile pull of the surface film. It is believed to account for the spherical form of such objects as soap bubbles or drops of oil suspended in water; for the surface of these bodies has contracted to the greatest possible extent, in as much as a sphere has the least surface in proportion to its mass. According to *Bütschli* and *Rhumbler,* who proposed this theory, Amœba is a fluid body which would be spherical in a homogeneous medium, but in a heterogeneous medium like pond water it encounters conditions on one side that lessen the surface tension. At this weakened point the surface bulges out into a pseudopod. Constantly changing conditions cause the local weakening of surface tension to shift from one place to another and, consequently, the withdrawal of one pseudopod and the thrusting out of another. Experiments with rancid oil drops in aqueous solutions seemed to substantiate this theory; for they could be made to change shape and send out blunt processes when substances known to lower surface tension were applied locally to portions of the surface. It was noted that in a region of lowered surface tension currents were set up which flowed backward along the surface and forward in the center. *Dellinger* has demonstrated that currents in a pseudopod of Amœba do not flow in that way but in exactly the opposite directions; yet this theory held sway for some time in spite of its weaknesses.

c. Contraction Theories.—An early notion obtained that the thrusting out of pseudopods was due to protoplasmic contractility of some sort; but the ideas of the exact nature and location of the contraction impulse were somewhat naïve. Amœba was looked upon as a fluid-filled, elastic sac which could undergo contraction of parts of the surface, causing the weakest part of the wall to bulge out. According to this view, currents in the protoplasm should be observed first in the region of contraction and subsequently in the out-pushed region. But it was soon seen that currents begin at the point of pseudopod formation and not at the point supposed to be contracting—an observation which disproved the older contraction theories.

Two American investigators have reinstated the contraction theory by putting the matter in an entirely new light. *Jennings*

had the ingenious notion of marking in some way the surface of
an Amœba in order to watch the fate of any point under observation. This he did by dropping on an Amœba's back a particle of
lamp black. This adheres firmly and furnishes a fine landmark by
means of which the relative rates of flow of ectoplasm and endoplasm can be followed and shifts in position of the ectoplasm may
be mapped out. Jennings' diagram of a progressing Amœba is

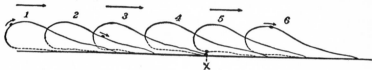

FIG. 36.   Diagram of the movements of a particle attached to the outer sur-
            face of *Amœba verrucosa*, in side view. (From Jennings.)

shown in Figure 36. An analysis of the locomotion of an Amœba
is thus given by Jennings:—

"In an advancing Amœba substance flows forward on the
upper surface, rolls over at the anterior edge, coming in contact
with the substratum, then remains quiet until the body of the
Amœba has passed over it. It then moves upward at the posterior
end and forward again on the upper surface, continuing in rotation as long as the Amœba continues to progress. The motion of
the upper surface is congruent with that of the endoplasm, the
two forming a single stream. The movement can be imitated
roughly by making a cylinder of cloth, laying it flat on a plane
surface, and pulling forward the anterior edge in a series of waves.
The entire cylinder then rolls forward just as Amœba does."

Two points in connection with Jennings' work should be mentioned: first, that he does not state definitely the location of
the contractile substances which pull the Amœba forward; second,
he used a species of Amœba (*A. verrucosa*) which is almost devoid
of pseudopodia and actually does seem to roll along as simply as
he describes. The rolling theory, however, does not apply at all
well to *Amœba proteus*.

We owe to **Dellinger** the best explanation of how Amœba walks.
This author had frequently observed that small organisms swam
under a large Amœba as though the latter were supported on legs.
This gave him a clue to the real situation. If one were to try to
discover the mode of locomotion of a horse by looking down upon
it from the top of a skyscraper, he might get an entirely wrong

impression: so with Amœba. We have always looked down upon
Amœba from a great height above. Dellinger conceived the idea
of looking at the animal from the side exactly as one would look
at a horse from the sidewalk. He made a promenade for the
Amœba in the following way: one edge of a glass slide was ground
smooth and flat. Two long cover slips were cemented with edges
protruding somewhat beyond the flat edge of the slide, as shown
in Figure 37. The microscope was then bent over into a hori-

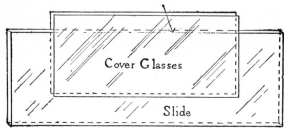

FIG. 37.   Diagram of apparatus used for the study of locomotion in Amœba.
By mounting this slide in a horizontal microscope the Amœbæ may be
seen in side view. (From Dellinger.)

zontal position, thus bringing the troughlike slot of the slide
uppermost and putting the flat surface parallel with the earth's
surface. Amœbæ were then placed in the trough along with
water, and observations and microphotographs were taken as they
paraded before the observer. Dellinger noted that advancing
Amœbæ "extend the anterior end free in the water and attach
it at or near the tip and then contract. At the same time the
posterior end is contracting and the substance thus pushed and
pulled forward goes to form the new anterior end. This continues
as long as the Amœba advances (Fig. 33, D, E, F). Often the
anterior end is pushed along the substratum but no attachments
form except at definite points. . . . In other cases the anterior
end is lifted free and then curves down to the substratum and
attaches, forming a long loop. The posterior end is then released,
and the substance flows over to the anterior end. At the same
time another anterior end is extended." Dellinger showed that
Amœba can walk on the ceiling as well as the floor. The important
point to note is that the animal actually *walks*, putting one foot
out and then another. When a forward step is made, a foot (pseudopod) is stretched out, takes hold and then shortens (contracts).

This is the locomotor act: for contraction involves mechanical work. We do not know for certain exactly what makes a pseudo-pod extend and then contract, but the prevailing theory is that protoplasm, especially the ectoplasm, is a colloid substance that expands when it takes up water and tends to flow outward. Attachment is believed to stimulate the reverse phase of the proto-plasm, causing it to undergo loss of water together with local contraction and shortening. There is a rhythmic alternation of exchanges of water between the ectoplasm and endoplasm, and this give alternate contractions and expansions. If this be the correct explanation of pseudopodial movement, it is not unlikely that all rhythmic protoplasmic movements, such as those in cilia or those in muscle fibers, are due to the same reversible changes in colloids.

d. Mast's Theory.—The latest interpretation of the mechanics of locomotion in Amœba has been worked out by **S. O. Mast** and his pupils. Working with relatively simple Amœbæ, they have been able to determine that the forward flow of the pseudopod is caused by contraction of the more viscous ectoplasm, especially in regions back of the pseudopodia. There is a forward current in the more fluid endoplasm which causes an outflow at points where the ectoplasm is thinnest and less solid. As the plasmasol flows out through the aperture it becomes transformed into plasmagel around the base of the pseudopod, building it out "much as a chimney might be extended by carrying bricks and mortar up through it and depositing them on the wall surrounding the opening." To carry out this figure, it must be supposed that the wall at the bottom of the "chimney" is constantly undergoing disintegration into bricks and mortar, thus providing more ma-terial for transportation to the top. Thus plasmasol changes to plasmagel at one end and the reverse change takes place at the other. The flow is initiated by contraction of the ectoplasm and a sort of bursting forth of the endoplasm to form pseudopods. This latest view then appears to be a refinement of the earlier contraction theories.

3. *The Behavior of Amœba*

All activities of the whole organism in response to internal or external stimuli are included within the definition of the word "behavior." Many studies have been made of the ways in which

Amœba responds to different kinds of external stimuli. *Jennings* has grouped the reactions of Amœba into positive responses, negative responses, and food taking responses. We have already dealt with the food taking reaction, and shall omit further consideration of this process.

When a stimulus strikes an Amœba, it behaves either as though it likes it or dislikes it. If it likes it, it moves toward it or at least it goes on undisturbed. If it dislikes it, it moves away. The words "like" and "dislike" are open to objection. Instead, let us say that an Amœba that reacts favorably toward light, for example, is positively phototactic or exhibits positive phototaxis; that, if it reacts unfavorably to light, it is negatively phototactic. The movements toward or away from the stimulus are called TROPISMS. Thus we speak of positive and negative phototropism.

In Amœba we distinguish the following tropisms:—

1. Phototropism (reaction to light),
2. Thermotropism (reaction to heat),
3. Thigmotropism (reaction to contact),
4. Chemotropism (reaction to chemicals),
5. Galvanotropism (reaction to the galvanic current),
6. Geotropism (reaction to gravity),
7. Rheotropism (reaction to currents).

Amœba reacts to all of these stimuli in either a positive or a negative way. Sometimes a positive response will be given to a stimulus of a certain intensity, and a negative response to one of a greater or less intensity. Studies of the behavior of Amœba under a great variety of stimuli have shown that it behaves in much the same ways as do higher organisms. This has interested the students of psychology. They feel that a complete understanding of Amœba's activities might reveal the beginnings of mind, of intelligence. Without going into detail in this place, it may be said that Amœba seems to show evidences of possessing mental faculties which are, in the words of Jennings, "comparable to the habits, reflexes, and automatic activities of higher organisms" and, "if Amœba were a large animal, so as to come within the everyday experience of human beings, its behavior would at once call forth the attribution to it of states of pleasure and pain, of hunger, desire, and the like, on precisely the same basis as we attribute these things to a dog." It is no more difficult to believe that

Amœba has a kind of mind than that a germ cell has a mind. Yet, according to **Conklin,** an egg cell or a spermatozoön has sensitivity and responds to stimuli by appropriate tropisms or reflexes, thus exhibiting the beginnings of mental activity. A germ cell and an Amœba probably possess minds of about the same sort.

D. Reproduction in Amœba

The life cycle of *Amœba proteus* is unexpectedly complex for so lowly an organism. According to **Calkins** who has studied the

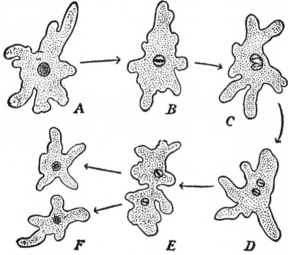

Fig. 38. Fission of *Amœba.* **A,** *Amœba* before the onset of fission; **B,** most of the chromatin has become concentrated in chromosomes about the equator of the nucleus; **C,** each chromosome has divided into two, the two sets of daughter chromosomes are moving apart and the boundary of the nucleus is becoming indented between them; **D,** the nucleus has become completely divided into two daughter nuclei; **E,** the two nuclei have moved apart and the cytoplasmic body of the *Amœba* is undergoing constriction; **F,** the process has been completed. (From Hegner, after Kerr.)

life cycle in great detail, Amœba has an infancy, a youth, a period of maturity, and an old age. Starting out as a tiny thing called a pseudopodiospore, which has but one pseudopod, it goes through a period of growth and increasing complexity until it reaches the full grown stage. When it reaches the maximum size, it divides by binary fission (Fig. 38) into two daughter Amœbæ. Each of these grows to twice its initial size and binary fission again

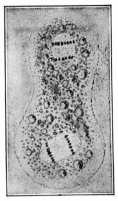

Fig. 39. *Amœba binucleata* beginning to divide. Both nuclei have formed mitotic figures. (From Lang, after Schaudinn.)

occurs. How many times this phase of multiplication may be repeated depends upon the particular strain of Amœba used and the favorableness of the environmental conditions. During binary fission the nucleus sometimes appears to divide by amitosis, but more often clear evidences of a sort of simplified mitosis are observed (Fig. 39). After the period of binary fission comes to an end a period of encystment and sporulation intervenes. This appears to be a very complicated process and the observers of the process fail to agree upon its details. Obviously, however, the period is one of senescence. The final stage is the formation of pseudopodiospores—essentially infant Amœbæ. Thus we are back where we started. This cyclical feature of reproduction is universal for organisms and is dealt with here to emphasize that Amœba in one stage may be fairly simple, but when we come to study all of its varied phases, it loses for us its simplicity and makes an impression of confusing complexity.

CHAPTER XII

PARAMECIUM

(SUBKINGDOM PROTOZOA)

Paramecium caudatum and *P. aurelia* are zoölogical classics. While the first species is somewhat commoner, the latter is more frequently figured in the illustrations. Paramecium is called the "slipper animalcule" because of a fancied resemblance to a crude slipper. In outline one can see that the anterior end is blunt and narrow like the heel and that the posterior end is broader and pointed like the toe. Perhaps the oral groove may be thought of as like the opening to the inside of the slipper. Paramecium is one of the most abundant of Protozoa and is perhaps the most readily obtained for laboratory work. It is therefore a favorite denizen of the zoölogical laboratories. Quite commonly one finds Amœba and Paramecium living together in the same environment. While Amœba may be considered as a good example of the simpler types of Protozoa, Paramecium may be contrasted with it as one of the more complex members of that group.

A. General Morphology

1. *Paramecium and Amœba Contrasted*

Amœba was seen to be a shifty individual, never looking the same any two successive minutes, with a changing axis and with a nucleus and contractile vacuoles floating about in the endoplasm. Paramecium (Fig. 40), on the other hand, has a fixed axis, with permanent anterior and posterior ends and a permanent semi-spiral groove—the ORAL GROOVE—running from the anterior end down to the permanent MOUTH. The mouth opens into a funnel-like depression called the CYTOPHARYNX, or GULLET. Instead of temporary locomotor organs like the pseudopodia of Amœba, Paramecium has the entire surface covered with numerous whiplike motor organs called CILIA. The ectoplasm is not naked as in Amœba, but is covered with a thin, tough CUTICLE, or

PELLICLE. Under this there is a definitely differentiated layer called the CORTEX, which contains closely packed TRICHOCYSTS that give this layer somewhat the appearance of a cellular layer. The endoplasm is fluid, as in Amœba, but both the MACRONUCLEUS

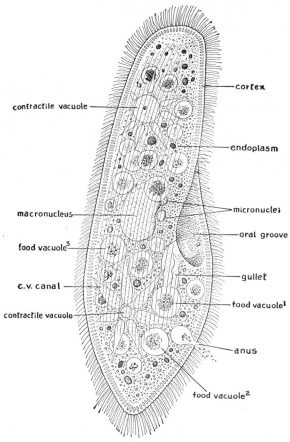

FIG. 40.   *Paramecium aurelia.* Note especially the two micronuclei. (Redrawn after Pfurtscheller wall chart.)

and MICRONUCLEUS, as well as the two CONTRACTILE VACUOLES appear to be anchored definitely at fixed points. There is also a fixed ANUS situated just back of the oral groove.

The general impression one gets from a comparison between Amœba and Paramecium is that the latter has a much more highly specialized organization: its organs are much more definite and fixed. If one were asked to say which is the higher organism, one would undoubtedly answer that Paramecium is higher. When pinned down as to what is meant by higher or lower, one would have to reply that it is all a matter of degree of specialization. Paramecium is probably no more capable of meeting the world struggle than is Amœba. Both must be eminently successful and well adapted animals, else they could hardly have survived all these ages of competitive life. One is as fit as the other. Perhaps we are all wrong in ranking one organism as high and another low. This at least is a problem that the student had best be thinking about as he surveys various animal groups.

2. *Finer Details of Structure*

The permanency of form of Paramecium is due to the fact that the ectoplasm is a well defined, fairly stiff body wall. The external layer, or PELLICLE, is a separate layer which can be blistered free from the cortex by adding a little weak alcohol to a drop of water containing Paramecia. The pellicle, viewed from the surface, appears to be sculptured into rows of hexagonal areas, each of which has a cilium attached to its center (Fig. 41, A). Between the hexagonal areas occur little pores that seem to be holes through which TRICHOCYSTS are extruded. Trichocysts are characteristic structures of the cortex (the layer of ectoplasm beneath the pellicle). These bodies are arranged perpendicularly to the surface (Fig. 41, B). Just what trichocysts are, how they arise, and how they function, are matters incompletely understood. They seem to be semi-fluid in consistency; they arise in the endoplasm near the nucleus, possibly being a product of the latter; they migrate to the exterior and locate themselves in a very accurately spaced fashion. When the animal is strongly irritated, the trichocysts are discharged as long sticky threads through pores in the pellicle. The trichocysts serve primarily as organs of defense in that they adhere to and entangle organisms, such as Didinium, that attack Paramecium (Fig. 41).

The ENDOPLASM has a bubbly or alveolar appearance. There are in it many food vacuoles and various large granular bodies which are probably reserve food materials. The whole endoplasm seems to circulate about in one distinct current which carries with it the food vacuoles and all other movable structures. Such a food path may be likened to an alimentary tract.

The two CONTRACTILE VACUOLES can hardly be assigned definitely to either ectoplasm or endoplasm. They seem to be mainly in the latter but are definitely fastened to the former. Their posi-

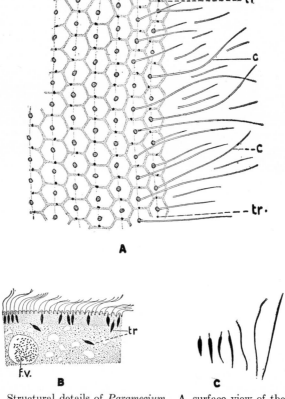

FIG. 41.   Structural details of *Paramecium*.   **A,** surface view of the pellicle, showing hexagonal areas produced by striations; *tr*, the position of the ends of the trichocysts; and the cilia, *c*.   **B,** part of a cross section of the surface of *Paramecium* showing surface ridges, cilia attached to microsomes and trichocysts, in black, cut longitudinally and usually lying in the ectoplasm, though some are seen arising in the endoplasm; *f.v.*, a food vacuole in the endoplasm.   **C,** seven stages in the discharge of trichocysts; the one on the left just beginning to discharge and that on the right completely discharged.   (Redrawn, **A,** after Schuberg; **B, C,** after Maier.)

tion is on the ABORAL surface (that away from the mouth).   Each vacuole is provided with from six to ten long radiating canals that reach out so far as to communicate with most of the parts of the body.   Each canal receives water from the endoplasm that lies in contact with it. When the canals are all full and distended at their inner ends, they simultaneously discharge their contents into the vacuole, which then contracts and forces the liquid out through a pore in the pellicle. Then the canals fill again. The two contractile vacuoles work alternately, one being in the full condition while the other is empty. The rhythm of discharge of the vacuoles in a quietly feeding individual is rather exact, for one can note that a definite time interval elapses between discharges. The functions of the contractile vacuoles are doubtless the same as those described for

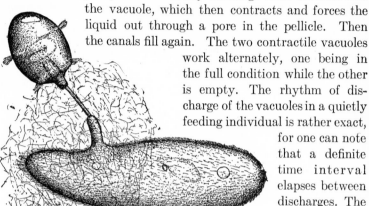

Fig. 42. *Paramecium* making use of its trichocysts in defending itself against the attack of *Didinium*, a predaceous protozoan. The mass of trichocysts swells up into a voluminous jelly and seems mechanically to force the enemy away. (From Mast.)

Amœba. It has recently been shown by Weatherly that the function of the vacuole (in Paramecium) is not the elimination of nitrogenous waste products of metabolism, but is probably the regulation of hydrostatic pressure within the cell. The method of feeding necessitates taking a great deal of excess water, and if this could not be eliminated fast enough the animal would swell up and dissolve in the excess of water.

B. Physiology of Paramecium

1. *How Paramecium Swims*

The Equipment of Cilia.—The swimming unit is the cilium (plural, cilia), a whiplike process projecting from the center of each hexagonal area of the pellicle. The cilia at the posterior end in *Paramecium caudatum* are longer than elsewhere and this little caudal tuft has given it the specific name, *caudatum* (meaning tailed). A cilium is believed to be equivalent to a long, permanent pseudopod. The mechanics of ciliary motion is still an unsolved problem, but in the light of what we have discovered about the basis of pseudopodial movement, it seems highly probable that the movement is due to rhythmic contraction and expansion of colloidal elements in the cilium. Flagella, which are much like cilia in structure and in function, have been shown to have distinct contractile fibrils running throughout their length, and it is probable that cilia are similarly constructed. This theory would imply that, when the animal is moving forward, fibrils on the posterior side of each cilium contract more strongly than those on the anterior side. When the animal moves backward, however, as it frequently does when avoiding unfavorable regions of the environment, the anterior contractile substances contract more vigorously than the posterior. The cilia of the oral groove and of the mouth are stronger and more vigorous than elsewhere, and serve to cause a vortex of water to be pulled into the mouth. This serves as a feeding mechanism. The cilia of the dorsal part of the oral funnel, or mouth, are fused together side by side into a flat sheet called the UNDULATING MEMBRANE, which serves the function of guiding food particles into the mouth.

The Spiral Path of Paramecium.—When Paramecium swims through the water, it does not follow a straight course but, when unobstructed, describes a distinct spiral, such as one would describe in going up a steep spiral staircase on all fours. The explanation of this spiral course is somewhat complicated. In the first place the beat of the cilia is not straight backward but diagonally over to the left. This would, of itself, make the animal go forward in a straight course, spinning on its long axis like a shell shot from the rifled bore of a cannon. In the second place, the beat of the cilia in the oral groove is much stronger than elsewhere and is continually pulling a vortex of water toward the oral surface. This has the same effect as pulling the oral groove side of the Paramecium off its course. As the animal is continually revolving, the oral groove is pointed successively to all radii of the axis, and that produces the spiral course. This may need a little figuring out on the part of the student. If a Paramecium could be attached by its tail to a swivel and its ciliary action kept up as in normal locomotion, it would describe a cone. Imagine this cone projected forward and you would have a spiral. The adaptive features of the spiral path, as discussed by *Jennings,* are that the spiral path, as contrasted with a straight course, affords a much more extensive range for food hunting operations. As Paramecium goes forward it dives now up, now down, now to one side, and now to the other, and always it draws in a cone of water from ahead of it. If the cone of water contains food, the direction is altered so that the animal runs into the food region. If, however, the animal went straight ahead like a bullet, it could not cover anything like so much territory and its chances of finding food would be correspondingly less. It will soon be shown how the spiral path aids in keeping out of danger.

2. *How Paramecium Feeds*

We have already shown how Paramecium hunts for food. When it enters a region of abundant food, such as a mass of bacteria, it seems to quiet down and come to rest. The stimulus of the food seems to act as a depressant upon the body cilia and they move very slowly; but the cilia of the oral groove show increased activity. A vortex of food-laden water is swept down the oral groove and is focused by means of the undulatory membrane into the mouth. So forcibly does the vortex of water play upon the naked protoplasm inside of the mouth that a pocket is made in the endoplasm (see Fig. 39). The pocket grows larger and larger like a bubble on a bubble pipe, and bacteria continue to collect within it until the bubble breaks off and floats away with its load of food. It is then a FOOD VACUOLE. Vacuole after vacuole is formed in this way, and they move off as though caught in a current and follow one another in a procession. As the food vacuoles drift along a well defined path, which is functionally equivalent to a digestive tract, the process of digestion takes place; the digested food is passed out into the surrounding protoplasm, assimilated, and used up in energy and growth. It has already been shown how the contractile vacuoles serve to remove the excess water from the food vacuoles. All that now remains is for the indigestible material to be discarded. This takes place when the old food vacuoles drift to the posterior end and give off their débris through the ANAL OPENING.

3. *Behavior of Paramecium*

Paramecium has been used as experimental material by many investigators interested in the analysis of the behavior of lower organisms. It has been discovered, as was the case for Amoeba, that Paramecium exhibits in more or less definite fashion all of the types of tropism. There is practically no controversy as to the *fact* that the animals are guided by stimuli of all sorts so that they collect in regions of favorable stimuli and depart from regions of unfavorable stimuli. The real controversy centers about the exact *method* by means of which Paramecium directs its course to or from the sources of stimulation. Two contrasting interpretations of the directed behavior of Paramecium, and similarly of many other animals, have been offered: the one implying that the organism is a pure automaton driven helplessly by the external forces, and the other that the organism has a good deal to do with directing its own course and choosing its own location. The former is the Tropism Theory of animal behavior and the second the Trial and Error Theory.

Tropism versus Trial and Error.—A decade or so ago zoölogists were much more interested in the analysis of the behavior of the lower organisms than they are today. Most of the pioneer work in the field of animal behavior was done by the zoölogists; but now this field has been lifted almost bodily out of the zoölogical laboratories and transferred to those of comparative psychology. Some zoölogists with ecological propensities are still interested in animal behavior as a phase of the response of organism to environment. While interest in animal behavior was still strong and fresh among zoölogists, two distinct schools of animal behaviorists developed. One school, strongly inclined to take an extreme mechanistic attitude toward animal responses, looked upon Paramecium, for example, as a helpless, blind automaton driven about by external stimuli after the fashion of John Hayes Hammond's automatic torpedo. This torpedo is provided with selenium cells on the two sides, which are so sensitive to light that a searchlight thrown on the moving torpedo from straight behind stimulates both sides equally; but if it turns to one side, the selenium cell of the side nearer the light is more affected and operates some mechanism that will straighten the course. Paramecium is thought to be thus guided by stimuli in such a way that when the directed lines of energy strike it on one side, they will either stimulate or quiet that side, thus rendering the beat of cilia on the two sides unequal in strength. This will cause the animal to turn until the two sides are equally stimulated, when it will swim directly toward or directly away from the stimulus. This is, in outline at least, a statement of the tropism theory of animal behavior as applied to Paramecium by the late *Jacques Loeb.*

Professor H. S. Jennings was the first to take issue with this theory. In his studies of Paramecium under all sorts of environmental conditions he was never able to see any evidence that Paramecium behaved in this simple, direct fashion. Anyone who observes the animals swimming about gets quite a different impression of their activities. They seem to start, stop, back up, start off in another direction, and never to maintain a straight course. Jennings' explanation of why a Paramecium comes to find the most favorable part of its environment is quite different from that implied in the Tropism Theory. When a Paramecium is swimming forward in a spiral path, testing the water ahead and to one

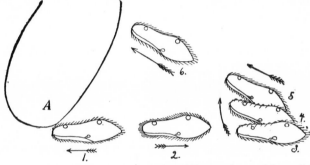

Fig. 43.   Diagram of the avoiding reaction of *Paramecium*.   A is a solid object or other source of stimulation.   1–6, successive positions occupied by the animal.   (The rotation on the long axis is not shown.)   (From Jennings.)

side of it by means of the test cone of water drawn into the oral groove, it comes to a region where the content of the water is unfavorable. If markedly unfavorable, the animal gives a prompt negative response, the so-called "AVOIDING REACTION" (Fig. 43). The direction of ciliary beat is suddenly reversed, sending the animal backward for a short distance until it is out of range of the adverse stimulus. Then the forward beat of cilia is resumed. While overcoming the momentum of the backward motion, the body simply whirls on its tail like a top slightly off balance, the anterior end describing a circle. As it spins around, the oral groove samples the water in all directions, and, when the sample is satisfactory, forward progress is resumed along one of the axes of the cone which the body is describing. This spinning around and trying a number of directions before selecting a favorable one is called the TRIAL AND ERROR method of orientation.

The avoiding reaction and the trial and error process may be repeated a great many times and doubtless will be kept up as long as there are unfavorable stimuli in the environment. When Paramecium by this more or less experimental method finally gets into the most favorable neighborhood, it either comes to rest for feeding purposes or, if still stimulated, keeps moving about. Whenever it swims toward a less favorable region, the avoiding reaction drives it back, and it is thus practically trapped in the favorable region, unable to get out of it. That is Jennings' explanation of why we find great aggregations of Paramecia on one side or other of a dish placed in some position where light enters from one direction. By continually avoiding the less favorably lighted regions they finally come to comparative rest at the region of optimum (most favorable) light intensity. Thus they are not forced directly into the favorable region or away from the unfavorable region, as the Tropism Theory claims, but reach their destination in a much less direct fashion, by trying and trying, rejecting and rejecting, until finally, more or less by chance, the best region is found. When once the most favorable region is found, the animal will give the avoiding reaction to all regions less favorable. This whole explanation of Professor Jennings seems to imply that Paramecium is not a pure automaton driven by forces outside of itself, but that it is very much in control of its own activities. Some critics have claimed that this view borders on a vitalistic interpretation, but this criticism is quite unjustified. Though small in size, Paramecium is not a very simple organism and it behaves very much like many metazoan organisms. It is only when we ignore the organic complexity of the Protozoa that we make the mistake of oversimplifying their activities. The activities of Paramecium compare very favorably with those of Metazoa as high in the scale as worms and mollusks. Moreover, even human beings learn by trial and error: we try a variety of methods of doing a thing and select the most effective one; we have our avoiding reactions, our protective reflexes of various sorts; and many of our mental activities are as automatic as those of Paramecium.

C. Reproduction and the Life Cycle of Paramecium

The life cycle of Paramecium is a complex one, involving many intricate changes in both nucleus and cytosome. It consists of a

series of divisions of whole individuals by transverse binary fission, interrupted at long intervals
by a temporary union or conjugation of two individuals—the latter a sexual act. There is thus
a sort of alternation between
asexual and sexual reproduction.

Binary Fission.—When a Paramecium is about to begin fission
the micronucleus—there are two
of these in *P. aurelia*—the small
inconspicuous body that normally lies imbedded in the side
of the much larger macronucleus,
leaves its position and undergoes a peculiar sort of mitotic
division (Fig. 44). In the anaphases the mitotic figure is long
and slender with two knoblike
ends where the daughter chromatin lies; while in the middle
the spindle of fibers is much like
that seen in typical mitotic division. Subsequently the middle
parts of the spindle fade away,
leaving the two rounded ends
widely separated, one near the
anterior and one near the posterior end of the individual.
The macronucleus follows suit,
elongates, and becomes dumbbell
shaped; the two halves pull apart
and nuclear division is complete.
The gullet buds off a small posterior branch which migrates
backward to form the gullet of
the posterior daughter individual.
The undulating membrane remains in the old gullet and a new

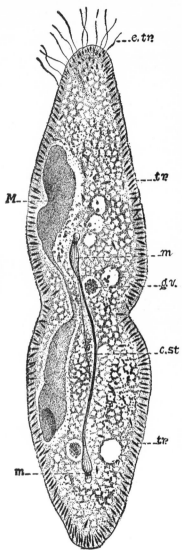

Fig. 44.   Section of a dividing *Paramecium caudatum*. *M*, dividing
macronucleus; *m*, *c.st.*, dividing
micronucleus; *g.v.*, gastric vacuole; *tr.*, trichocysts; *e.tr.*, extruded trichocysts. (From
Woodruff after Calkins.)

one arises in the new gullet. A new contractile vacuole arises in each of the two prospective individuals. While these changes have been in progress a constriction has arisen around the body at about equal distances from the two ends. This cuts deeper and deeper into the body until the last threadlike junction between the two bodies is broken and two completely separate daughter individuals are produced. This all takes place in about two hours, more or less, depending on the temperature and other growth controlling factors. Normally, this process is repeated about once every twenty-four hours, and it may continue without variation for weeks or even months. The daughter Paramecia are not exactly like the parent at first, and they also differ from each other, for they have been derived from two quite different portions of the body. Moreover, each is only half as large as the parent. A period of DEDIFFERENTIATION ensues, during which the inherited structural differences between the two are gradually done away with, and each individual then redifferentiates the structural characteristics of its species and grows up to full size.

Heredity.—It is easy to understand why a daughter Paramecium inherits its characters from its parent. It is merely a continuation of the parent, for the production of offspring eliminates the parent. The PHYSICAL BASIS OF HEREDITY is well illustrated here. An offspring resembles the parent because it arises through the isolation from the parent body of a representative living part of the latter, a part endowed with a capacity to redevelop the specific differentiations possessed by the parent.

Conjugation.—There are some nonconjugating strains of Paramecium, but the rule is that after a certain number of fissions, varying in different strains, conjugation ensues. An experienced investigator, watching his pedigreed cultures from day to day, soon learns to detect the signs of approaching conjugation. The individuals look unhealthy, appear somewhat opaque, and move about as though excited. When two Paramecia are ready to conjugate, they come into contact by their oral surfaces and adhere in this position because of the sticky character of the surface protoplasm. At about the middle of the surface of contact a protoplasmic bridge is formed, uniting the internal protoplasm of the two individuals. This union, together with the ensuing events, is interpreted as a sexual act.

Our attention must now be focused upon the changes in the micronucleus, which up till now has been quiescent, imbedded in the side of the macronucleus. The micronucleus (two of these in

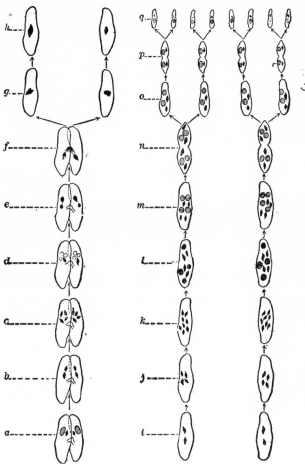

FIG. 45. *Paramecia* conjugating. a-q, stages in the nuclei during conjugation and the subsequent divisions of the conjugants during the period of nuclear reconstruction. The original macronuclei have been omitted except in stage a. (From Hegner, after Calkins and Cull.)

P. aurelia) frees itself and then undergoes a mitotic division about like that described for binary fission. Almost immediately the two daughter nuclei divide again, making four. Three of these resultant micronuclei disintegrate, while the fourth divides again

into a smaller and a larger nucleus. In each animal the smaller
nucleus migrates across the protoplasmic bridge, enters the other
individual, and fuses with the larger nucleus of that individual.
Both individuals have thus exchanged nuclear material and now
possess a new nucleus composed of chromatin materials from
two individuals. This whole series of changes has been compared
to the processes of maturation and fertilization of germ cells in
the Metazoa, and doubtless there is a deep-seated analogy between the two processes. The two preliminary divisions remind
one of the two MATURATION DIVISIONS in Metazoa, which result
in the formation of four cells out of one, and especially call to
mind the maturation divisions of the egg in which are produced
one functional egg and three abortive eggs, or polar bodies. There
is no division in Metazoa corresponding to that which gives rise
to the stationary and the migrating nucleus; but the large stationary nucleus is like an egg nucleus, while the small migrating nucleus
is like the sperm nucleus. Finally, the union of the two nuclei
appears to be the equivalent of FERTILIZATION. The story of conjugation in P. aurelia is shown diagrammatically in Figure 45.

Soon after fertilization the CONJUGANTS separate. Even before
separation, however, the macronucleus has begun to show clear
signs of a break-up. It becomes irregular in shape, constricts,
breaks into pieces, and these disintegrate more or less completely,
leaving only a few dispersed granules. While the macronucleus
has been disintegrating, the fusion nucleus has divided three
times, giving rise first to two, then to four, and finally to eight
micronuclei, four located near one end and four near the other
end. The fate of these eight nuclei has been studied by various
authorities and their accounts differ in minor details. One account has it that the four micronuclei near the anterior end enlarge and transform themselves into four macronuclei. Of the
posterior group of four micronuclei, three disintegrate and dissolve
up into the cytoplasm, the remaining one becoming a new micronucleus. This then divides and the process of fission is resumed.
Probably the only difference between these earliest fissions and
subsequent ones is that the four macronuclei have been preformed
and need only be distributed to four prospective individuals.
These two distributing divisions occur at short intervals. From
then on, the binary fission period is kept up until it is time for
another conjugation.

The first few fissions are rapid and have been compared to the period of youth; the later divisions that go on for some time are comparable to the period of maturity; and the period just before conjugation corresponds to the period of old age. If a Paramecium cannot conjugate, it dies. Conjugation appears to be to some extent a process of reorganization or rejuvenation.

The Problem of Age and Natural Death.—It has been said that, except as the result of accident, Paramecium never dies. The body of one individual goes on living in the daughter individuals derived by fission. The parent ceases to exist but it does not die. After a long series of fissions the individuals grow old and would die, often do die in fact; but life may be saved by conjugation which involves a complete reorganization of all parts of the body, a breakdown of old structures and a rebuilding of new. The protoplasm takes a fresh start, becomes, as *Calkins* so aptly says, "germinal." Conjugation is believed by him to transform ordinary body cells into germ cells. An individual after conjugation is like a fertilized egg, or an organism in its earliest infancy: vigorous, renewed in its energy. We shall see later on that the physical immortality of Paramecium is no different from the physical immortality of germ cells of the higher organisms. The parent lives on in its offspring although part of it dies, namely, that part which has become specialized for maintaining the life of the individual. Even tissue cells of the higher organisms can go on living indefinitely if placed in proper culture media. Nerve cells, connective tissue cells, muscle cells, have been caused to grow when removed from the body. Natural death then is not due to any necessary playing out of vitality in individual cells, but seems to be "due to some defect in the interrelations of the many differentiated cells and organs of the body of the Metazoa and a defect which is cumulative until the organisms are unable to carry on the necessary functions, and die."

Is Conjugation Necessary?—If conjugation serves as a means of rejuvenating a race of Paramecia that has run down or become senescent, could other agencies accomplish the same end? *Woodruff,* working with a race of Paramecia that was conjugating every six months, showed that by making a daily change in the culture medium he was able to prolong the unbroken series of binary fissions for thirty-seven months or even longer. It appears then that the same rejuvenating effect is attained by a varied food as is normally attained by conjugation.

The same author discovered one race of *Paramecium aurelia* that never conjugates. For seven years this race was watched

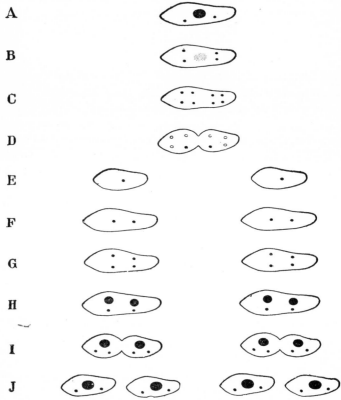

Fɪɢ. 46.   Diagram of the nuclear changes during endomixis in *Paramecium aurelia*.   A, typical nuclear condition; B, degeneration of macronucleus and first division of micronuclei; C, second division of micronuclei; D, degeneration of six of the eight micronuclei; E, division of the cell; F, first reconstruction micronuclear division; G, second reconstruction micronuclear division; H, transformation of two micronuclei into macronuclei; I, micronuclear and cell division; J, typical nuclear condition restored.   (From Woodruff.)

with care and there were no signs of conjugation nor of lowered vitality.   On microscopic examination, however, it was found that at regular intervals the separate individuals went through the same nuclear behavior as if they were conjugating, except that no nuclear material was exchanged between different individuals. This so-called ENDOMIXIS (Fig. 46) is interpreted as the equivalent of PARTHENOGENESIS, a type of germinal reproduction found quite commonly among the Metazoa, in which eggs undergo maturation and develop without fertilization.

D. Conclusion

One of the most important generalizations that one arrives at after the study of a fairly complex protozoan organism such as Paramecium is that there is not any very pronounced difference between such an animal and a metazoan animal. We find that in its behavior, in the performance of its metabolic functions, and in its reproduction, it shows striking parallelism with such animals as Hydra or Planaria. The fact that in Paramecium differentiation of organs takes place within the somewhat narrow confines of a single cell, while the others are much larger in size and have many cells regionally specialized for different functions, constitutes an important distinction; but this is not so important a consideration as that both are organisms, whole individuals, in which the parts are held together by a centralized controlling region. Thus the Organismal Theory is somewhat more fundamental in understanding the relative status of Protozoa and Metazoa than is the Cell Theory.

CHAPTER XIII

THE PROTOZOA AND THE METAZOA

A. Protozoa and the Cell Theory

In terms of the Cell Theory a protozoan organism is merely a single independent cell equivalent to one of the many dependent cells making up the tissues of metazoan organisms. We have already shown the inadequacy of this point of view. A whole protozoan is in a larger sense the equivalent of the whole metazoan. In spite of this, however, there is nothing to be gained by denying that Protozoa are cells. The whole situation is well explained by *Ritter,* as follows:—

"I wish to point out that while there can be no doubt about the great importance of the fact that in metazoa and metaphyta (multicellular plants) cells are parts of the organism, I am unable to see that the fact necessitates, as held by Huxley and Dobell, the exclusion of the protozoa from the cell-theory. It simply establishes in the most uncompromising way the subordination of the cells to the organism in the metazoa and metaphyta. If the idea be grasped that cells are among the instrumentalities produced by organisms in the course of their development, individual and racial, with which to carry on their various activities, it will become apparent that there can be no objection to modifying the conception of the cell to make it apply to any structure whether a part of or the whole of an organism, which satisfies certain well established criteria. When, for example, it is recognized that certain species of amœbæ resemble so closely the white corpuscles of the blood of many animals as never to fail of recognition by good observers, the established principles of biological definition and classification dictate that the two sorts of bodies be given a common, that is, logically speaking, a generic name."

But it must not be forgotten that Amœba is more than a cell; it is a whole organism. A white blood corpuscle is only a dependent element playing one useful function in the blood and lymph of a higher organism.

146

From the point of view of the Cell Theory a whole race of Paramecia derived from the repeated binary fissions of one individual is in a sense equivalent to a metazoan organism produced by the repeated process of the mitotic division of a single cell, the egg cell; but this is not the whole story. Even if we could collect and cement together all the products of fission of a Paramecium so that they formed a coherent harmonious mass, we would not have anything equivalent to a metazoan; for the mass would lack unity and

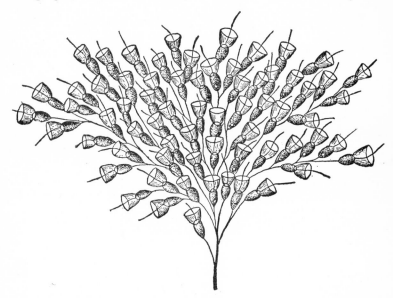

Fig. 47.   An arboreal colony of flagellated protozoa, *Codosiga cymosa*. (From Calkins after Kent.)

organization.   All the cells would be alike both in form and in function.   No part of the mass would be in control so as to confer organization or individuality upon the whole.   As a matter of fact, there are Protozoa that hang together after fission so as to form colonies.   Such a colony is seen in the protozoan species *Codosiga cymosa* (Fig. 47).   This collection of Protozoa is, however, a cell aggregate, not an organism.

B. Germ Cells and Body Cells

Certain other colonies, instead of forming arboroid, or treelike, colonies like Codosiga, adhere closely so as to form spherical

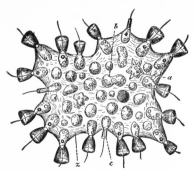

Fig. 48. *Proterospongia hæckeli*, a colonial CHOANOFLAGELLATE. *a*, amœboid cell; *b*, a cell dividing; *c*, cell with small collar; *z*, jelly. (From the Cambridge Natural History, after Kent.)

colonies in which all the cells remain embedded in a continuous gelatinous matrix secreted by the cell membranes. Some such colonies as Proterospongia, for example (Fig. 48), show a certain small amount of regional differentiation of the constituent cells. Those on the outside are typical collar-flagellate cells like those in Codosiga, but some of these collar cells, when well fed, migrate to the interior of the colony, where they lose their collars and flagella and divide to form cells that wander back to the surface and reassume the characteristic collar-flagellate form. Here we have a temporary differentiation into vegetative or body cells and reproductive or germ cells. Permanently differentiated body cells are found in the spheroidal colonial protozoan, Pleodorina, where four out of the thirty-two cells forming the colony are purely vegetative and do not reproduce, while the remaining twenty-eight may be considered as germ cells. In the species *Gonium pectorale* the vegetative condition consists of sixteen cells arranged

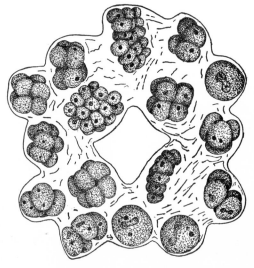

Fig. 49. Reproduction of *Gonium pectorale*. Each of the sixteen cells of the ordinary colony divides until a sixteen-cell stage results; the old colony then breaks up and the sixteen young colonies grow independently. (From Calkins.)

in a ringlike fashion (Fig. 49). In the process of reproduction each cell in the colony acts like a germ cell, dividing into two, four, eight, and then sixteen cells, after which the original colony breaks up into sixteen young colonies. The process of division in Gonium is extremely like that of a dividing egg in a metazoan organism even in having the first two cleavage planes vertical and the third horizontal.

We see then in the colonial Protozoa that we have multicellular aggregates that are almost equivalent to individuals of a higher order, but not quite so, because they lack centralized control and axiate organization. There is no apical end; no axial gradient. It is only the introduction of centralized control that makes possible a true organism or individual.

C. Possible Connecting Links between Protozoa and Metazoa

Some writers have said that there is no sharp line between the Protozoa and the Metazoa. They point to the series of cell aggregates seen among the Protozoa and claim that one group merges over by imperceptible steps into the other. In order to make the series more complete they introduce into it a number of simple plants such as Pandorina, Eudorina, and Volvox, in which the differentiation of somatic cells and germ cells is clearer and in which the germ cells differentiate into macrogametes and microgametes, usually spoken of as the equivalent of eggs and sperms in animals. Without entering upon a controversy as to whether these organisms are plants, as the botanists confidently claim, or animals, as some zoölogists prefer to think, we doubt the advisability of drawing from such an artificial series any important conclusions as to the relationship existing between the Metazoa and the Protozoa or as to whether the Metazoa may have been derived from the Protozoa through steps similar to those shown in this series. It seems logical to believe that the original ancestral living organisms were unicellular and, if so, it seems a necessary consequence that the multicellular organisms have descended from unicellular organisms. It does not follow, however, that the ancestor or ancestors of the metazoan groups were ever very much like present-day colonial Protozoa.

One therefore has difficulty in accepting the statement that there is no hard and fast line between the Protozoa and the

Metazoa. Protozoa as a group are organized on quite a different principle from Metazoa. They may be very simple or very complex, but their differentiation is attained without making use of the scheme of cell multiplicity. Colonies of Protozoa are not comparable with single metazoan individuals, but with colonies of the latter. There is, for example, a very close similarity between a colony of protozoans such as Zoöthamnium (Fig. 50) and a colony of metazoans such as Obelia or Bougainvillea (Fig. 66). Each is a loosely connected group of organized independent individuals, all derived by the asexual division of one original in-

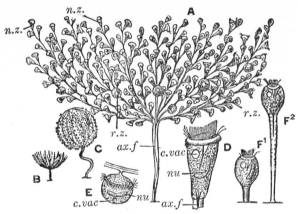

Fig 50. *Zoöthamnium arbuscula*, a colonial ciliate protozoan. **A,** entire colony; **B,** the same, natural size; **C,** the same, retracted; **D,** nutritive zooid; **E,** reproductive zooid; **F¹, F²,** development of reproductive zooid; *ax.f*, axial fiber; *c.vac*, contractile vacuole; *nu,* nucleus; *n.z,* nutritive zooid; *r.z,* reproductive zooid. (From Parker, after Kent.)

dividual and remaining in contact by their basal ends. In each case zooids become specialized as reproductive individuals that break off and swim away. These free individuals in both cases reproduce sexually, and thus give rise to new colonies.

There is also no essential difference between the process of transverse binary fission by means of which Paramecium multiplies itself and the equivalent process by means of which the flatworm Planaria reproduces (Fig. 72). In both cases an organism divides into two daughter organisms, which at first are incomplete in certain respects but soon reconstitute the lacking parts. Thus it is not correct to compare the products of fission of a Paramecium

to the tissue cells of a metazoan organism: these fission products
are whole individuals comparable with whole daughter Planaria,
which have been produced in the same way. This process of transverse fission is found in much higher animals, such as the segmented
worms, in which whole chains of individuals are produced that hold

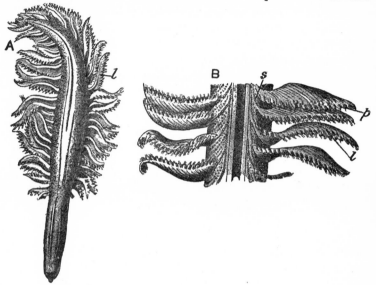

Fig. 51. *Pennatula sulcata,* a colonial hydroid showing the individuals ar-
        ranged according to a system that approximates that of an individual of
        a higher order. A, entire colony; B, portion of the same magnified; *p,*
        polyp; *l,* lateral branch; *s,* siphonozoöid. (From Parker and Haswell,
        after Koelliker.)

together for life and constitute a new order of individuality. Even
more striking cases of the organization of colonies of zoöids into
coherent, organized groups, that exhibit greater unity than do
those of any of the Protozoa, are seen among some of the colonial
Hydrozoa. An excellent example of this kind of thing is furnished
by the Sea Pens (Fig. 51). Here the whole colony has a very definite symmetrical and axiate arrangement, and experiments have
shown that those situated at one level of the axis have different
physiological properties from those at another level. Here we have
a case of metazoan individuals forming aggregates that tend to
lose their individuality in the process of coöperating in the formation of a corporate individuality of a higher order.

An equally good illustration of a superindividual consisting of an organized group of component individuals is furnished by Physalia, the Portuguese Man-of-War (see Frontispiece). Here the hydranths (individuals), some nutritive, some protective, some locomotor, some reproductive, are so organized that the whole complex resembles a single individual.

Some writers go so far as to say that a swarm of bees, or even a community of human beings, is in a sense a unit, an organism. If, then, we bear in mind all of these important considerations, we may well conclude that it is hardly a safe procedure to use colonial types of Protozoa as a phylogenetic bridge connecting the two great subkingdoms, Protozoa and the Metazoa. It seems more in accord with the facts to look upon the two groups of organisms as totally independent, neither one derived from the other, but both derived from a very ancient common ancestor. In one of them differentiation is attained without the use of cellular multiplicity and in the other differentiation is attained chiefly through the instrumentality of cellular multiplicity.

If our arguments are valid, *there is then a sharp line between the Protozoa and the Metazoa* which cannot be bridged by means of colonial types of PROTISTA. These colonial types are not leading toward a condition equivalent to a single metazoan individual, but to conditions like colonies of Metazoa. By taking this position we are not discarding the Cell Theory as an important principle, but merely restricting it within reasonable bounds and applying the Organismal Theory in a field where it has been neglected.

Stop Tues.

CHAPTER XIV

SPONGES

(PHYLUM PORIFERA)

A. GENERAL CHARACTERISTICS

EVEN though they fail to meet the popular criteria of what animals ought to be, sponges are truly animals. In the adult state they are sessile organisms, fastened down for life to rocks, shells, or wharf piles, and therefore incapable of moving about as one expects animals to do. They do not visibly respond by movements when touched, and they display no other signs of animation under casual observation. Why then do we insist that they *are* animals?

In the first place, they are made up of living cells, usually many thousands of them, each in itself a characteristic animal cell. Moreover, these cells are arranged in definite layers and differ from one another structurally and functionally in accord with the position

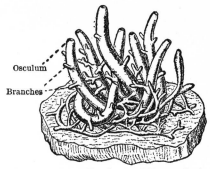

FIG. 52. A small colony of *Leucosolenia*, a simple sponge. (From Lankester.)

they occupy in the individual. A sponge then is a real organism, an individual in the technical sense, but its organization is loose and the interdependence of part upon part is relatively slight. An example of a simple sponge is *Leucosolenia* (Fig. 52), a species common along the New England coast. Individuals of this species grow in colonies or clusters, and reach a length of about one inch. Each sponge looks like a little slender urn or flask with the bottom fastened to the substratum and the mouth uncorked. This opening is not a real mouth in the sense that it is the portal for the entrance of food, yet it is called the OSCULUM (meaning little mouth). Nothing enters the body through the osculum. On the contrary, it acts as an exit for water and wastes. The mouths of the sponge are myriad, consisting of countless little INCURRENT PORES (OSTIA) that dot the whole external surface. It is the presence of these pores that gives the name "Porifera" to the phylum.

An animal with hundreds of mouths cannot be thought of as very highly organized, for there is no well defined apical region and no single gradient. That a sponge is in truth loosely organized is shown by the fact that if an individual be torn to fragments and these be strained through the meshes of closely woven silk fabric, the various kinds of cells will be separated one from another. In spite of this complete breaking down of organization, the cells can go on living separately and are able to aggregate into small bunches or masses out of which new sponges arise. These and other considerations have led to the conclusion

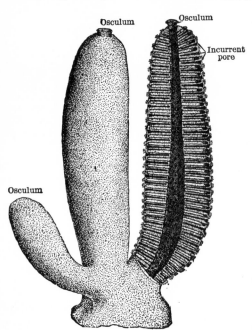

FIG. 53. A typical sponge, *Sycon*, The right-hand individual is shown in longitudinal section. (From Parker and Haswell.)

that sponges are hardly entitled to full rank as Metazoa, but are only slightly more advanced than some of the more elaborate colonies of Protozoa. They differ from protozoan colonies, however, in the fact that definite tissues are differentiated, including a protective external tissue, an internal nutritive tissue, and an intermediate tissue that contains skeletal cells, reproductive cells, and some cells that assist in nutrition. There are also muscular tissues associated with the openings of pores and passageways, and these serve to regulate the flow of water through the body. Because the Porifera are multicellular organisms, but lack sufficiently definite organization to be considered true Metazoa, they have been assigned by some biologists to a separate minor subkingdom, PARAZOA.

B. THE ANATOMICAL PLAN OF A SPONGE

If one cut open a sycon sponge, such as that shown in Figure 53, and examine it under the low power of the microscope, he will find it a rather definite labyrinth of canals or passageways. In the center is a large cavity, the CENTRAL CAVITY, which is in no sense comparable to a stomach or intestine. Radiating from this cavity and in communication with it are numerous canals (EXCURRENT CANALS) that end blindly near the surface (Fig. 54). Between the excurrent canals are similar canals (INCURRENT CANALS), each opening to the outside by a pore (incurrent pore, or OSTIUM) and ending blindly near the central cavity. Numerous tiny passages (PROSOPYLES) place the incurrent canals in communication with the excurrent canals, so that it is possible for

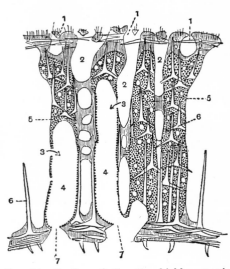

FIG. 54. Section of *Grantia*, highly magnified, showing:—1, openings of incurrent canals; 2, incurrent canal; 3, prosopyles; 4, excurrent canal; 5, collar cells; 6, spicules; 7, openings of excurrent canals. (From Dendy.)

currents of water to pass from the surface into the central cavity. The incurrent canals are apparently merely water conduits, for they are lined with flat pavement cells without other function than that of furnishing a firm, smooth surface.

The cells lining the excurrent canals, however, are very different. Each cell is provided with a funnel, or collar, opening at the surface and a flagellum, or animated whip, which lashes water and suspended food particles into the cell mouth at the base of the collar (Fig. 55). These then are the food capturing cells of the sponge.

Small nutritive particles are taken into the cell protoplasm, digested, and part of the nutrition passed on to deeper lying cells. The combined movements of the flagella, or whips, are in such a direction that water currents are created toward the central cavity. This is the whole mechanism of water flow, the only superficial sign of life in the sponge. The central cavity is merely a common conduit for conducting to the outside the water expelled from the excurrent canals.

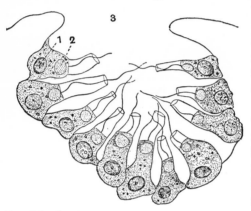

The current may be checked by contracting the muscle cells surrounding the incurrent pores.

It is to be noted that all digestion is INTRACELLULAR, that is, within the individual cell bodies. Similarly, respiration and excretion is carried out by each and every cell; for there are no special tissues for these functions.

FIG. 55. Section of portion of excurrent canal, highly magnified, showing collar cells and flagella. 1, nucleus; 2, vacuole; 3, opening into central cavity. (From Shipley and MacBride.)

The external surface of a sponge is covered by a layer of relatively tough protoplasm in which occur many nuclei. Such a layer, with no distinct cell boundaries but with numerous nuclei, is known as a SYNCYTIUM.

Since the living tissues of the sponge are in themselves quite soft, and since the whole life of the animal depends upon the maintenance of a more or less constant form with open passageways for the water circulation, a supporting framework is highly essential. Throughout the deeper layers of the body there is an intricate trestlework composed of calcareous rods and other, more complex units. These may be composed of rods fused together into symmetrical forms, some being shaped like a T, others not unlike the little iron "jacks" used in the favorite game of schoolgirls. These SPICULES, as they are called, constitute the skeleton of the sponge and serve to keep the water passages from collapsing.

Compound sponges of various grades of complexity are essentially of no higher level of organization than the simpler types just described, for they are merely like an apartment building composed of repeated units, each like the rest. If we think of the Leucosolenia type of sponge as a single apartment we may properly designate compound sponges apartment buildings of varying degrees of size and complexity. Some of the stages of increasing complexity are shown in Figure 56.

The various subclasses, orders, and families of sponges differ rather sharply from one another in the material used for the skeleton and in the shape of the skeletal units. One class (CAL-CAREA) has calcareous (limestone) spicules that are sometimes quite elaborate; a second class (HEXACTI-NELLIDA) has spicules of glasslike silicon; a third class (DEMOSPON-

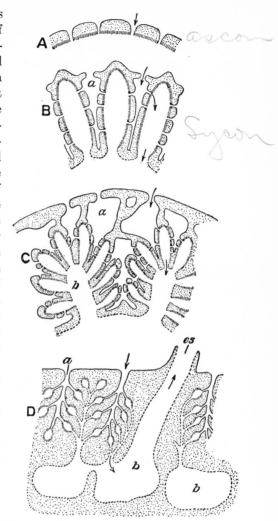

FIG. 56. Diagram of the canal system of various sponges. **A,** section through part of wall of simplest type; **B,** section through wall of Ascon type, *e.g., Grantia;* **C,** section through wall of a complex sponge which is constructed like a colony of Grantias; **D,** longitudinal section through a portion of a specialized type of sponge with small, restricted flagellated chambers. *a,* incurrent canals; *b,* central cavities; *os,* osculum. (From Parker and Haswell.)

GIA) has either no skeleton at all, or a skeleton composed of SPONGIN fibers, or a combination of spongin and silicious spicules.

The sponge of commerce is the cleaned and dried skeleton of certain species of Demospongia, having a pure spongin framework. Spongin is a soft, fibrous material capable in the dry state of absorbing much water. The principal sponge of commerce is *Euspongia*. A million or more pounds of sponge skeletons are marketed annually in the United States.

C. REPRODUCTION

The sponge reproduces both sexually and asexually. Asexual reproduction is accomplished by two methods: (*a*) ordinary budding, involving the branching off of a new individual from the external surface of an old one; and (*b*) internal budding, or gemmulation, a process involving the aggregation of small bunches of cells of different sorts in the form of spherical GEMMULES, each of which is literally an infant sponge. The sexual method is much like that of the true Metazoa. Eggs and sperms are produced in the MESOGLŒA, or deeper tissue, of a single individual, for Grantia is HERMAPHRODITIC. Sperms come in contact with eggs and the latter are fertilized in typical fashion. Embryonic development takes place within the tissue of the parent and the young are later released by breaking out into the canals and being swept out with the current.

D. COMMERCIAL VALUE OF SPONGES

So important has the sponge industry grown, especially since the vast development of the automobile industry, that marine sponge farms have been established in which sponges are planted and harvested in the most systematic fashion. Live sponges of the best types (seed sponges) are cut up into very small cubes, each cube being wired to a cement disk, which is sunk to the bottom in those parts of the sea known to be favorable for sponge growth, such as, for example, along the Bahama coasts. In a few years these pieces grow to a size suitable for the market. This is but one instance of sea farming, a relatively undeveloped industry. In the future we shall do much more with the products of the sea than we have even dreamed of doing in the past.

E. Phylogenetic Relationships of the Sponges

There exist today no close relatives of the sponges. The closest affinities noted are with a group of Mastigophora (a phylum of Protozoa), known as Choanoflagellata, or collar-flagellates, and especially with the genus *Proterospongia*. These Protozoa are remarkably like the cells of sponges that line the excurrent canals. Sometimes the choanoflagellate Protozoa form small, but rather massive colonies with internal collarless cells that resemble the mesogloea cells of sponges (see Figs. 46 and 47). Granted then that the sponges have been derived from a group of Protozoa that became extensively colonial and attained a certain degree of division of labor and organization, what relation might they have to other metazoan phyla? The belief today is that the sponges went up an evolutionary blind alley and have never given rise to any higher forms. The early adoption of sessile life and the failure to acquire well defined axiate organization may have doomed them to a permanent lowly status. As we have already said, the sponge branch of the phylogenetic tree comes off near the bottom and is distinctly a side branch ending in many minor twigs, all of which are only sponges.

CHAPTER XV

HYDRA

(PHYLUM CŒLENTERATA)

THE fresh-water polyps, *Hydra (Chlorohydra) viridissima*, the green Hydra, and *Hydra (Pelmatohydra) oligactis*, the stalked Hydra, have long been favorite objects for laboratory study (Fig. 57).

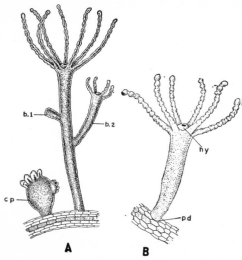

They are easily obtainable and, perhaps more important than anything else, they may be studied alive. Their feeding reactions and responses to changes in the environment are also readily observed. Hydra represents metazoan organization in almost its simplest terms. Relatives of Hydra (Protohydra and Microhydra) are considerably simpler than Hydra itself, and indeed rank as the very lowest expression of true metazoan organization.

FIG. 57. Hydras attached to aquatic vegetation. **A,** two specimens of *Hydra viridissima*, the one on the right moderately extended; the one on the left in the fully contracted position (*c p*); *b.1* and *b.2* are, respectively, a young bud and an older bud. **B,** a specimen of *Hydra fusca; hy,* hypostome; *pd,* pedal disk. (Redrawn after Pfurtscheller wall chart.)

Hydra lives in fresh water, usually attached by its "foot," or basal extremity, to aquatic plants. It is not fixed in one position, though one might get this impression after watching it for a short time. It slides slowly about on its PEDAL DISK (*pd*) and in the course of some time it may travel considerable distances. We may characterize Hydra as a SEDENTARY organism in order to contrast it with SESSILE organisms that are permanently fixed.

A. GROSS ANATOMY

Plan of Organization.—Hydra is a true individual with a definite axiate organization. Roughly speaking, the body is an elongated cylinder. At the free end is the mouth and just back of the mouth a crown of tentacles radiating out from the mouth. The rest of the cylinder shows no differentiated organs except at the base, where there exists a pedal disk that functions as an adhesive and locomotor organ. A line drawn through the Hydra from the mouth and HYPOSTOME (Fig. 57, B, *hy*) to the pedal disk represents the primary axis of the animal. This is the oralaboral axis and is not equivalent to the anteroposterior axis of higher animals, as will be made plain in a later chapter. The mouth and the ring of tentacles represent the apical or controlling region of the individual and the rest of the body is subordinate. It has been shown by *Child* and others that the rate of metabolism is greatest at the mouth end and that there is a gradient of lessening rate of chemical activity as one proceeds down the axis. The tips of the tentacles and the lips of the mouth are the most active regions of all and have the highest rates of metabolism. Most authors lose sight of the primary organization of Hydra in their efforts to emphasize the fact that the repeated parts are radially arranged. In the plan of organization this RADIAL SYMMETRY is secondary to the axis of polarity, which is essentially equivalent to what is called the dorsoventral axis of higher forms; while the radial symmetry is in contrast with the bilateral symmetry of these groups. All Metazoa have at least a primary axis. They vary with reference to their secondary plan of organization. Sessile and sedentary organisms are likely to be characterized by radial symmetry; while free-living organisms usually exhibit bilateral symmetry.

The Two-layered Structure of Hydra.—Another feature of the general plan of organization in Hydra is that it is DIPLOBLASTIC (Fig. 58, A)—by which is meant that the body consists of but two layers of cells, an ECTODERM (*ec*) layer on the outside and an ENDODERM (*en*) layer on the inside. The ectoderm is a protective, sensory, and contractile layer; while the endoderm is muscular and alimentary in character.   One might compare the two-layered condition of Hydra to that of a thermos bottle, which consists of an outer and an inner cylinder, with the inner cylinder opening at the mouth.   In Hydra there is no open space between the two layers, but only a thin sheet of noncellular substance.   The central cavity is known as the GASTROVASCULAR CAVITY (*gc*).   It

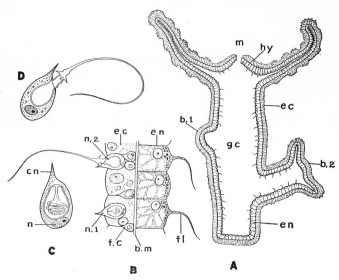

FIG. 58.   Cellular structure of *Hydra*.   **A,** a semidiagrammatic view emphasizing the diploblastic, or two-layered, condition: *b.1* and *b.2* are a younger and an older bud; *ec*, ectoderm; *en*, endoderm; *gc*, gastrovascular cavity; *hy*, hypostome; *m*, mouth.   **B,** a semidiagrammatic section through the body wall of *Hydra*, showing: *b.m*, basement membrane or mesoglœa; *ec*, epitheliomuscular cell of the ectoderm; *en*, epithelio-muscular cell of the endoderm; *fl*, flagellum of latter cell; *f.c*, formative or subepithelial cells; *n.1*, nematocyst ready for discharge; *n.2*, nematocyst discharged.   **C,** enlarged figure of a nematocyst before discharge; *cn*, cnidocil or trigger; *n*, nucleus of cnidoblast or cell in which nematocyst was formed.   **D,** enlarged view of discharged nematocyst.   (Redrawn after Pfurtscheller wall chart.)

is the only cavity present in the body, for there is no cœlom nor any blood nor lymph spaces.   This type of cavity differs from similar cavities of most higher organisms in having but one opening, the mouth, and no posterior opening, or anus.   It also subserves two functions, that of digestion and that of circulating the products of digestion about the body.   It is therefore both a digestive tract and a vascular system; hence the name, "gastrovascular."

B. Histology of Hydra

We have already considered the main features of the general organization of Hydra and shall now turn our attention to the cellular composition of the animal. We have before us a true metazoan organism that makes use of cells to gain specialization of regions of the body. There is a physiological division of labor among the cells, some performing only one function, others performing two or three functions. In so far as more than one function is performed by one kind of cell, there is incomplete specialization. A study of the cellular details of the two layers of Hydra, the ectoderm and the endoderm, affords a good introduction to that important branch of morphology known as Histology. We may conveniently describe first those types of cells that are confined to the ectoderm; second, those confined to the endoderm; and third, those present in both ectoderm and endoderm.

1. *Cells Confined to the Ectoderm*

There may be distinguished three types of cells that are characteristically ectodermal: (*a*) epithelio-muscular cells; (*b*) nematocysts, or nettle cells; (*c*) reproductive cells.

a. Epithelio-muscular Cells.—Hydra has no cells that are purely muscular in function, but each of the epithelial cells possesses

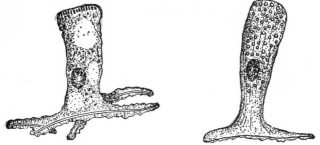

Fig. 59. Epithelio-muscular cells of *Hydra oligactis*, showing myofibrils and secretory granules. (From Schneider.)

elongated basal processes which extend up and down the cylinder of the body and contain contractile fibers (Fig. 59). The contraction of these muscular processes serves to shorten the body or to bend it from side to side. The bodies of the epithelio-muscular cells lie side by side like paving blocks with free ends rounded. They serve the double function of covering the outer surface of the body and, by contraction, shortening the body when it is necessary to withdraw the oral end. In addition to this, ectoderm cells of the basal disk have the power of sending out pseudopodial processes by means of which the Hydra moves slowly from place to place.

b. Nettle Cells.—These cells are peculiar to the phylum Cœlenterata to which Hydra belongs. They occur over nearly the entire outer surface, being absent only on the basal disk. They are most abundant on the tentacles and on the HYPOSTOME, the crater-like prominence around the mouth. On the tentacles the stinging cells are usually arranged in batteries composed of one piece of heavy artillery (a large, specialized nematocyst) in the center and a ring of smaller fieldpieces about it. These curious cells serve as offensive or defensive weapons and are the only means a Hydra has of defending itself or of capturing prey. A nettle cell, or NEMATOCYST (Fig. 58, B, *n.1* and *n.2*), as it is called when fully formed, is possessed of a coiled thread that lies inside of its body and that may be everted or shot out with great violence so as to penetrate the body of enemy or prey. From the end of the thread, a minute drop of poison exudes, which has a paralyzing effect upon animals struck by it. When many nettle cells strike at once, animals much larger than a Hydra may be paralyzed. Each nettle cell is provided with a sensory hair or CNIDOCIL (Fig. 58, C, *cn*), which plays the part of a trigger. When certain stimuli affect the trigger, it reacts in such a way as to bring about the discharge of the stinging thread.

A detailed study of the *origin and development of nematocysts* has shown that they are cytoplasmic derivatives of certain cells of the formative ectoderm. Within such a cell there arises a vesicular body, which in the course of development acquires a tough membrane. This vesicle or cyst increases in size until it crowds the nucleus to one side. While the cyst is growing, one part of its surface pouches inward and elongates into a slender coiled tube, the "thread" of the nematocyst (Fig. 58, C). This shoots out when the cell functions as a stinging cell (Fig. 58, D). The method of uncoiling is similar to that observed when the inturned finger of a glove is flipped out by blowing into the opening of the glove. The *exact mechanism of this discharge* is not fully understood, but there is evidence that the force exerted in the discharge is due to an increase in the water content of the cyst. This increased internal pressure becomes focused upon the one part of the cyst that can yield, namely, the inturned threadlike tube, which everts with such incredible velocity that, even though it is slender and delicate, it is able to penetrate resistant tissues such as the skin of larger animals. In endeavoring to show how this is possible, certain writers call our attention to the alleged penetration of straws into tough wood when driven at high speed in a tornado.

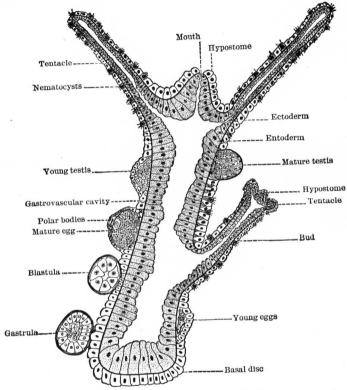

Fig. 60. A longitudinal section of *Hydra*. Not all the structures shown occur in one animal at the same time. (From Hegner.)

c. **Reproductive Cells.**—Like most sedentary and sessile organisms, Hydra may be MONŒCIOUS, or HERMAPHRODITIC; that is to say, each individual produces both male and female germ cells (Fig. 60). The germ cells are aggregated into more or less compact masses, called GONADS. The male gonad is called a TESTIS and the female, an OVARY. In certain regions of the body and under certain environmental conditions, a group of undifferentiated formative cells begins to grow and to multiply. At first the two types of gonads and their contained primordial germ cells are indistinguishable, but later they become very different indeed. In the ovary there is a cannibalistic warfare among the primordial germ cells, the stronger engulfing and eating up the weaker until only one is left, a huge gorged cell filled with the remains of its sisters. In the testis the chief activity has been of another sort: the cells have gone on multiplying until there are immense numbers of minute very active sperms with swimming tails. In the case of ova, numbers have been sacrificed for the sake of a large accumulation of food for the prospective embryo; while in the case of the sperms, size and food have been sacrificed for great numbers and activity.

2. Cells Confined to the Endoderm

There are three kinds of cells found only in the endoderm: (a) nutritive-muscular cells; (b) slime cells; (c) albumen cells. These cells are all concerned with the processes of securing or digesting the food.

a. Nutritive-muscular Cells.—These cells are larger and longer than the corresponding cells of the ectoderm; their free ends bear flagella (Fig. 58, B, en) and also send out processes resembling pseudopodia. At their basal ends these cells have elongated muscular processes that run around the cylindrical body at right angles to the processes of the ectodermal muscular cells. Contraction of these muscles elongates the body, while contraction of the ectodermal muscles shortens it. The two sets of muscles together control all movements except the slow sliding movement of the basal disk. The cytoplasm of the endodermal nutritive-muscular cells is much vacuolated in well fed Hydras and contains considerable food matter. In the green Hydra small green algæ live SYMBIOTICALLY inside alimentary cells. We see then that these cells are quite versatile, performing a variety of functions, each being almost able to take care of itself.

b. Slime Cells.—These cells are used to lubricate the food in order to facilitate swallowing. They are located between the epithelial cells of the mouth region.

c. Albumen Cells.—These are widely distributed elongated cells with slender bases attached to the basement membrane. Not infrequently the free ends of these cells are provided with one or more flagella.

3. Cells Found in Both Ectoderm and Endoderm

There are three kinds of cells not confined to either body layer, but distributed more or less at random throughout the body of Hydra: (*a*) nerve cells; (*b*) sensory cells; (*c*) formative or reserve cells.

a. Nerve Cells.—Specialized nerve cells in Hydra are few in number and confined to the most active region of the body, namely the hypostome or cone of tissue around the mouth. In a sense

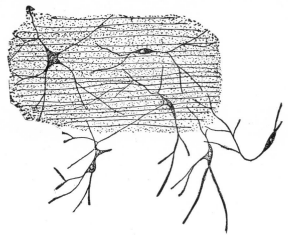

FIG. 61. Plexus of nerve cells in the ectoderm of *Hydra oligactis;* the parallel lines represent the longitudinal muscle fibers on the supporting lamella. (From Schneider.)

this region of Hydra is its brain, or central nervous system, the center of its coördinated activities. It is this region that directs and unifies the activities of the whole organism. The nerve cells are not in the form of a compact tissue, or ganglion, but lie in a loose interlocking network, the processes of the various cells being united or at least in contact with one another (Fig. 61). As has already been said, the regions where nervous tissue predominates may always be considered as the center of organization of an animal, and it is interesting to find that in Hydra the nervous system exists in the form of a band around the mouth, a very primitive situation and one that persists even among many of the higher organisms. This seems to imply that, for Hydra, the mouth is the most important region and that feeding is its dominant activity. The only difference between the nerve cells of the ectoderm and those of the endoderm is that they are much more numerous in the former than in the latter.

b. Sensory Cells.—Cells specialized for receiving stimuli are found chiefly around the mouth and the basal disk. These are slender cells, lying crowded between the epithelial cells and sending out from their bases branching fibers connecting them with the muscular processes of the contractile cells and with the nerve cells. Sensory cells are much more numerous in the endoderm than in the ectoderm; in addition, those of the endoderm sometimes bear flagella.

c. Formative or Reserve Cells.—There are always present, in the corners made by the tapering basal ends of the epithelial cells, little groups of roundish cells that are not specialized for any particular function, but are always ready for any one of several various lines of specialization (Fig. 58, B, *f.c*). Those in the ectoderm differentiate into epithelio-muscular cells, nettle cells, germ cells, and probably also into nerve and sensory cells. Those in the endoderm seem to specialize into various types of endodermal tissues only when repair work is necessary as the result of injury, or when a bud is being formed. Formative cells are far more abundant in the ectoderm than in the endoderm.

4. *The Basement Membrane, or Mesoglœa*

A thin homogeneous layer, secreted mutually by the ectoderm and the endoderm, lies between the two body layers (Fig. 58, B, *b.m*). In Hydra and in the other polypoid types of Cœlenterata the mesoglœa remains relatively inconspicuous, assuming the form of a thin basement membrane, but in the jellyfish types it becomes voluminous and constitutes the main bulk of the body.

C. Physiology of Hydra

1. *How Hydra Feeds*

Hydra is a carnivorous animal, voracious and greedy beyond compare. It feeds upon whatever forms of animals it may be able to reach and to sting with its batteries of nettle cells. Usually it has to be satisfied with the capture of small crustaceans or larvæ of aquatic animals. *Jennings,* however, has described a case that breaks all records for greed. A Hydra was found that had swallowed a caterpillar about fifty times its own size. The Hydra's body was stretched like a thin film over the body of its prey, and the mouth and tentacles formed the only clearly visible evidence that the Hydra was on the outside of the caterpillar. Whether the meal was ever digested is not known, but it seems certain that there must have ensued a severe attack of indigestion. Hydras are rarely so greedy as this, their favorite food consisting of creatures of more convenient size, such as the water flea, Cypris. One of these water fleas in swimming about comes into contact with a stretched out tentacle of Hydra and is at once stung by the poisoned darts of the nettle cells. The poisonous material, HYPNO-TOXIN, paralyzes the prey, while the threads hold it firmly. With the aid of other tentacles it is passed to the mouth, which opens in anticipation, indicating a nervous connection between the tentacles and the mouth. The Cypris is then forced into the gastro-vascular cavity, where it is digested, just as a piece of meat would be digested in a human digestive tract, by means of a pouring forth into the cavity of digestive ferments. Indigestible parts of the animal are voided through the mouth. Small organisms or other minute food particles are engulfed by the pseudopodial action of the endodermal cells and are digested within the bodies of the cells.

2. *The Behavior of Hydra*

The green fresh-water polyp (*Hydra viridissima*) is a good deal livelier than other species and is therefore a better form for the study of behavior. The more sluggish forms have much the same activities, but in a slowed down form. Hydras are usually found attached to the glass bottoms or sides of aquaria, clinging to water plants or hanging head downward from the surface film of the water. They tend to take up a position perpendicular to the surface of attachment. Movements of Hydra while attached to the substratum are confined to those produced by contraction of the muscular processes of the two kinds of epithelial cells. All they can do is to contract by shortening the muscular processes of the ectodermal cells or to elongate through contraction of endodermal muscular processes. Movements may be stimulated by internal conditions, such as hunger, or by external stimuli.

3. *Hunger Movements*

A hungry Hydra goes through a regular routine of activities. It contracts the endodermal cells and in so doing extends the body as far as possible, spreading out the tentacles to all points of the compass. If no food is encountered, it contracts and then extends in a different direction. If this new direction brings no success, it will suddenly contract again and try still another direction (Fig. 62). This is the equivalent of the TRIAL AND ERROR MOVEMENTS of Paramecium. If the now very hungry Hydra can find no food after repeated trials, it adopts another type of behavior involving a change of headquarters. At first it will simply slide along on its

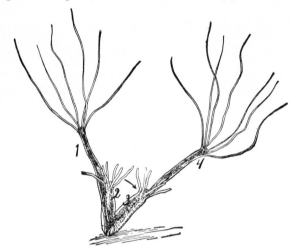

FIG. 62. Spontaneous changes of positions in an undisturbed *Hydra*. Side view. The extended animal (1), contracts (2), bends to a new position (3), and then extends (4). (From Jennings.)

basal disk until it has gone a short distance; it then goes through trial and error movements again. If still unsuccessful, it adopts more strenuous measures, bending over sideways toward the plane of attachment, attaching itself by the tentacles, releasing the basal disk, contracting the body, and then taking an upright position in a new place. This may be repeated much after the fashion of a measuring worm looping along a twig (Fig. 63). If no food be encountered—and none is likely to be under the conditions of the experiment—the ravenous Hydra resorts to extreme measures, somersaulting instead of looping. This is its last resort in the attainment of speed. The head is bent over and attached; then the foot is thrown forward over the head and attached again far in advance; then the head does as the foot has done. Even this gives no satisfaction, and the Hydra finally contracts down to a lemon-shaped mass and becomes very quiet, as though discouraged. It will live for a long time in the contracted quiescent condition. All of this behavior seems to indicate that Hydra is intelligent; and doubtless it really is intelligent, if we are somewhat liberal in our definition of the term.

If ability to modify behavior according to the changing conditions of life is intelligence, Hydra is intelligent.

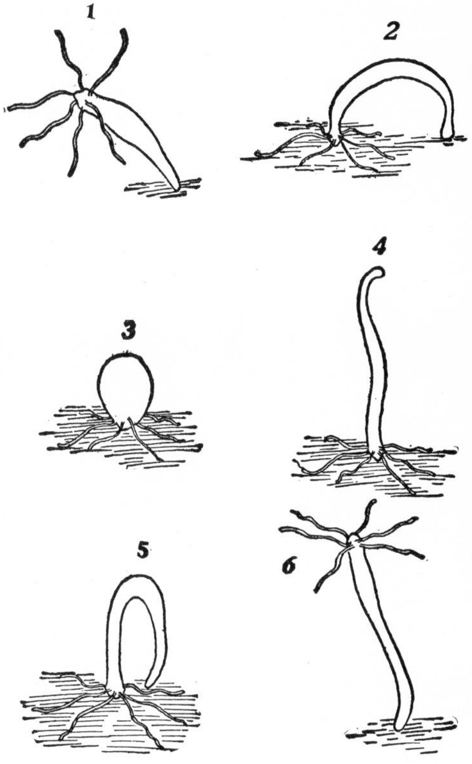

4. Reactions to External Stimuli

A good many different kinds of stimuli affect the behavior of Hydra, the following being its most important reactions: reactions to contact, reactions to chemicals, reactions to light, reactions to temperature changes.

a. Thigmotropism (reactions to contacts).—Because Hydra is a sedentary organism, fixed at all times to a substratum, contact stimuli are of

FIG. 63. Hydra looping like a measuring worm; 1–6 show successive positions of a single individual. (From Jennings, after Wagner.)

primary significance. The normal position of Hydra with the foot attached, and both looping and somersaulting movements, have definite reference to contacts. Hydras are also very sensitive to mechanical shocks such as jarring of the vessel in which they are contained, or to being touched with a solid object such as a glass rod. If one tentacle be touched, others contract, showing transmission of stimuli to the central nervous region and out to other tentacles. If one side of the body be touched, it contracts on that side and bends away at the point of local stimulus.

b. Chemotropism.—Hydra does not discharge its nematocysts when mere mechanical stimulation is applied unless the mechanical shock be severe or oft repeated. To cause the discharge a definite combination of both chemical and mechanical stimuli is necessary. This combination is furnished when solid protein food is brought in contact with the tentacles.

c. Phototropism.—One may easily observe that, if the aquarium be placed in such a position that the different sides have different illumination, the Hydras are likely to be found on one or possibly two sides, depending on the intensity of the light. Green Hydras tend to gather on the lighter sides of the aquarium unless there is too much direct sunlight. The method by which they reach the area of optimum light is that of trial and error; that is, continual avoidance of the less favorable of two alternatives will inevitably result in reaching the most favorable region and in remaining there.

d. Thermotropism.—If Hydras are placed in a long aquarium warmed at one end and chilled at the other, they will find by trial and error the region of optimum temperature, and stay there. If the whole environment be warmed, the Hydras become at first more active; but no migratory movements take place unless the temperature goes above 31° C. If the temperature be lowered, Hydra merely becomes less active, finally ceasing all movement when the freezing point is approached.

D. Reproduction of Hydra

Two phases are to be distinguished in the life cycle of Hydra and these are comparable to those described for Paramecium. There is an ASEXUAL method of reproduction, much like binary fission, which is called budding; and there is a SEXUAL method involving the production of male and female gametes—eggs and spermatozoa—and the union of gametes, or fertilization.

1. *Budding*

Hydras reproducing by budding are not uncommon in aquaria kept in laboratories (Figs. 57, A, 58, A, and 60). The first sign of budding is seen in a slight bump on the side of the body (Fig. 58, A, *b.1*), usually midway between the mouth and the basal disk.

This bump grows out at right angles to the parent body as a cylindrical branch (Fig. 57, A, *b.1*), and soon develops a crown of tentacles and a mouth at the free end (Fig. 57, A, *b.2*). While growing, the gastrovascular cavity of the bud remains in communication with that of the parent; but, when full grown, the budded individual pinches off and becomes independent. Not infrequently two or more buds may be seen attached to the parent body at the same time, so that there exists, for a while at least, a simple colony of polyps. Budding takes place only in well fed, large Hydras. If a budding individual be starved, the bud ceases to grow and will be resorbed by the starving parent.

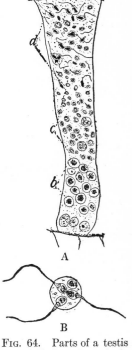

2. *Sexual Reproduction*

In our account of the histology of Hydra we have already shown that both male and female sex cells, or gametes, arise through the differentiation of formative or undifferentiated cells of the ectoderm. While these primordial germ cells are at first alike, the history of differentiation of the male cells is quite different from that of the female. The two histories are now to be described separately. This history of the differentiation and maturation of spermatozoa is known as SPERMATOGENESIS; that of ova, or eggs, as OÖGENESIS.

FIG. 64. Parts of a testis of *Hydra*. **A,** a single cyst showing spermatogonia, primary spermatocytes (*b*), secondary spermatocytes and spermatids (*c*), and spermatozoa (*d*); **B,** developing spermatozoa. (After Tannreuther in Biol. Bul.)

a. Spermatogenesis.—The male gametes are formed in small conical enlargements, which project from the surface of the body. These enlargements are the male gonads, TESTES, or SPERMARIES (Fig. 60). The testes are the result of regional rapid mitotic division of a group of formative cells in the ectoderm. These cells come to arrange themselves into a number of vertically placed elongated sacs or cysts (Fig. 64), each of which is a continuous

mass of cytoplasm containing many nuclei. After the period of
multiplication of nuclei is over each nucleus contains the diploid,
or somatic, number of chromosomes and is known as a SPERMATO-
GONIUM. Soon after this the chromosomes unite in pairs, giving
half as many double chromosomes as there had previously been
single chromosomes. The cells are now full grown and are known
as PRIMARY SPERMATOCYTES. These then divide, one member of
each of the double chromosomes going to each daughter cell. This

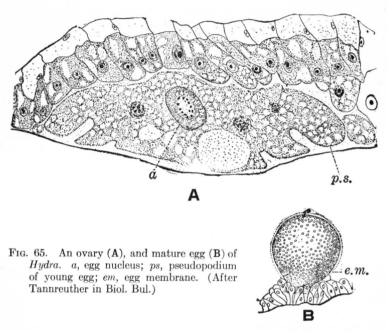

Fig. 65. An ovary (**A**), and mature egg (**B**) of
Hydra. a, egg nucleus; ps, pseudopodium
of young egg; em, egg membrane. (After
Tannreuther in Biol. Bul.)

is the first maturation division and is a REDUCTION DIVISION, for
the number of chromosomes in each cell has been reduced to one
half. These reduced cells are called SECONDARY SPERMATOCYTES.
They divide again, without reducing the chromosome number,
into SPERMATIDS, which in turn gradually differentiate into the
tailed SPERMATOZOA. Any one cyst may contain all the stages of
male germ cells from the spermatogonia up to spermatozoa, the
former occupying the inner end and the latter the outer end of the
cyst. When a considerable number of ripe spermatozoa is formed,
the testis ruptures and releases them into the water where they
are able to swim about rapidly, and thus to reach the egg.

b. **Oögenesis.**—The female gonads, ovaries (Fig. 60), arise nearer the basal disk than do the testes. The formative cells destined to become the female germ cells divide less rapidly than do those in the testis, and on that account grow larger in size. They are first to be distinguished from ordinary formative cells by their larger, rounder form and by their larger nuclei. A considerable number of primordial egg cells constitutes the female gonad, or ovary; yet all but one of these potential egg cells are sacrificed for the purpose of enriching one of them. The one egg engulfs all of the other formative cells and uses their substance as a kind of yolk (Fig. 65, A). Finally, the egg, which during the growing and feeding period has been amœboid in shape, rounds up into a sphere, surrounded by a single somewhat stretched layer of epithelial cells (Fig. 60). Maturation ensues, consisting, as in spermatogenesis, of two divisions; but here the divisions are very unequal in so far as the cytoplasm is concerned. Two very tiny cells, the POLAR BODIES, really abortive eggs, are formed (Fig. 65, B). During maturation the number of chromosomes, in the same manner as in spermatogenesis, is decreased to half of the original number. After maturation the ectodermal covering of the egg ruptures and the naked egg is exposed except at its base.

c. **Fertilization.**—The exposed egg seems to attract any spermatozoa that may be in the neighborhood. These swim to the egg in considerable numbers and several attach themselves to its surface. Only one, however, actually enters the egg. After the sperm is inside of the egg membrane it rounds up into a nucleus and the egg and sperm nuclei unite to form a fusion nucleus in which the full specific number of chromosomes is reinstated. Unless it be fertilized the egg dies and disintegrates within a period of about twenty-four hours.

3. *Embryology*

After the egg is fertilized the development of a new individual begins. While still attached to the parent body it undergoes cleavage by mitotic division into cells known as BLASTOMERES. Cleavage continues until a hollow ball of cells, the BLASTULA (Fig. 60) is formed. This consists of a single layer of cells inclosing a SEGMENTATION CAVITY. Cells from the outer layer then begin to migrate into the cavity and ultimately fill it up. The inner cells are destined to form the endoderm, and hence the process of GAS-

TRULATION, though not at all typical, has taken place; for, irrespective of just how the condition be arrived at, the attainment of the two-layered condition is considered as gastrulation (Fig. 60). While gastrulation has been going on, the ectoderm secretes about itself a horny layer, which acts as a protective envelope and effectually slows down and practically stops development for a considerable period. The young embryo drops to the bottom and rests for some time, usually passing the winter months in the dormant state. When environmental conditions again become favorable, the shell about the embryo is ruptured and the embryo is freed. The whole body undergoes expansion; the endoderm, hitherto solid, opens up so as to form the gastrovascular cavity; the mouth breaks through; the tentacles develop; and a young Hydra with its foot attached to the substratum starts out on its lifelong hunt for food.

4. Regeneration

An artificial method of reproducing Hydras is that of cutting a single individual into two or more parts and letting each part reproduce the whole. Regeneration is the process of reconstituting a whole individual or a whole organ from a part. It is a process characteristic of lowly organisms in which there is not too much regional specialization, or of young organisms that have not yet become specialized. A piece of Hydra as small as one twenty-fourth of the whole is capable of regenerating an entire animal.

E. The Relatives of Hydra

The Phylum Cœlenterata, to which Hydra belongs, is a very large and highly diversified group of animals, consisting of polyps, jellyfishes, corals, and sea anemones. They all agree in having but two body layers (diploblastic); in having no cœlom, or cavity, between body wall and alimentary tract; in having a gastrovascular cavity with one opening, the mouth; and in possessing nematocysts.

There are three classes of Cœlenterata:—

CLASS I. HYDROZOA—including fresh-water polyps, colonial hydroids, some small jellyfishes, and a few coral-like forms.

CLASS II. SCYPHOZOA—including most of the larger jellyfishes.

CLASS III. ANTHOZOA—including the sea anemones and most of the corals.

Hydra is probably a degenerate type of the Class Hydrozoa and is therefore hardly representative of that class. Most of the Hydrozoa are colonial in the polyp phase of their life cycle and form

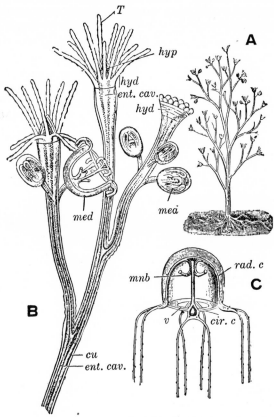

FIG. 66. *Bougainvillea ramosa*, a colonial hydroid. **A,** entire colony, natural size; **B,** portion of the same, magnified; **C,** immature medusa; *cir.c*, circular canal; *cu*, cuticle, or perisarc; *ent. cav*, enteric, or gastrovascular cavity; *hyd*, polyp, or hydranth; *hyp*, hypostome, or manubrium; *med*, medusa bud; *mnb*, manubrium; *rad.c*, radial canal; *T*, tentacle; *v*, velum. (From Parker and Haswell, after Parker.)

rather elaborate branching systems of polyps derived from the budding of one young polyp. A good example of the Hydrozoa is Bougainvillea (Fig. 66), in which each individual polyp is the equivalent of a Hydra bud that has failed to detach itself from the parent body. Certain colonial Hydrozoa (Siphonophora) have some of their polyps specialized for locomotion, others for floats, others for defense (see Frontispiece). In fact, it is rather general for the members of a colony to differ somewhat in function. Bougainvillea shows a differentiation into generalized vegetative polyps (Fig. 66) and reproductive polyps or MEDUSÆ, which are characteristically umbrella-shaped and swim about freely in the sea. The medusa is a sexually mature individual that produces either eggs or sperms. The egg becomes fertilized and develops into a polyp, which in turn, by repeated asexual budding, forms a colony. Thus we have an alternation between the asexual and the sexual modes of reproduction quite similar to that seen in Paramecium. This is called METAGENESIS, or ALTERATION OF GENERATIONS. Hydra is a degenerate form which has no true medusa stage, though the ovaries and testes may be viewed as reduced medusa buds. There are many intermediate conditions that serve to bridge the gap between species like Bougainvillea and Hydra.

In the Scyphozoa the medusa stage is highly developed and the polyp stage greatly reduced or suppressed; while in the Anthozoa the polyp stage is highly specialized and the medusa stage totally suppressed.

CHAPTER XVI

PLANARIA

(PHYLUM PLATYHELMINTHES)

A. HABITS AND HABITAT

PLANARIA is a common flatworm belonging to the PHYLUM PLATYHELMINTHES. It occurs only in fresh water, usually crawling on the under sides of stones or other smooth objects. The body is several times as long as it is broad. It always moves about with the blunt anterior end foremost. The head end is rather broad with two lateral earlike processes, the AURICLES, which act as tactile organs. The posterior end tapers off to a sharp point. A well-grown animal may be half an inch long by about an eighth of an inch wide. When viewed from the side, the body is seen to

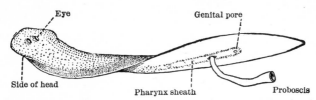

FIG. 67. *Planaria polychroa* seen in approximately side view, showing the flatness of the body and the way in which the proboscis may be thrust out. (From Shipley and MacBride.)

be extremely flat, a character which gives the common name flatworms to the group (Fig. 67). While a Hydra is in contact with solid objects only at its base, Planaria maintains contact along its entire length, about half of its body surface being kept constantly flat against the substratum.

Planaria has a very steady, gliding type of locomotion that seems to have no reference to any muscular movements of the body. Its progression is, in fact, due to cilia, which cover the entire surface but are particularly abundant on the ventral side. The worm lays down a smooth roadbed for itself by secreting mucus at the anterior end and then sliding along on it by backward whipping of the cilia.

179

As it glides along, the head moves from side to side and the auricles extend outward and forward, now to one side, now to the other, as though the animal were feeling its way.

B. General Morphology

1. Four Advanced Characters of Planaria

One can readily note that there are present in Planaria four characters not shown in Cœlenterata, but possessed also by higher groups: (a) anteroposterior axis, dorsoventral axis, and bilateral symmetry; (b) a distinct third body layer, the mesoderm; (c) an excretory system; (d) a true central nervous system. These require detailed description:—

a. **Anteroposterior Axis, Dorsoventral Axis, and Bilateral Symmetry.**—A modern theory as to the relation between the oral-aboral axis and radial symmetry of the cœlenterates, on the one hand, and the anteroposterior axis, dorsoventral axis, and bilateral symmetry of the flatworms, on the other, deserves careful consideration.

This theory holds that the flatworms have descended from some flat bodied jellyfish-like ancestor. Such a form would have had its mouth at the free end of a long hypostome resembling a handle hanging down from the top of the flat umbrella-like body. The pharynx of such a form would divide into a number of branching radial subdivisions of the gastrovascular cavity. The central nervous system would consist of radially arranged ganglia, repeated at regular intervals along the margin of the umbrella and connected with one another by nerve cords, the whole forming a nerve ring.

If in the course of evolution such a jellyfish were to lose the habit of swimming about freely in the water, as many other types of aquatic organisms seem to have done, and were to settle to the bottom for feeding purposes, it would settle down on the oral surface with the mouth next to the bottom. In feeding upon the rich food supply of the bottom it would tend to slide about on the oral surface by muscular and ciliary action, and it would progress sometimes in the direction of one radial axis, sometimes in others. For some unknown reason one of the several radial axes seems to have gained the ascendancy, becoming the new apical end, or head, and the ganglia of that region became the new brain. The acquisition of dominance by the new brain seems to have suppressed all rival nerve centers, and all that was left of the ancestral ganglionic ring are one enlarged pair of ganglia and a pair of widely separated nerve cords.

The establishment of a new dominant region, the head, would influence the direction of growth of the rest of the body, involving an elongation perpendicularly to the apical region, and oval or elongated bodies would be produced. The mouth would still be centrally located and the hypostome would now be used as a proboscis. The digestive tract would still be a more or less radially branched gastrovascular system with the branches coming off from the pharynx and running to all parts of the body, but mainly forward and backward because of the elongation of body.

In short, were these changes to take place, a primitive flatworm would be the result. There are numerous flatworms today, relatives of Planaria, that are so wide across the body as to be broadly oval or nearly circular in shape. A comparison of these with a flat jellyfish lends probability to the above theory.

According to this theory the oralaboral axis of the cœlenterates becomes the dorsoventral axis of flatworms and the radial symmetry of cœlenterates becomes not merely the bilateral symmetry but the anteroposterior axis of the flatworms, for one of the secondary radial apical points of the circular marginal nervous system of the jellyfish ancestor becomes the new anterior end, head, of the flatworm. Hence it is not the dorsoventral axis that is new, as is usually supposed to be the case, but the anteroposterior axis, while bilateral symmetry is merely a kind of distortion of radial symmetry consequent upon the elongation of the body perpendicular to the new apical end. Although it must be admitted that this theory is somewhat speculative, it is undoubtedly the most satisfactory theory of the ancestry of the flatworms and is in harmony with the Diphyletic Tree Theory.

In all animals except vertebrates the ventral surface is the one where lies the nervous system; it is the superior or controlling surface, and there is a gradient in the rate of metabolic activity running from ventral to dorsal surfaces. One might call such a gradient a ventrodorsal gradient to distinguish it from the dorsoventral gradient of vertebrates. An animal with a ventrodorsal axis is related to the environment equally on the two sides, the right and the left; and in accord with this we find that the two sides are equivalents or mirror images of each other. One can draw a line down the body from head to tail so as to divide the animal into two equivalent halves. Some organs occur singly in the median line, such as mouth and proboscis, penis, uterus, genital pore, and the median branch of the intestine; but all organs that occur away from the median line are likely to be paired. Thus we have a pair of brains, a pair of eyes, a pair of auricles, a pair of posterior gastrovascular branches, and pairs of gonads. This paired arrangement is known as BILATERAL SYMMETRY. All of the higher animals are, at least primitively, bilaterally symmetrical.

b. The Mesoderm.—Hydra is diploblastic, having only two body layers, ectoderm and endoderm, with a noncellular mesoglœa between. Planaria, however, is a three layered animal (TRIPLOBLASTIC), as are all higher animals. In addition to the ectoderm and endoderm there is a third body layer known as mesoderm.

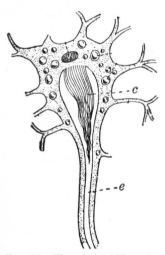

The ECTODERM consists of a thin layer of external cells called the EPIDERMIS. The cells are ciliated. Embedded in the epidermis are characteristic rodlike bodies, called RHABDITES, which are discharged to the exterior when the animal is irritated, and are believed to serve an offensive purpose. The skin is also provided with unicellular mucous glands.

The MESODERM consists largely of a sort of packing tissue, or PARENCHYMA, which rather loosely fills in the space unoccupied by other organs between the body wall and the alimentary tract. Thus there is no definite cœlom, or body cavity. Other mesodermal tissues are the muscles which occur in four systems: circular muscles, longitudinal muscles, oblique, and dorsoventral muscles. The circular muscle cells form a thin layer next to the epidermis; then comes an ill-defined layer of longitudinal and oblique muscles; the dorsoventral muscles extend between dorsal and ventral surfaces between the branches of the intestine.

FIG. 68. Flame cell of *Planaria*. *c*, cilia; *e*, opening into excretory tubule. (From Lankester's Treatise.)

The ENDODERM consists of a single layer of elongated epithelial cells lining the much-branched digestive tract.

c. **Excretory System.**—This consists of a network of tubules running lengthwise through the body along the two sides. Each tube branches and rebranches giving off fine terminal twigs to all parts of the body. Each ultimate branch terminates in a peculiar cell termed a FLAME CELL (Fig. 68), a large hollow cell in the cavity of which there is a bunch of cilia. These cilia extend into the cavity of the tubule and their synchronous beat produces a flicker like that of a flame. Their movement serves to propel the fluid contents of the tubule and thus to drive it to the exterior.

d. **Nervous System.**—The central nervous system consists of a bi-lobed mass of nerve cells (CEPHALIC GANGLIA) near the anterior end and beneath the black EYESPOTS. This double ganglion, or BRAIN, gives off two ventral nerve cords that run the length of the body at some distance from each other. Transverse nerves connect the two ventral nerve cords like the rungs of a ladder. The brain also gives off nerves to the various sensitive areas of the head, the AURICLES, and adjacent surfaces.

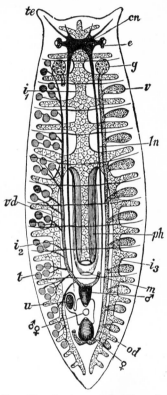

FIG. 69. Anatomy of *Planaria*. *cn*, brain; *e*, eye; *g*, ovary; i_1, i_2, i_3, branches of intestine; *ln*, lateral nerve; *m*, mouth; *ph*, pharynx; *od*, oviduct; *t*, testis; *te*, auricle; *u*, uterus; *v*, yolk glands; *vd*, vas deferens; ♂, penis; ♀, vagina; ♂♀, common genital pore. (From Lankester's Treatise, after V. Graff.)

2. *Improvements on Earlier Systems*

The systems showing most distinct improvement over equivalent systems of Hydra are: the alimentary system, the reproductive system, and the muscular system.

a. Alimentary System.—About midway between anterior and posterior ends of Planaria is the pharyngeal chamber in which lies a cylindrical muscular tube, the PHARYNX (Fig. 69). This organ is continuous anteriorly with the walls of the PHARYNGEAL CHAMBER and with the STOMACH-INTESTINE. It is free at the posterior end and has a wide terminal opening near the MOUTH. The pharyngeal chamber opens to the exterior through a circular opening, and, when feeding, the pharynx may be protruded by elongation through this opening, as a long trunk or PROBOSCIS (Fig. 67). The digestive tract is a true GASTROVASCULAR CAVITY, like that of Hydra, but much more elaborately branched, so as to be in close contact with nearly every part of the body. It is thus able not only to digest food but also possibly to circulate it. There is only one opening into this cavity, namely, the mouth, no anus being present. Fæces are voided through the mouth, as in Hydra.

b. Reproductive System.—Planaria, like most flatworms that reproduce sexually, is HERMAPHRODITIC, *i.e.*, it has both male and female reproductive organs in the same individual (Fig. 69). Some Hydras were shown to be hermaphrodites also; so this is not a new but an old character. As a rule, the hermaphrodite condition is found in groups that are of sedentary habits, or are likely to lead isolated lives. It makes the process of fertilization of eggs more certain when a single individual can fertilize its own eggs, or when any two individuals that chance to meet can mutually supply sperm for each other's eggs.

The MALE REPRODUCTIVE ORGANS consist of a large number of small spherical bodies (TESTES) located in the mesoderm and scattered almost from one end of the body to the other. They are connected by tubules with a pair of ducts, the VASA DEFERENTIA, that lead to a median muscular organ, the PENIS, which lies in a pouch of the body wall called the PENIAL SHEATH; this opens to the outside by means of a single opening, the GENITAL PORE. When the free end of the penis is protruded, it is of considerable length and is able to pass into the long slender duct of the uterus of another individual to which it transfers spermatophores or packets of spermatozoa.

The FEMALE REPRODUCTIVE ORGANS consist of two spherical OVARIES lying near the anterior end. Each is provided with a long oviduct which runs backward to the posterior end of the body and enters the genital atrium. As the eggs pass down the oviduct they

become associated with yolk from the numerous yolk glands that
empty into the oviduct. Thus eggs mixed with yolk enter the
genital atrium where sperm cells have been
stored, and there fertilization takes place. After
the eggs are fertilized groups of them together
with masses of yolk are parceled up into cocoons.
These capsule-like bodies are commonly deposited
upon stones or other objects in water where they
remain until the young worms emerge. One cannot
but be impressed with the elaborateness of the
whole equipment for sexual reproduction. It is,
indeed, a well known fact that flatworms, more
than almost any other group of animals, have
developed a high degree of specialization in the
organs accessory to sexual reproduction.

    c. Muscular System.—In the Hydra we saw
that the contractile function was played by cells
that had also a number of other duties. In
Planaria there are cells that are specialized for
the contractile or muscular function alone.

3. *Systems That Planaria Lacks*

    A number of important systems that are prom-
inent features of higher animals are not definitely differentiated in Planaria nor in other
flatworms: (1) There is no true body cavity or
cœlom; (2) there is no separate circulatory system, but this rôle is played by the gastrovascular
cavity; (3) there is no respiratory system, respiration taking place over the whole surface of the
body; (4) there is no skeletal system, all parts of
the body being soft, without any hardened protective covering of any sort, and without any
spicules.

Fig. 70. *Planaria
dorotocephala*,
outline, indi-
cating several
zoöids in ba-
sal region; *f*,
f, usual level
of fission.
(From Child.)

C. Asexual Reproduction

    Some species of Planaria, notably *P. dorotoce-
phala*, rarely develop sexual organs. They have been reared in
laboratory cultures for years without ever showing any gonads.
Yet they reproduce quite effectively in another way. Large

animals of a relatively mature age, when their activity has slowed down, undergo transverse fission, the fission plane being about at the level of the line f—f in Figure 70. The separated posterior piece pulls loose and becomes a new animal, while the anterior portion regenerates a new posterior end. The posterior piece is not merely one individual, but there are several other potential individuals represented in it, as is indicated in the illustration by the lines drawn across the body.

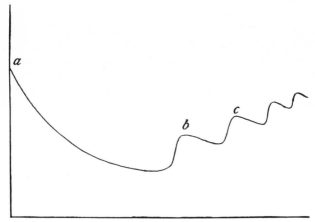

Fig. 71. Graphic representation of major axial gradients in a *planaria* with several zoöids: *a*, head of animal; *b*, *c*, apical regions of secondary zoöids. (From Child.)

A physiological explanation of the fission process has been given by **Child**. The animal has a well-defined axiate organization, owing to the fact that the head, or apical end, is the region of highest metabolic activity. From the apical region there is a gradient of decreasing metabolic rate until the level f—f is reached. "There a sudden rise occurs, and then again a downward gradient toward the posterior end. The region where the rate rises suddenly represents the apical end of the second individual and the downward gradient following is the gradient of the major axis of this zoöid. In the shorter animals only one of the zoöids is present, but as the length increases the basal body region may show two, three, or more distinct gradients (Fig. 70). Represented graphically, the metabolic gradient in such an animal is like the curve in Figure 71: *a* is the head region, the long slope the body of the anterior chief zoöid, which forms most of the body of the worm, *b* represents the apical point of the second zoöid, c that of the third, etc. These zoöids are the result of successive physiological isolations of the basal region as the animal grows in length."

Certain principles involved in this situation need further elucidation. When a Planarian is young, it is relatively short and its whole body, especially the head, has a relatively high rate of metabolism. As it grows older it becomes longer and its whole metabolic rate slows down. When young, the high metabolic rate of the head was able to exercise a dominance, through the transmission of stimuli down the gradient, over the entire length of the animal. With a slowing down of the metabolic rate of the apical end and an increase in the length of the path over which the impulse travels, there comes a time when the apical end can no longer maintain a physiological dominance over the entire axis. At the point where dominance fades out, an independent part of the body arises through what is known as PHYSIOLOGICAL ISOLATION. The isolated piece, the second zoöid, has its own gradient, the metabolic rate of the anterior end being the highest. This region now becomes a new apical end or, morphologically speaking, the head of a new zoöid. No structural indications of a new individual are visible, however, at this time. The only tests of the presence of a second or third individual are physiological tests. It has been shown in many ways that the metabolic gradients are as shown in Figure 71. Then, too, the posterior zoöid shows lack of coördination with the rest of the animal, often holding on when the latter goes ahead. Thus the body becomes greatly stretched as in Figure 72 and sooner or later a separation occurs at the fission level, *f—f.* The isolated posterior zoöid now forms a new head, with eyes, brain, and other parts. The new head then re-organizes the rest of the piece into a complete new individual.

Fig. 72. *Planaria dorotocephala* in the act of fission. (From Child.)

It is important to note that, even in flatworms like Planaria, there is a tendency for the animal to become a chain of individuals consisting of one dominant individual with a well developed head and one or more subordinate individuals formed posteriorly.

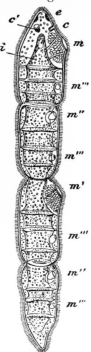

In MICROSTOMUM, a flatworm belonging to the same class as Planaria, the production of a series of zoöids goes some steps further. Here the new individuals are morphologically differentiated but not completely cut off, since the alimentary tract remains continuous through the whole chain. Note (Fig. 73) a chain of sixteen zoöids more or less completely formed. The original head is seen at the top, with a large mouth, relatively large brain, eyespots, and ciliated pits. None of the other individuals have eyespots, nor so large a brain, nor a fully formed mouth. Evidently the first fission occured about halfway back, for the apical end of this second zoöid has the brain rather large and a mouth broken through into the intestine. This evidently dominates all of the minor individuals of the posterior half. The third fission divided the anterior zoöid again, producing a third zoöid with a small brain and a mouth partly

FIG. 73. Process of repeated fission in *Microstomum. c, c',* ciliated groove; *e,* eyespot; *i,* intestine; *m, m', m'', m''',* mouths of primary, secondary, tertiary, etc., zoöids. Note that there are sixteen zoöids belonging to four grades. (From Parker and Haswell, after von Graff.)

formed. The second zoöid then gave off the fourth zoöid posteriorly, which is somewhat less well developed than the third. Each of the first four zoöids is in process of dividing again, as shown by incipient mouths and fission planes across the body. Subsequently the series of individuals breaks apart and each zoöid becomes an independent worm. If the chain were to remain permanently under the dominance of the original head, we would have a condition in many respects similar to that seen in the Annelida (the segmented worms), which constitute the subject matter of our next chapter.

D. REGENERATION IN PLANARIA

It has been shown how Planaria can break its own body into two parts and regenerate a whole individual from each of the parts.

Essentially the same thing takes place when with a sharp knife one cuts a Planaria into two pieces. The posterior piece constricts itself more or less at the cut surface and new colorless tissue forms over the wound. Out of this new tissue a small head is differentiated. The new head then takes command of the piece and reorganizes its materials into the body of a complete worm. Small pieces may be cut out of the worm at various levels of the primary axis. For example, pieces *a*, *b*, and *c* may be removed from a worm like that shown in Figure 74. This might be repeated in fifty worms and a comparison made of the average success in regeneration of *a*-pieces, *b*-pieces, and *c*-pieces. It is found that heads form nearly always in *a*-pieces, less frequently in *b*-pieces, and relatively rarely in *c*-pieces. Moreover, the heads that do form in *a*-pieces are normal, those in *b*-pieces frequently subnormal, and those in *c*-pieces mostly subnormal. This seems to indicate: first, that there is a gradient down the axis of the original worm, and second, that as one goes further down the axis there is less difference between the apical end and the basal end of the piece, so that

FIG. 75. Reconstitution of single and biaxial apical structures from short pieces of *Planaria*. (From Child.)

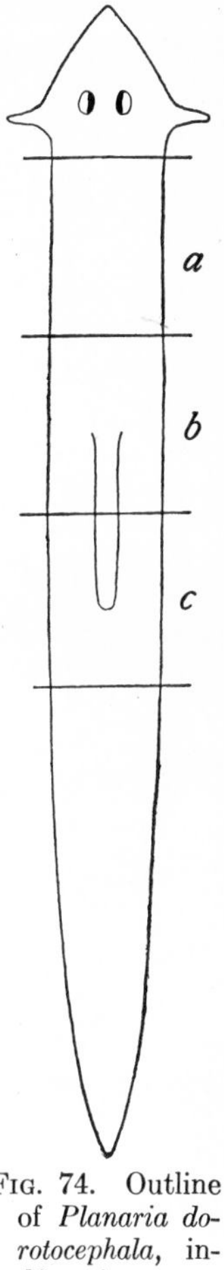

FIG. 74. Outline of *Planaria dorotocephala*, indicating regions, *a*, *b*, *c*, from which pieces are taken. (From Child.)

it is difficult for the apical end to gain ascendancy over the rest of the piece and thus to produce normal apical structures.

If a small piece is cut out very close to the head, there is so little difference in the rate of metabolism at the apical and basal ends of the piece that neither end dominates the other and a head is formed on both ends (Fig. 75).

By artificially controlling the rate of metabolism of regenerating pieces it is possible to alter the prospective fate of such pieces— to increase or to decrease the normal frequency of heads or the degree of normal development of heads and other parts. In brief, the interpretation of animal organization in terms of the rate of metabolism at different levels of the axis has enabled the experimenter to control development with a great deal of nicety, and to obtain results that have thrown much light on the nature of the processes of development and of reproduction.

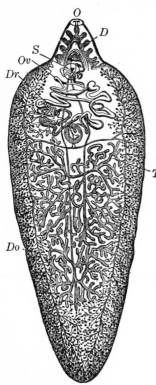

FIG. 76. The liver fluke, *Fasciola hepatica. D*, anterior part of intestine (posterior part not shown); *Do*, yolk-glands; *Dr*, ovary; *O*, mouth; *Ov*, uterus; *S*, sucker; *T*, testes. (From Sedgwick, after Sommer.)

E. OTHER FLATWORMS

The PHYLUM PLATYHELMINTHES consists of three classes:—

CLASS I. TURBELLARIA (Planarians, etc.).—Free-living, carnivorous, ciliated worms, with fairly well developed head and sense organs.

CLASS II. TREMATODA (Flukes).— Small, always parasitic flatworms, destitute of cilia and with a cuticle; having usually two sucking disks, and with head parts greatly reduced. This group is well illustrated by the common liver fluke (*Fasciola hepatica*), parasitic in the gall bladder of the sheep (Fig. 76). As compared with Planaria, it should be noted that the anterior or prepharyngeal part of the body has been greatly shortened, so that almost the whole body corresponds to the postpharyngeal part of Planaria. The mouth, provided with a sucker, is anterior in position and opens into a two branched digestive tract. The second sucker, which is for attachment only, is on the ventral side near the anterior end. The reproductive system is even more complex than in Planaria.

A remarkable and characteristic peculiarity of the flukes is their complicated life history. In addition to the fact that they have a long series of larval generations between the egg and the adult, they spend part of the life cycle in the body of an intermediate host, a water snail. The life cycle is represented in the accompanying illustration (Fig. 77).

Eggs in large numbers are fertilized in the body of the adult fluke, are given off into the bile duct of the sheep, pass out

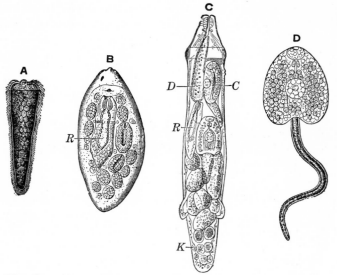

Fig. 77. Stages in the life-history of the liver fluke, *Fasciola hepatica*. **A,** miracidium (ciliated embryo). **B,** sporocyst containing rediæ (*R*). **C,** a redia; *C*, cercaria; *D*, gut; *K*, germ cells; *R*, redia. **D,** cercaria. (From Sedgwick; **B,** after Leuckart; **C** and **D** from Hegner, after Thomas.)

through the digestive tract, and are voided with the fæces. The egg hatches out when it rains and a tiny ciliated aquatic larva, the MIRACIDIUM (Fig. 77, A), emerges and, if lucky, finds a snail of the genus Lymnea, into whose body it bores. Here it rounds up into a saclike thing called the SPOROCYST. Some of the cells of the sporocyst appear to be parthenogenetic ova, each of which develops into a larval form much more elaborate than a miracidium, called a REDIA (Fig. 77, C), which has a definite alimentary canal and two processes, like paired legs, on the outside of the body. The rediæ break out of the sporocyst and, in turn, produce parthenogenetic ova that develop into more rediæ. This is repeated for several generations. Then some of these later rediæ give rise parthenogenetically, as before, to a generation of still more advanced larvæ called CERCARIÆ (Fig. 77, C). Each cercaria is shaped something like a tadpole, but with flattened body and long swimming tail (Fig. 77, D). It is a true larval form which changes without further multiplication into an adult fluke. The young cercaria bores its way out of the snail's body, loses the tail, and rounds up into a cyst. These cysts are eaten by grazing sheep and the cyst is digested off, releasing the young fluke in the stomach or intestine, whence it finds its way to its favorite abode, the gall bladder. There it attaches itself and grows up to the adult condition.

CLASS III.   CESTODA (Tapeworms).—Internal parasites with a complex life history involving two hosts. They are extremely degenerate forms, with no mouth nor digestive tract. The original young BLADDER WORM multiplies by transverse fission, producing a long ribbonlike series of secondary individuals (PROGLOTTIDES), which are little more than bags of reproductive organs.

An example of the Cestoda is a common tapeworm of the human intestine, *Tænia solium* (Fig. 78). The adult animal (A) consists of a headlike anterior part, called the SCOLEX (B), which is provided with a ring of hooks (C) and several suckers. Behind the scolex is a short part called the NECK, and this is followed by a long series of rectangular flattened individuals, proglottides, which are smallest next to the neck and largest at the posterior end. A single worm may be ten feet or more in length and contain nearly a thousand proglottides. New proglottides are constantly being produced from the neck region, so that those farthest from the neck are the oldest. The larger proglottides are sexually mature and seem to be practically filled with reproductive organs of both sexes. The long, tapelike series of proglottides becomes folded one part against another, bringing the proglottides together in pairs so that they are able to effect a mutual exchange of spermatozoa. The fertilized eggs develop while in the uterus of a proglottid into small spherical embryos armed with six hooks (D). Proglottides, laden with these embryos, break off and pass out of the body of the host along with fæces. Hogs pick up the proglottides as the result of filthy feeding habits. The proglottides are digested in the alimentary tract of the hog, and the freed embryos work their way through the walls of the alimentary tract, reach their destination in the

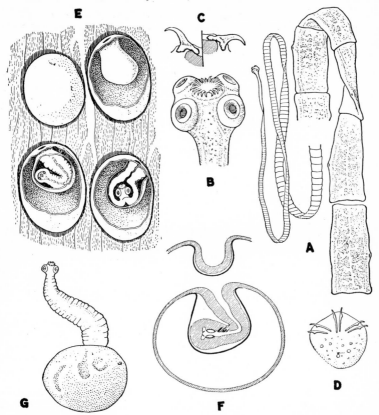

FIG. 78. The human tapeworm, *Tænia solium.* **A,** shows representative portions of a single tapeworm including the scolex, the region of fission, many young proglottides, and a few sexually mature proglottides, the posterior one being the oldest and now free. **B,** the scolex enlarged, showing the four suckers and the apical crown of hooks. **C,** separate hooks showing method of grasping. **D,** hexacanth, or six-hooked embryo. **E,** a group of bladder worms (cysticerci) embedded in the muscle fibers of the hog. **F,** shows two stages in the invagination that results in the bladder-worm condition. **G,** Bladder worm with head evaginated and ready to attach itself to the wall of the human intestine. (Redrawn after Pfurscheller wall chart.)

voluntary muscles, in the liver, and in other organs, where they become encysted, and during encystment develop into BLADDER WORMS with inverted heads (E and F). If underdone pork infested with these parasites be eaten by man, some bladder worms (CYSTICERCI) are released in the intestine. Each bladder worm shoots out its hooked head (as in G) and attaches itself to the wall of the intestine. The bladder is soon lost and the series of transverse fissions ensues, giving rise to another chain of proglottides.

This process of multiplication by transverse fission doubtless has the same physiological basis as has the formation of zoöids in Planaria. It begins, however, while the worm is still an embryo, or at least no more than a larva. This is significant, because it has some points of resemblance to the formation of metameres or segments in the Annelida.

CHAPTER XVII

CLAM-WORM AND EARTHWORM

(PHYLUM ANNELIDA)

THE marine worm, *Nereis*, and the earthworm, *Lumbricus*, are chosen as representatives of the large and important PHYLUM ANNELIDA. They are SEGMENTED WORMS; all other worms—flatworms, roundworms, etc.—being unsegmented. Nereis is a much more typical annelid than is the earthworm. The latter is a degenerate type with reduced head and locomotor structures; it leads a semisedentary life; and, appropriately enough, it is HERMAPHRODITIC. Nereis, on the contrary, is a marine form, relatively active, has a well developed head, and is DIŒCIOUS (*i.e.*, the sexes are separate). Although it is customary to introduce students first to the earthworm and later to other worms, we shall depart from custom and present Nereis first as a very typical annelid, showing annelid characteristics at their best and in their least modified phases. Laboratory work on living Annelida and many details of internal anatomy will necessarily be worked out upon the earthworm, because, except along the seashore, living specimens of Nereis are unobtainable, while the earthworm is available practically everywhere.

A. HABITAT AND HABITS OF NEREIS

Nereis virens is a relatively large worm common on our Atlantic Coast. It is usually called the "clam-worm" or "sand worm" because it lives in burrows in the sand along with marine clams. They spend nearly all their lives in their burrows, emerging partially for the purpose of seizing pieces of seaweed and small animals that live upon seaweeds. Pieces of food are seized with their grasping jaws and swallowed by inverting the everted PHARYNX. The numerous bristles or SETÆ on the paired PARAPODIA (Fig. 79) doubtless function chiefly in enabling the worm to get a purchase on the sides of the smooth, slime lined burrow. One wonders that an animal so well provided with aquatic locomotor organs leads so quiet a life, and swims about so little. We do not know much about

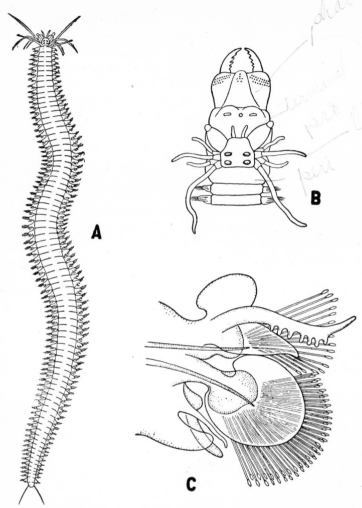

FIG. 79. The clam-worm, *Nereis*. **A,** the entire animal showing the head parts in the normal position when not feeding. **B,** the head with jaws and pharynx protruded in the position assumed when grasping food; note the squarish prostomium with four eyes and short pair of tentacles, the large peristomium with palpi and four pairs of long tentacles, and the first two trunk metameres. **C,** a single parapodium showing numerous locomotor setæ and flattened respiratory flaps. (Redrawn after Leuckart wall chart.)

the free life of *Nereis virens*, but *N. limbata* becomes, during the breeding season, a swift swimming marine creature. When the swarming period comes, they leave their burrows and swim up toward the surface, darting about in great numbers and giving off clouds of eggs and spermatozoa. It is at such times as this that the collector with a bright light at the bow of the boat may attract and capture with the dip net large numbers of worms; for they are strongly phototropic.

B. General Morphology of Nereis

1. *General External Characters*

The body is long, narrow, and nearly cylindrical, tapering somewhat toward the posterior end (Fig. 79, A). The HEAD is well defined, and provided with EYES, PALPI, TENTACLES (Fig. 79, B). The rest of the body consists of a series of ringlike segments, or METAMERES, each practically like all the others, except that the posterior one is rounded off and provided with a pair of ANAL CIRRI. Each metamere is provided with a pair of movable appendages —flat, paddlelike structures known as PARAPODIA that are fringed with bundles of bristles (SETÆ, or CHÆTÆ). The head consists of a PROSTOMIUM and a PERISTOMIUM. The prostomium is relatively small and bears two pairs of well developed eyes, a pair of anterior tentacles, and further back a pair of conical PALPI. The peristomium resembles a broad metamere without any parapodia. Instead of parapodia it bears four pairs of long tentaclelike structures. Situated in an anterior position and just ventral to the prostomium is the MOUTH, an opening surrounded by the first true segment, the peristomium.

2. *Advanced Characters*

Several innovations have been introduced by the annelids: metameric organization, a true cœlom, a circulatory system, and respiratory organs:—

a. Metamerism.—This is the most important advance made by the annelids. An understanding of the characteristics and significance of this segmental type of organization is of importance, because it is upon this plan that the most successful of the higher groups of animals—the arthropods and the vetebrates—have been built up. There are differences of opinion as to how the metameric condition arose and how it has become modified. Before entering upon a discussion of this problem, let us examine the metameric structure of Nereis. We may note that, back of the eleventh, each metamere is like all the others. Each is partitioned off from the others by a mesodermal wall perforated by the intestine, nervous system, NEPHRIDIA, and blood vessels. Each has its own pair of nephridia, its own pair of subsidiary brains, or ganglia, its own vascular ring. In the breeding season nearly every metamere produces ova or spermatozoa. In a sense, then, each metamere is a sort of subordinate, incomplete individual. We have already seen that Planaria has a tendency to build up a chain of subordinate zoöids, and that Microstomum actually does build up a temporary series of zoöids. If such zoöids were to remain permanently attached to the anterior individual, the latter might play the rôle of a head and dominate the whole series. If so, the subordinate zoöids would become merely a series of repeated body parts, semi-independent in their functions, but under the general control of the head. This is the ZOÖID THEORY as to the nature and origin of metamerism. It seems to agree with many of the facts, but is not accepted by all zoölogists. According to this theory, however, the prostomium is looked upon as the original individual, which, while still in the larval stage, begins to elongate posteriorly and undergoes repeated transverse fission so as to form a whole series of secondary individuals. These remain closely integrated, both morphologically and physiologically, as parts of the single individual. Thus we have a higher level of individuality built up out of a series of individuals each of an order equivalent to a short, simplified planarian. Just as it is a mistake to overemphasize the fact that the Protozoa are one-celled animals, so it would be a mistake to call planarians and other unsegmented worms one-metamered individuals, and the annelids many-metamered. Two terms which seem most appropriate are "unsegmented" and "segmented"; which reminds one of Dobell's characterization of the Protozoa as noncellular and the Metazoa as cellular organisms. The annelids, arthropods, and vertebrates may be looked upon as groups using the metamere as a very useful unit of organization that readily admits of regional specialization, just as the simpler Metazoa use the cell unit in gaining higher levels of specialization.

b. **The Cœlom.**—The cœlom may be defined as a cavity in the mesoderm, or middle body layer, lined with epithelium. Into it open the NEPHRIDIA, and its walls give rise to the reproductive cells. All of the higher animals develop a cœlom at some period. It becomes the true body cavity and plays an important rôle in distributing nutritive materials. It is filled with a fluid, the CŒLOMIC FLUID, in which there are numerous small colorless cells, resembling the leucocytes or white blood cells of the vertebrates. So radical a departure is the cœlom, that some zoölogists have divided all of the Metazoa into ACŒLOMATA and CŒLOMATA— animals without and animals with a cœlom. The Acœlomata are: Porifera, Cœlenterata, Ctenophora. The Cœlomata are: Echinodermata, Annelida, Mollusca, Arthropoda, Chordata, etc. The Platyhelminthes and Nemathelminthes seem to be forms in which the mesoderm is in process of developing a cœlom, but in which a real open cœlom is wanting.

c. **Circulatory System.**—In Hydra and in Planaria we saw that the function of digestion and that of circulation were both played by a single organ, the gastrovascular cavity. In the annelids these two functions are separated, leaving the digestive tract free for digestion only, and introducing a new system of BLOOD VESSELS that runs to all parts of the body. As a detailed study of the circulatory system of the earthworm comes later, we need here only mention this new acquisition.

d. **Respiratory System.**—With the introduction of a circulatory system carrying blood all over the body, it would appear highly advantageous to have some means by which the blood could reach the surface in order to obtain oxygen and get rid of its gaseous wastes, such as CO_2. In small or in relatively inactive animals this might readily be accomplished through the skin alone, but it becomes necessary in more active animals of the aquatic sorts to increase the area through which respiration can take place. In Nereis the parapodia are believed to aid materially in this way. In a number of marine worms that are more completely confined to tubes or burrows than is Nereis, elaborate gills or BRANCHIAL FILAMENTS develop in considerable numbers around the head region, which is the only part of the body usually exposed.

3. *Improvements in Old Systems*

Almost as striking as the innovations just described are some of the radical improvements in systems already dealt with in lower forms:—

a. The Alimentary Tract.—Freed from the circulatory function, the alimentary tract in Nereis has become a straight, unbranched food tube, running from the mouth to the posterior end, where a second opening, the ANUS, exists. It will be remembered that Hydra and Planaria, together with their relatives, have only one opening to the alimentary tract, the mouth.

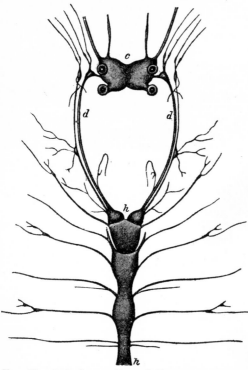

b. An Improved Nervous System.—The BRAIN, or CEREBRAL GANGLION, of Nereis (Fig. 80) is a considerably more clearly defined and specialized organ than that of Planaria. It gives off slender nerves to the tentacles and palpi and short thick nerves to the four eyes. Running backward are paired nerve bundles, the ŒSOPHAGEAL CONNECTIVES, that encircle the pharynx and unite on the ventral side behind the latter. This place of union marks the presence

FIG. 80. Anterior portion of the nervous system of *Nereis*. *c*, cerebral ganglion or brain; *d*, œsophageal connectives; *h*, anterior end of ventral nerve cord. (From Parker and Haswell, after Quatrefages.)

of a secondary ganglion, the SUBŒSOPHAGEAL GANGLION, which is located in the third segment. From œsophageal connectives are given off nerve branches to the peristomial tentacles. Then comes the VENTRAL NERVE CORD proper, which consists of two cords fused together along their inner sides. Each metamere shows a ganglionic enlargement of the nerve cord and gives off branches to the parapodia and other organs.

c. Improved Sense Organs.—The tentacles, palpi, and eyes are all more highly differentiated than equivalent structures in Planaria, and especially is this true of the eyes. An EYE of Nereis (Fig. 81) is a complex optical instrument many parts of which are similar to those in the human eye. We recognize a CORNEA (*co*); a LENS (*l*); a LAYER OF RODS (*r*) and a RETINA (*re*). The retinal cells communicate by means of processes with optic centers in the brain.

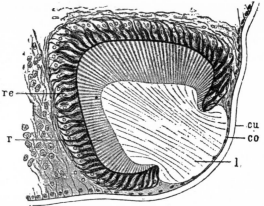

FIG. 81. Section through one of the eyes of *Nereis*. *co*, cornea; *cu*, cuticle; *l*, lens; *r*, layer of rods; *re*, retina. (From Parker and Haswell, after Andrews.)

d. Simple Reproductive System.—Nereis is unisexual (DIŒCIOUS). The gonads are simple masses proliferating from the walls of the cœlom during the breeding season. There are no special ducts for the exit of egg or sperms, but the distended body wall ruptures and emits quantities of eggs and sperms into the sea water. In contrast with this simple method of reproduction we shall find that of the earthworm very elaborate.

C. THE EARTHWORM CHARACTERIZED

Perhaps the most familiar of all worms are the earthworms, some six or seven families of which are known. They are practically cosmopolitan in distribution, living almost wherever man does, except in the Arctic regions, in deserts, and in a few other regions. Man has doubtless had a great deal to do with the geographic distribution of the earthworms, for he has carried them about with him in his agricultural operations, and especially when plants, with soil about their roots, have been transported and replanted. Earthworms of different species vary considerably in size, ranging from a small type of less than two inches in length to giant types three to four feet long. The common " dew worm," *Lumbricus herculeus*, found abundantly in humus soil throughout the Northern United

States, is very typical of the class. *Lumbricus terrestris* (Fig. 82) is another common species.

D. ACTIVITIES OF EARTHWORMS

Earthworms are expert tunnelers. They literally eat their way through the soil. The soil is swallowed and passed through the long alimentary tract, where it is put through a digestive process and its nutritive materials removed. The residue, mixed with the nitrogenous wastes of the worm, is deposited in the form of CASTINGS near the mouth of the burrow. *Charles Darwin,* who made a detailed study of the rôle of the earthworm as an agricultural agent, discovered that an enormous amount of new fertilized earth is brought to the surface by earthworms. He estimated that about eighteen tons per acre per year were brought up in certain regions. In addition, surface rocks are gradually buried and the ground is opened up by numerous tunnels and thus made more available for agriculture.

Earthworms are chiefly NOCTURNAL animals. During the day they lie quietly in their burrows with the head end near the surface. At night they become active, crawling partially out of their burrows and foraging about for food. The tail end is usually left in the burrow as an anchor, so that in case of danger a quick retreat to shelter may be made. Apart from soil, the chief food of earthworms consists of leaves. They pour out upon the leaf surface a sort of SALIVARY FLUID that softens the material and partially digests it. The softened parts are then sucked off and swallowed, leaving the veins of the leaf looking like fine lace. During the night they frequently take into the burrow whole leaves upon which they may feed during the day. They also carry small smooth pebbles into the burrow with which they line the enlarged chamber at the bottom.

In moving about in the burrow the worm makes use of its muscular system and of a set of SETÆ, or bristles. In moving forward the procedure is as follows: the posterior setæ are thrust out and take hold, thus anchoring the body at the rear; the circular muscles of the rest of the body contract, making the animal longer and narrower; this done, it must, of course, advance. When fully extended, the setæ of the anterior end are thrust out and that end is anchored; the posterior setæ are withdrawn; and the rest of the body shortens by contracting the longitudinal muscles. (This pulls forward the posterior region of the worm.)

E. General Morphology of the Earthworm

1. *General External Features*

a. The Head.—The head of the earthworm is a poor thing as compared with that of Nereis. It consists of a very small *prostomium* and a first metamere, which is thought to be equivalent to the peristomium of Nereis. There are no specialized sense organs present. The brain, while of closely similar pattern to that of Nereis, is proportionately smaller.

b. Metamerism.—There is a considerable amount of regional specialization of the metameres. The first thirty-seven segments are all different in their structure and functions. Back of that the metameres are practically all alike (Fig. 82). The reproductive organs are confined to metameres 9–14. Metameres 32–37 constitute the region of the CLITELLUM, a glandular region concerned in copulation and the formation of the COCOON. A considerable number of metameres near the posterior end are large and better provided with setæ than are those of other parts of the body. This region, which is usually somewhat flattened, may become at times the most active region; in fact, it is almost as dominant in the organization of the worm as the head region. This is shown by the facts that worms crawl backwards as easily as forwards, that the posterior end is nearly as sensitive as the anterior end, and has nearly as high a rate

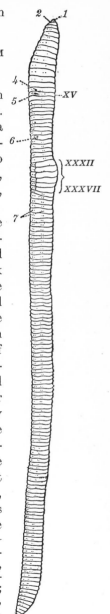

FIG. 82. Latero-ventral view of the earthworm, *Lumbricus terrestris*, slightly smaller than life-size. *1*, prostomium; *2*, mouth; *3*, anus; *4*, opening of oviduct; *5*, opening of vas deferens; *6*, genital chætæ; *7*, lateral and ventral pairs of chætæ; XV, XXXII, and XXXVII are the 15th, 32d, and 37th metameres, or segments. The 32d to the 37th form the clitellum. (From Hatchek and Cori.)

of metabolism. The earthworm, on this account, has been described as BIAXIAL, with two apical ends and gradients running toward the middle.

c. The Setæ.—In the earthworm the setæ are few and small as compared with those of Nereis. There are eight of them to a metamere and they are arranged in four double rows, two ventral and two lateral. Each seta is contained in a SETA SAC which is provided with muscles for thrusting out or withdrawing the seta. There are no parapodia in the earthworm and the setæ are the only organs that suggest that the ancestors of the earthworm may have had parapodia.

d. External Openings.—Besides the mouth and anus, the following openings are present: On the ventral side of the fifteenth segment are the openings of the male ducts or VASA DEFERENTIA; the OVIDUCTS open on the fourteenth segment; two pairs of SEMINAL RECEPTACLES open on the ninth and tenth segments; a pair of NEPHRIDIAL OPENINGS occurs on each segment except the first three and the last; minute DORSAL PORES connect the cœlom with the exterior, but they are so small as to be very difficult to find.

2. *General Internal Anatomy*

a. Body Wall, Cœlom, Mesenteries.—The body wall consists of several layers. The thin CUTICLE is a layer secreted by the epidermis and is noncellular. It is iridescent because of its striated structure which refracts the light. Numerous pores are present which represent the openings of gland cells. Beneath the cuticle is the EPIDERMIS (an epithelial layer sometimes called the HYPODERMIS) which contains gland cells and nerve cells. Beneath the epidermis is a layer of CIRCULAR MUSCLES, then a thick layer of LONGITUDINAL MUSCLES, and, on the inside, the peritoneal lining of the cœlom. The CŒLOM or true body cavity is metameric in origin. It arises in the form of paired cavities hollowed out in the primary mesodermal bands. These paired pouches meet above and below the intestine and fuse to form the DORSAL and VENTRAL MESENTERIES, sheets of membrane that sling the intestine in position and inclose between the two sheets the main blood vessels. The anterior and posterior walls of each cœlomic cavity meet and fuse with those of adjacent metameres, making the double walled partitions (SEPTA or, DISSEPIMENTS).

b. Alimentary Tract

(Fig. 83).—The mouth opens directly into the BUCCAL POUCH, which occupies segments I–III. This opens into an enlarged muscular region, the PHARYNX, which acts as a suction apparatus. Back of the pharynx is the long ŒSOPHAGUS, running from about the sixth to about the fourteenth metamere. Two pairs of CALCIFEROUS GLANDS, believed to secrete calcium carbonate into the œsophagus, occur in the region of the seminal vesicles. Then comes the CROP, or PROVENTRICULUS, a thin-walled storage sac. Behind this is the thick muscular GIZZARD, which acts as a grinding mill. From the gizzard to the anus extends the brown, thin-walled STOMACH-INTESTINE; a deep dorsal fold of the latter (TYPHLOSOLE) runs lengthwise and adds greatly to the digestive surface. A detailed study of the wall of the intestine shows that it is composed of five layers: (1) an external CHLOROGOGUE LAYER composed of pear-shaped cells, believed to have an excretory func-

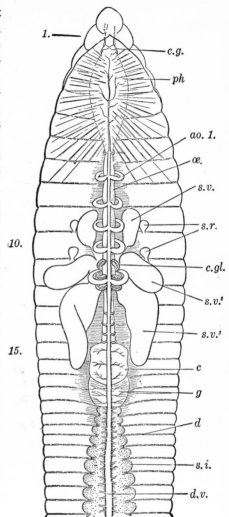

FIG. 83. Anterior part of the body of the earthworm, *Lumbricus*, as it appears when the dorsal wall is removed. *ao*, aortic arches or loops; *ph*, pharynx; *c.g.*, cerebral ganglia; *œ*, œsophagus; *s.v*, seminal vesicles; *s.r*, seminal receptacles; *c.gl*, calciferous glands; *c*, crop; *g*, gizzard; *d*, dissepiment; *s.i*, stomach-intestine; *d.v*, dorsal vessel. (From Sedgwick and Wilson.)

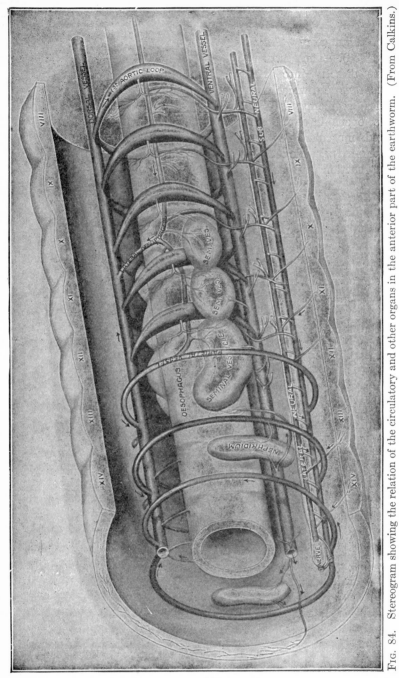

FIG. 84. Stereogram showing the relation of the circulatory and other organs in the anterior part of the earthworm. (From Calkins.)

tion; (2) a thin layer of LONGITUDINAL MUSCLES; (3) a thin layer of CIRCULAR MUSCLES; (4) a VASCULAR LAYER; (5) a lining EPITHELIUM, consisting of glandular digestive cells.

c. Circulatory System (Fig. 84).—This consists of: a DORSAL BLOOD VESSEL, lying on the digestive tract; a VENTRAL BLOOD VESSEL, lying beneath the intestine; a SUBNEURAL BLOOD VESSEL, lying beneath the nerve cord; the HEART ARCHES, or "AORTIC LOOPS," five pairs of enlarged connective vessels running between the dorsal and ventral vessels in the region of the seventh to the eleventh metameres; two LATERAL NEURAL BLOOD VESSELS running longitudinally one on each side of the nerve cord; various branches of the trunk vessels repeated metamerically.

The BLOOD consists of plasma, colored by a dissolved red pigment, HÆMOGLOBIN, the same substance that gives color to the blood corpuscles of vertebrates. In the PLASMA are suspended many colorless cells, resembling the white blood cells of vertebrates.

The COURSE OF THE BLOOD is forward along the dorsal vessel, the propulsion being due to peristaltic contraction of the vessel, reenforced by the heart arches. Valves in the walls of the dorsal vessel and in the heart arches prevent back flow. After passing through the heart arches the blood flows both forward and backward in the ventral vessel, and thence is distributed to the body wall and to the nephridia. In the subneural vessel the flow is backward and then upward through parietal vessels to the dorsal vessel. The blood that goes to the epidermis is brought in contact with oxygen. From there it flows back to the dorsal trunk vessel.

d. Cœlomic Circulation.—In addition to the blood vascular system proper there is a second circulatory mechanism consisting of a voluminous CŒLOMIC FLUID, which fills the cœlomic cavities and passes freely about the body through openings in the DISSEPIMENTS connecting adjacent segmental cœloms. This fluid consists of a colorless plasm in which are suspended many colorless blood cells, or leucocytes. When the worm contracts or expands locally, the cœlomic fluid moves about from segment to segment and bathes the surfaces of all cells lining the cœlom. It is highly probable that both plasm and leucocytes play much the same physiological rôles as do their equivalents in vertebrates, especially those of maintaining the chemical equilibrium of the system and protecting the body against the invasions of disease producing bacteria and Protozoa.

e. Excretory System.—This consists of a series of paired NE-
PHRIDIA (Fig. 85), one pair to each metamere except the first three
and the last. Each nephridium is a coiled tube occupying part of
two adjacent metameres. The ciliated funnel (NEPHROSTOME) of
each tubule projects through the septum anterior to the one in

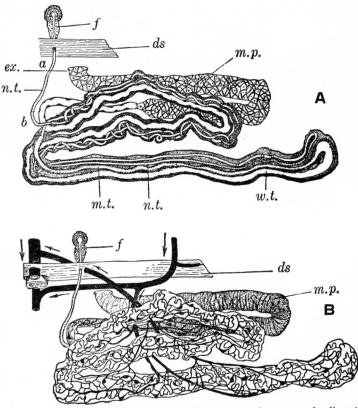

FIG. 85. **A,** nephridium of *Lumbricus*. *f,* funnel or nephrostome; *ds,* dissepiment; *n.t,* narrow tube ciliated between *a* and *b;* *m.t,* middle tube; *w.t,* wide
tube; *m.p,* muscular part; *ex,* external opening. **B,** another nephridium,
showing blood supply. (From Sedgwick and Wilson.)

which it mainly lies. The whole tube is ciliated, and a considerable
part of it is glandular. The cilia in the funnel and in the lumen of
the tube serve to create a current, which carries out solid waste
particles from the cœlomic fluid and also carries off the liquid
wastes secreted by its glandular walls. The external opening is
through the lateral ventral region of the body wall.

f. Muscular System.—The muscular system of the earthworm consists mainly of a fairly thick sheath of muscle fibers in the body wall (Fig. 86). It might be said that the body wall is made up chiefly of muscular elements. Just beneath the HYPODERMIS, or skin proper, is a thin sheath of muscle fibers running around the

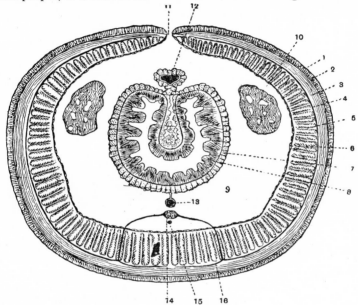

FIG. 86. Transverse section through *Lumbricus terrestris* in the region of the intestine and of a dorsal core. Magnified. 1, cuticle; 2, ectoderm, or epidermis; 3, circular muscles; 4, dorsal nerve; 5, longitudinal muscles; 6, somatic epithelium; 7, splanchnic epithelium or yellow cells; 8, endoderm or epithelium lining the intestine; 9, cœlom; 10, nephridium cut in section; 11, dorsal pore; 12, dorsal blood vessel lying along the typhlosole or groove in the wall of the intestine; 13, subintestinal blood vessel; 14, ventral nerve cord; 15, subneural blood vessel; 16, ventral nerve. The dorsal and ventral nerves are added diagrammatically. The other structures are drawn from nature. (From Shipley and MacBride.)

body, covering each somite like an elastic belt. Their contraction causes the elongation of the body. Beneath this layer is a much thicker and more complex layer of muscle fibers running lengthwise, those of one segment overlapping those of the next. Their contraction causes a shortening of the body either locally or as a whole. The continuity of these bands of muscle is interrupted by the four pairs of setæ in each somite. Each seta lies in a SETA SAC, and to the base of each seta is attached a set of special muscles for moving it, enabling it to be thrust out or retracted. There are also special muscles in the pharynx, the gizzard, the walls of the stomach-intestine, and the walls of the hearts and blood vessels.

g. **Central Nervous System.**—As in Nereis, the central nervous system consists of a brain and a double ventral nerve cord with paired segmental enlargements, or ganglia. Each pair of ganglia

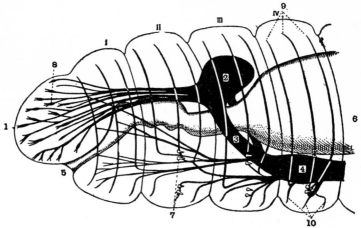

FIG. 87. Diagram of the anterior end of the earthworm showing the arrangement of the nervous system. 1, prostomium; 2, brain; 3, circumœsophageal commissures; 4, subpharyngeal ganglion; 5, mouth; 6, pharynx; 7, setæ; 8, tactile nerves of the prostomium; 9, dorsal nerves; 10, ventral nerves; I, II, III, IV, first four segments. (From Shipley and MacBride.)

is to be thought of as a subordinate brain. The nerve cells of one somitic ganglion are connected with those of several others by means of numerous nerve fibers. These interconnections serve to coördinate and integrate the activities of the animal as a whole.

Running laterally from the cord at definite intervals are paired nerves, three pairs to each somite, branches of which run to the peripheral sense organs, to the muscles of the body wall, and to all other parts of the body. Each nerve is a complex of nerve processes, or axones, some of which belong to the ganglion cells and others to nerve cells in the periphery. The fibers conducting impulses from the ganglia are known as motor, or efferent fibers; those conducting impulses from the peripheral sense organs are called sensory, or afferent, fibers.

The most anterior pair of ganglia in the ventral series is larger than the others. These are the subpharyngeal ganglia (Fig. 87). A pair of circumœsophageal commissures connects these with another pair of ganglia situated above the buccal pouch, known as the cerebral ganglia, or true brain. This brain is so small as to be almost degenerate, being hardly larger than a pair of segmental ganglia. For this reason and others it is believed that the earthworm has undergone regression with regard to the specialization of the head. Such an animal would hardly be expected to exhibit much intelligence. As a matter of fact, its activities indicate an intelligence of the purely reflex or instinctive sort.

Any simple REFLEX ACTION (Fig. 88) involves a mechanism consisting of a sensory cell, which receives a stimulus from the environ-

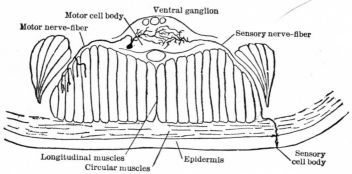

FIG. 88. Transverse section through the ventral nerve cord and surrounding structures of an earthworm, showing the path of a simple reflex. (From Hegner, after Parker.)

ment, a sensory axon, or nerve cell process, carrying the impulse to the ventral nerve cord, where it comes into contact through its processes with dendrites of another nerve cell, a motor neurone with an axon running to a muscle or some other tissue. When once the neurone of one somite is stimulated, the stimulus is usually passed backward and forward to the neurones of other somites causing a wave of muscular contraction up and down the body. There are also coördinating neurones in the ganglia that serve to bring about orderly movement of the organism as a whole and thus prevent internal discord.

h. Reproductive System.—The earthworm is HERMAPHRODITIC, provided with organs of both sexes located in definite metameres (Figs. 83, 84). The FEMALE SYSTEM consists of a pair of small OVARIES (o) in the thirteenth metamere and a pair of OVIDUCTS

with ciliated funnels opening into the thirteenth metamere, leading
back through the septum into the fourteenth metamere, and making their exit through small pores. The oviducts are modified
nephridia. Two pairs of SEMINAL RECEPTACLES are also considered
as female organs. These are merely narrow necked pockets in
the body wall which temporarily hold spermatozoa received from
another worm until the eggs are ready for fertilization. The MALE
ORGANS are larger and more elaborate. They consist of two pairs
of TESTES, each shaped like a hand, located in the tenth and
eleventh metameres; three pairs of large SEMINAL VESICLES, located
in metameres nine to twelve; and two pairs of VASA DEFERENTIA,
with large ciliated funnels, in the same metameres as the testes.
These ducts, which are much coiled, unite into one tube on each
side and make their exit in the fifteenth metamere.

F. Breeding Habits of the Earthworm

During the breeding season worms reach out from their burrows
and seek mates. Since each individual is a male-female, any one
will do for a mate. Though having both
eggs and spermatozoa they do not fertilize
their own eggs, but mutually fertilize each
other's eggs. The whole process of fertilization and cocoon formation is somewhat
elaborate. Two worms meet and overlap each

A   B

Fig. 89. **A,** the anterior segments of two copulating earthworms. Slime
tubes encircle the pair from the 8th to the 33d segment. **B,** cocoon,
freshly deposited, of an earthworm, surrounded by one half of a slime
tube. (From Hegner, after Foot, in *Journ. Morph.*)

other for about a third of their lengths, heads facing in opposite
directions and with ventral sides in contact (Fig. 89, A). They
then secrete quantities of viscous mucus, which dries out so as to
form a thick band about the clitellar region of the body. This
mucous band surrounds both bodies and serves to bind the copulating individuals tightly together. Each worm then acts as a male

giving off a quantity of seminal fluid that is conducted along grooves to the seminal receptacles of the other, where it is picked up and stored. This is all that happens during copulation. After the worms separate, the SLIME TUBE, which is formed about the clitellum of each worm, is worked forward over the body, collecting albumen from the glands on the ventral side. As it passes over the fourteenth metamere, it collects a few eggs from the oviducts; and when it passes the ninth and tenth metameres, it receives spermatozoa from the seminal receptacles. The sperms then fertilize the eggs. The slime tube is gradually slipped off over the head, closing up as though with a drawstring as first its anterior end and then its posterior end slips off over the sharp prostomium. This closed slime tube, with its contained fertilized eggs and nutritive fluid, constitutes the COCOON (Fig. 89, B). In this cocoon the eggs develop directly into complete young worms that, when ready to emerge, crawl out through one end of the cocoon after the slime plug has been dissolved away.

G. Development of the Earthworm

Because of the cocooning habit the development of the earthworm and its allies is in some respects peculiar and difficult to understand. It will be better understood when compared with the development of Polygordius, an account of which follows the present section.

In the earthworm we have an example of a somewhat foreshortened embryonic history. The whole period of development from the fertilized egg to the complete young worm takes place within the confines of the cocoon. Hence there is no true larval period. We shall study only the early embryology of the earthworm and shall then resort to Polygordius for a study of the larval period.

One reason for presenting the embryology of the earthworm is that it well illustrates the methods of mesoderm formation and cœlom formation characteristic of the Annelid-arthropod series.

The fertilized egg, or zygote, divides in typical fashion, the cells derived from the animal (apical) pole dividing more rapidly than those at the vegetative (basal) pole. In the sixteen-cell stage there are twelve small cells at the animal pole and only four large cells at the basal pole. The remaining developmental stages may best be followed by means of illustrations (Fig. 90). Note that in E, m, a single cell is set aside to form the mesoderm. This cell is technically termed 4D and its equivalent is found in most of the animals belonging to the Annelid-arthropod series. Repeated divisions of this cell give rise to a pair of mesodermal bands, one on each side

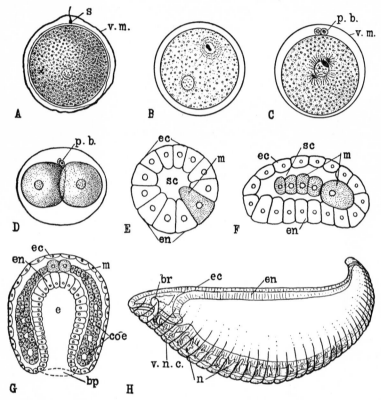

Fig. 90. Stages in the development of the earthworm within the cocoon. A to C shows fertilization processes; D, two-cell stage; E, late cleavage stage showing 4D cell (m); F, early gastrula stage showing mesoderm bands; G, gastrula, showing origin of segmental cœlom; H, embryo showing segmental structure; br, brain; bp, blastopore; cœ, cœlomic cavities; e, primitive gut; ec, ectoderm; en, endoderm; m, mesoderm; n, nephridia; p.b., polar bodies; sc, segmentation cavity; s, spermatozoön; v.m., vitelline membrane; v.n.c., ventral nerve cord. (From Curtis, after Wilson.)

of the archenteron. These bands become hollowed out into a series of paired segmental cœlomic cavities that do not fuse with one another but remain separated by septa as in G and H.

Gastrulation is begun as in F and completed as in G. In F we

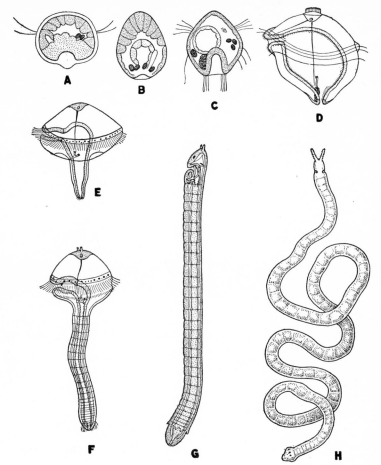

FIG. 91. The development of *Polygordius*. **A,** ciliated blastula; **B,** gastrula; **C,** early trochophore larva; **D,** optical section of typical trochophore larva, showing apical plate with eye spot, head kidney and prototroch, or preoral band of cilia; **E,** trochophore larva with posterior growth region, ready for the first segmentation; **F,** larva in which segmentation has made considerable progress; the apical plate now has a pair of tentacles and the original trochophore is seen to be changing to form the head of the segmented organism. **G,** advanced larval condition in which the original trochophore larva is seen to be the head, with mouth, eye spots, and tentacles. **H,** the adult worm. (From an unpublished chart by Whitman.)

see the three primary germ layers (ectoderm, endoderm and meso-derm) well defined. The ectoderm gives rise to the outer skin, the nervous system, and a few minor tissues. The endoderm gives rise to the epithelial lining of the digestive tract and its derivatives. The mesoderm gives rise to the lining of the cœlom, muscles, blood vessels, nephridia, reproductive organs, connective tissues, and several other tissues.

H. Development of Polygordius

There is nothing distinctive about the cleavage or the blastula and gastrula stages (Fig. 91, A, B, C). A well defined TROCHO-PHORE larva (Fig. 91, D), whose counterpart is found in flatworms, annelids, and mollusks, is characterized by having an equatorial band of cilia and an apical plate with a pair of eye spots. The mouth opens posterior to the PROTOTROCH, as the ciliated band is called. The alimentary tract consists of three well defined regions (œsophagus, stomach, intestine) and is curved dorsoventrally. A single pair of nephridia, the so called HEAD KIDNEYS, open near the posterior end. This larva swims about for some time as an independent individual, feeding and growing. The region of great-est growth is the posterior region, and a considerable elongation of this region takes place in the direction of the primary axis (Fig. 91, E). When the posterior prolongation has reached a stage when it is about as long as the rest of the larva, metamerism begins to be evident. A first segment is cut off at the posterior end. This end grows and another segment is cut off, and thus a large number of metameres are produced (Fig. 91, F). The original trochophore goes over directly to form the head of the adult (Fig. 91, G). A pair of tentacles develops out of the apical plate, and the worm then grows long and slender as in Fig. 91, H.

We see then that transverse fission, the asexual process of pro-ducing a series of subordinate zoöids, takes place in the annelids during an embryonic or larval period; that the metameres are always decidedly subordinate to the original individual, the troch-ophore larva, and are quickly and completely integrated into a single well correlated individual or organism.

CHAPTER XVIII

THE SNAIL AND THE CLAM

(PHYLUM MOLLUSCA)

A. Mollusca in General

THE snail belongs to the great PHYLUM MOLLUSCA, one of the most important subdivisions of the Animal Kingdom. In addition to the snails and other snail-like forms, the phylum includes such well known animals as oysters, clams, mussels, squids, and octopi. As the name signifies, the Mollusca are soft bodied, without any true skeleton. In lieu of a skeleton most of them secrete from the body surface one or more external shells, composed mainly of carbonate of lime. The group appears to be as old as the echinoderms, for shells of various types of mollusks are among the commonest of the very early fossils. The various groups of mollusks that are now living were, for the most part, well established even in Cambrian times, but have all undergone steady progressive or regressive modifications and specializations as the ages have passed. So definitely and steadily have these cycles of change progressed that geologists are able to use the molluscan fossils as time markers. The finding of a given species or genus of mollusk in a newly discovered fossil bearing stratum serves to indicate the age of that stratum.

So different are the larger groups of mollusks from one another that they appear to have little, if anything, in common. What, you might ask, has the clam in common with the octopus? Careful study reveals many points of similarity highly significant to the comparative anatomist. These we shall now proceed to discuss.

All the other really advanced phyla of the Animal Kingdom (Annelida, Arthropoda, and Vertebrates) owe much of their complexity of organization and specialization of regions and parts to their segmental, or metameric, structure. In contrast with this, the Mollusca illustrate what can be done in the way of evolutionary advance without making use of the scheme of metamerism; for

217

they are nonmetameric. Like the Arthropoda, they have no open cœlom; for the embryonic cœlom becomes filled with loose tissue (PARENCHYMA) and blood sinuses.

The body has four main subdivisions: a, the HEAD, which is the seat of the major brain (cephalic ganglia), the eyes and the tentacles, the mouth with its jaws or radula, a rasping tonguelike

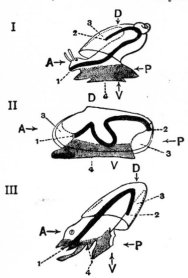

apparatus; b, the FOOT, which is typically a muscular ventral locomotor organ, has a minor brain of its own and not infrequently its own sense organ; c, the MANTLE, a fold of the body wall, is used primarily as a shelter for the branchiæ or other respiratory structures and as an organ of shell secretion; d, the VISCERAL MASS, which consists of digestive, excretory, circulatory, and reproductive organs, lies, as a rule, above the foot and under the mantle.

These four body regions are variously modified in the several molluscan classes (Fig. 92), sometimes one part and sometimes another being more or less profoundly altered. In the clams and oysters, for example, the head is almost entirely suppressed; in the squid and octopus the head and foot have been intimately fused to form the characteristic tentacled

FIG. 92. Diagrams of three types of mollusks,—I, a Prosobranch Gastropod. II, a Lamellibranch, and III, a Cephalopod, to show the form of the foot and its regions and the relations of the visceral hump to the antero-posterior and dorsoventral axes. A, anterior surface; D, dorsal surface; P, posterior surface; V, ventral surface; 1, mouth; 2, anus; 3, mantle cavity; 4, foot. (From Shipley and MacBride, after Lankester.)

head that constitutes their most striking feature; in the clam the visceral mass is partially inclosed within the foot, while in the snail it is coiled on top of the foot and inclosed in a spiral shell.

The group is so large and so varied that a general description cannot go very far without becoming involved in a maze of exceptions. We shall therefore now proceed to describe in greater detail a highly representative type of mollusk, a common garden snail. While the clam is the favorite mollusk for laboratory work, it is our conviction that its exclusive use is likely to give the student a wrong idea of molluscan organization; for the clam and its allies are degenerate, practically headless organisms, with many specializations for sedentary life. Of course the clam has its practical advantages as a laboratory type, being readily secured in the living condition, of a convenient size, and easily exposed for study. For a typical mollusk, however, we have no hesitation in selecting the snail.

B. The Snail

1. *General Features*

Snails belong to the Class Gastropoda (literally, stomach-footed). They are highly versatile in their habits, living in the sea, in fresh water, and on land. While the majority of the snails have coiled shells, there are many naked forms such as the terrestrial slugs and the sea slugs, or nudibranchs.

A good example of the snail tribe is *Helix pomatia* (Fig. 93). Although this animal is able to retire completely within its shell, the body may be extruded from the shell, leaving covered only the visceral mass and the mantle. The exposed part of the body, the head and the foot, constitute a relatively long and narrow region characterized by evident polarity and bilateral symmetry.

The HEAD is provided with four TENTACLES, a short anterior pair used as feelers and a long posterior pair upon the ends of which the EYES are borne. A snail can thus reach its eyes out in any direction in order to get a close up view of any adjacent object. The FOOT is a soft surfaced, flat bottomed, slime coated, flexible toboggan on which the animal slides slowly along on its own power. The lower surface of the foot, and especially a region near its anterior end, secretes mucous slime and lays it down as a slippery roadbed upon which the foot slides by means of an intricate system of wavelike muscular contractions, the exact mechanism of which is not adequately understood. Snails are proverbially unhurried in their movements, but they cover considerable distances in the course of each day.

The MANTLE (Fig. 92, I) covers the visceral mass and forms a lining for the entire shell. It is thin at all points except along the margin of the shell where it joins the foot; there it forms a thick collar-like edge, which is the active shell secreting portion. This thick-

ened rim of the mantle is fused down to the edge of the foot except
for a small opening, the RESPIRATORY APERTURE, which opens into
the mantle cavity. In the land snails the mantle cavity contains
no branchiæ or gills, but is merely highly vascular throughout its
surface and plays the rôle of a simple lung.

Asymmetry.—We shall see in a later chapter that the adult echinoderm acquired its radial symmetry through the asymmetrical

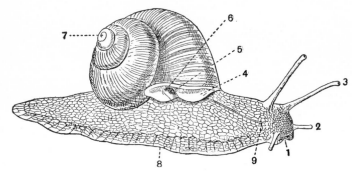

FIG. 93. *Helix pomatia.* Side view of shell and animal expanded. 1, mouth;
2, anterior tentacles; 3, eye tentacles; 4, edge of mantle; 5, respiratory
pore; 6, anus; 7, apex of shell; 8, foot; 9, reproductive aperture. (From
Hatschek and Cori.)

growth of the organs of the two bilateral halves of the larva. In
the snails a comparable phenomenon, involving unequal development of the two sides of the body, constitutes one of their most
interesting features. The spiral arrangement of the mantle, shell,
and VISCERAL HUMP, or MASS, is due to the unequal rates of growth
of the right and left embryonic primordia of the organs in those
regions. As a rule it is the left side, as in the echinoderms, that
grows more rapidly and therefore may be called the superior side,
but there are species in which the right side is superior and there
are occasional instances of right-handed individuals in species that
are characteristically left-handed. The inequality of the two
halves of the organism is foreshadowed even in the undivided egg,
for the cytoplasm is arranged in an asymmetrical manner and the
cleavage assumes a so called spiral form. Evidently the primordia
of the head and of the foot are less affected by this inequality of
growth, for they retain, to a large extent at least, their primitive
bilaterality. The SHELL may be considered as a permanent record
of the various stages of asymmetrical growth of the mantle, which,

in turn, reflects the asymmetry of the visceral mass. The first shell of the young snail is retained as the apex of the permanent shell, and a new and broader ring is added by the mantle edge each season. On account of the more rapid growth of one side of the body, the shell assumes the form of a true spiral coil.

2. Internal Anatomy of the Snail

a. The Digestive Tract.—Anteriorly, the mouth, which has a horny jaw in front, opens into the BUCCAL MASS, which consists of the RADULA (a filelike ribbon used for shredding the food before swallowing) and the RADULA SAC, together with its muscles and

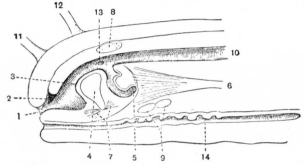

FIG. 94. Inner view of right half of head of *Helix*, showing the arrangement of the radula. 1, mouth; 2, horny jaw; 3, radula; 4, cartilage supporting radula; 5, radula sac from which radula grows; 6, muscle which retracts the buccal mass; 7, intrinsic muscles that rotate the radula; 8, cerebral ganglion; 9, pedal and visceral ganglia; 10, œsophagus; 11, anterior tentacle; 12, eye tentacle; 13, orifice of the duct of salivary gland; 14, mucous gland which runs along the foot and opens just under the mouth. (From Shipley and MacBride.)

cartilage (Fig. 94). Behind this is the œsophagus, which soon widens into the stomach (Fig. 96). Lying against the stomach are two large SALIVARY GLANDS that pour their secretion into the BUCCAL CAVITY. The rest of the digestive tract is long and slender and more or less coiled. The posterior part of it is directed forward toward the head and it ends in the ANUS, which opens on the left side just back of the mantle cavity. A large digestive gland, usually called the LIVER, occupies a considerable portion of the visceral hump and pours its secretion into the intestine.

b. Nervous System.—The central nervous system, like that of the annelids, is composed of paired ganglia, each of which is the nerve center of some important function or set of functions (Fig. 95). In a very real sense, each pair of ganglia is a brain; but they are all connected by means of commissures and are therefore not independent of each other. The two largest ganglia are, as in the annelids, situated above the œsophagus and are known as the CEREBRAL GANGLIA; they may well be called the principal brain, while the other ganglia mentioned below are secondary or subordinate brains, each presiding over some region of the body under the general superintendence of the principal brain. Beneath the œsophagus is a rather compact nervous mass composed of several pairs of ganglia (PEDAL, PLEURAL, PARIETAL, and VISCERAL) that are connected by means of pairs of commissures on either side of the œsophagus with the cerebral ganglia. A very small pair of BUCCAL GANGLIA is connected by means of its own commissures with the cerebral ganglia.

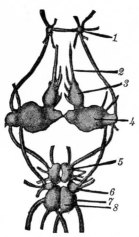

FIG. 95. Central portion of the nervous system of *Helix pomatia*. 1, buccal ganglion; 2, optic nerve with thickened root (3) arising from the cerebral ganglion (4); 5, pedal; 6, pleural; 7, parietal; 8, visceral ganglion. (From Lang, after Böhmig and Leuckart.)

c. **Reproductive System.**—Many snails have extremely elaborate reproductive systems, for they are hermaphroditic, having in one individual all the organs of both sexes. In spite of this they do not fertilize their own eggs but merely exchange sperms somewhat after the fashion described for the earthworms. Other snails are diœcious, that is, they have the sexes separate. Each individual of the hermaphroditic species, such as *Helix pomatia* (Fig. 96), has the following male organs: TESTIS, VAS DEFERENS, PENIS, DART SAC, and various accessory glands. Each individual has also the following female organs: OVARY, OVIDUCT, ALBUMEN GLAND, VAGINA, and several minor structures. In complexity this type of reproductive system rivals that of the flatworms.

d. **Circulatory System.**—This system differs from that of the annelids, vertebrates, etc., in that it is not a closed system of vessels, but an open system. By this we mean that the heart pumps blood through a few main arteries and arterial capillaries, which, in turn, pass the blood into venous capillaries. These instead of uniting directly into veins, open into a system of sinuses that penetrate all the tissues and bring the blood into intimate contact with

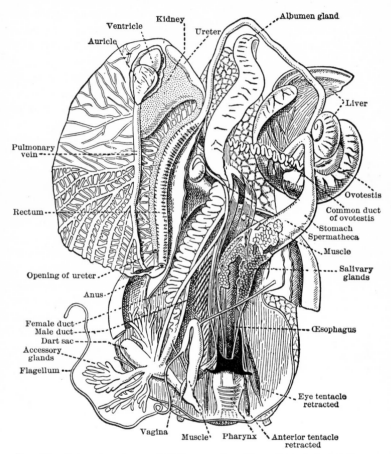

FIG. 96. Internal anatomy of *Helix pomatia*. (From Hatschek and Cori.)

the cells. Blood returns to the heart after traversing a series of veins (pulmonary veins) in the mantle roof. The heart lies in a cavity (PERICARDIUM) which corresponds to the cœlom of other groups and is not homologous with the pericardium of the arthropods, for the latter is a blood sinus.

The other systems of the snail are less distinctive and will not be described here.

3. *Activities of the Snail*

a. Homing Instinct.—Perhaps the most remarkable of the snail's activities are those associated with its strong instinct to maintain a fixed headquarters, or base of operations. Snails are, for the most part, nocturnal in their activities and need to seek a sheltered retreat during the day. As a rule, snails or slugs make excursions of considerable extent in search of food, but in spite of their varied wanderings they appear always to return to the same home retreat at the approach of day. One observer noted that a snail, which he had taken the precaution to mark with a spot of white paint, occupied a hole at some distance from the ground in a brick wall. Leaning against the wall with its end near the hole was a stick, the lower end of which rested among the herbs of the garden. As soon as it began to grow dark the snail habitually came down this improvised ladder and, after feeding over a considerable area during the night, always returned to and ascended its ladder and was at home by the first break of dawn.

b. Sense of Smell.—The snail has an exceedingly keen sense of smell, as is well illustrated by the following incident described by **Furtado:** "He noticed a *Helix adspersa* lodged between a column on a veranda and a flower-pot containing a young banana plant, and threw it away into a little court below, and six or seven yards distant. Next morning the snail was in precisely the same place on the flower-pot. Again he threw it away, to the same distance, and determined to notice what happened. Next morning at nine o'clock, the snail was resting on the rail of the staircase leading to the veranda from the court; in the evening it started again, quickening its pace as it advanced, eventually attacking the banana in precisely the same place where it had been gnawed before." Presumably the scent of the banana had guided the snail over a somewhat intricate path. Authorities agree that the sense of smell has its seat in the tentacles and that this sense is the snail's main dependence.

c. Tenacity of Life.—Land snails, especially those that live in arid regions, exhibit an almost unbelievable tenacity of life. One author states that he glued two specimens of *Helix desertorum* to a tablet in his collection of shells, and four years later, on reëxamining this case of shells, he found one of the snails alive and healthy but ravenously hungry. Many other cases are on record of snails surviving without food or water for periods of from two to six years. Doubtless their ability to seal themselves almost hermetically within their shells by means of the operculum accounts to some extent for their ability to avoid desiccation.

C. The Clam

1. *General Features*

The clam is a representative of a very large and important class of Mollusca, PELECYPODA, which includes oysters, scallops, and other important food animals. For reasons that are not difficult to understand, the clam is generally chosen as the type of Mollusca for laboratory use. These animals are easily obtained, of convenient size, and may readily be kept alive in aquaria. Except for these practical advantages, they are singularly ill suited to illustrate the characteristics of the Phylum Mollusca, for they are essentially degenerate, headless forms.

The Pelecypoda seem to have been one of the earliest of the molluscan groups to reach the end of their evolutionary progress, if their history may be called progress, for we find their fossil remains in almost the earliest fossil bearing strata. These ancient clamlike mollusks were essentially as specialized as are the modern types.

The characteristics of the Class Pelecypoda are as follows: They have bivalve shells, sheetlike gills, a wedge-shaped foot, and extremely reduced head. They are all aquatic in habitat. They range in size from tiny forms that in the adult state are no larger than a pinhead up to giant clams over three feet in shell length and weighing 500 pounds.

For the most part clams are burrowers and trenchers. Many species burrow about in mud or even excavate tunnels in soft rock. Some specialized forms such as the shipworm, or teredo, have the habit of excavating passageways in submerged wood, using the wood for food. In this way they riddle with their tunnels wharfing piles and the hulls of ships, causing an annual loss of many millions of dollars.

The common fresh-water clam, or mussel, may be a surface trencher as well as a burrower. In some regions they seem to prefer to move about over the surface of the muddy bottoms. As the animal moves slowly about on its plowshare-like foot it leaves a furrow. Often in quiet waters the bottom is sculptured with a labyrinth of these clam paths.

Moving about slowly as they do, they could not well capture active prey. Instead, they have adopted a scheme used by many other sedentary or semisedentary aquatic organisms: that of concentrating the organic particles suspended in all natural waters. The surface of the body, and especially that of the voluminous curtainlike gills, is covered with cilia that whip the water into currents and focus the streams into grooves that lead ultimately into the troughlike lips of the mouth, the so-called LABIAL PALPS. Feeding seems to be practically a continuous process and is intimately associated with respiration, for the steady current of fresh oxygen-bearing water serves admirably as a respiratory medium.

2. Anatomy of the Clam

a. General Description.—The clam is constructed more or less like a book. The two shells are like the covers; the hinge like the

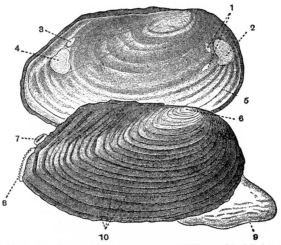

FIG. 97. Shell containing clam, *Anodonta mutabilis*, and behind it an empty left shell. 1, 2, attachment of anterior muscles; 3, 4, attachment of posterior muscles; 5, line of growth; 6, umbo; 7, dorsal siphon; 8, ventral siphon; 9, foot; 10, lines of growth. (From Shipley and MacBride.)

book back; the mantle folds like the pages pasted to the covers; the gills like the double fly leaves, front and back; while the body of the clam corresponds roughly to the body of the book, except that it is not divided up into pages.

Unlike the snail, the clam is bilaterally symmetrical. With a sharp instrument it is possible to sever the body into two equivalent halves, each a mirror image of the other.

The shell (Fig. 97) consists of two VALVES united dorsally by an elastic HINGE. The concentric rings seen on the outside of the shell

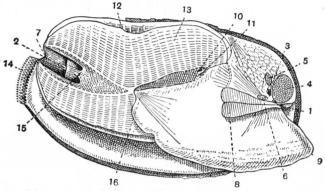

FIG. 98. Right side of *Anodonta* with the right mantle cut away and the right gills folded back. 1, mouth; 2, anus; 3, cerebropleural ganglion; 4, anterior adductor muscle; 5, anterior protractor muscle; 6, retractor muscle; 7, dorsal siphon; 8, inner labial palp; 9, foot; 10, opening of nephridium; 11, opening of genital duct; 12, outer right gill; 13, inner right gill; 14, ventral siphon; 15, epibranchial chamber; 16, posterior protractor muscle. (From Hatschek and Cori.)

are LINES OF GROWTH. A new ring is added to the outer margin each season. The original shell of the young clam, though usually worn and eroded, may be seen in the center of the UMBO, the somewhat elevated area situated dorsally and near the anterior end of the shell. The shell is three layered: the outside layer being horny, or chitinous; the middle layer being composed of crystals of calcium carbonate and of considerable thickness; the inner, or mother-of-pearl layer, being relatively thin and made up of a number of delicate sheets of nacreous material that has an iridescent appearance.

The muscles of the shell are used for closing the shell. These are two in number, the ANTERIOR and POSTERIOR ADDUCTORS. The shell opens automatically owing to the elasticity of the ligamentous hinge. This accounts for the fact that the shells of dead clams are widely open.

The MANTLE (Fig. 99) consists of two extensive folds of the body wall that come off from the dorsal part of the body and envelop the body proper. These mantle folds secrete the shell and also function after the manner of washers in a valve, enabling the shell to close up in water-tight fashion. Two regions of the mantle margin are specialized into two more or less elongated tubes, or siphons, the DORSAL and VENTRAL SIPHONS. These are openings through which

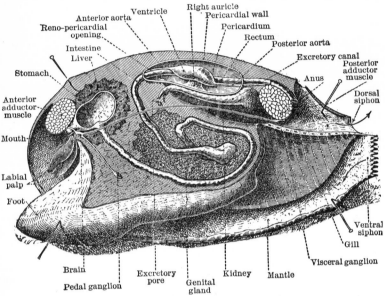

FIG. 99. Internal anatomy of a clam. (From Jammes.)

water enters the mantle cavity and makes its exit, the ventral siphon taking in water and the dorsal siphon expelling it. In some clams, such as the little neck clam, these siphons become very much elongated so as to enable the clam, even when buried some depth in the mud, to continue respiration and feeding uninterrupted.

The GILLS, or BRANCHIÆ (Fig. 98), are four in number. They hang down into the mantle cavity like curtains, two being suspended by their dorsal margins on each side of the body. They have a very elaborate sievelike structure, designed to present a vast amount of surface with relatively little bulk, an ideal arrangement for respiratory organs.

b. Digestive System (Fig. 99).—The digestive system consists of a MOUTH situated near the dorsal part of the foot between the two pairs of flaplike LABIAL PALPS. Each pair on one side is united along the inner edges to form a trough leading into the mouth. Cilia lining these troughs sweep the food particles, already concentrated by the gills and other organs, into the mouth. Next to the mouth is the very short ŒSOPHAGUS, that in turn opens into a fairly large STOMACH. The latter opens into a long, coiled INTESTINE, that takes several turns through the tissues of the dorsal part of the foot, passes through the PERICARDIUM, and opens to the outside through the ANUS, that lies near the dorsal siphon. The two lobes of the LIVER practically surround the stomach and furnish it with a digestive secretion.

c. Excretory System.—In the clam there is but one pair of U-shaped kidneys (NEPHRIDIA) that lie one on each side of the pericardium and discharge their waste products through two renal apertures near the dorsal siphon, whence it is carried away by the outgoing water currents.

d. Nervous System (Fig. 99).—A number of widely separated pairs of GANGLIA, connected by COMMISSURES comprise the nervous system. The BRAIN, if a headless creature may be said to possess a brain, consists of a pair of ganglia, the CEREBROPLEURAL GANGLIA, one on each side of the œsophagus and connected by a commissure that passes above the œsophagus. Two other pairs of ganglia are connected with the cerebropleural ganglia by means of commissures, namely, the PEDAL GANGLIA situated in the foot and controlling its activities, and the VISCERAL GANGLIA situated near the posterior adductor muscle and controlling the visceral functions. Minor ganglia are associated with the action of the chief muscles.

e. Circulatory System (Fig. 99).—The circulatory system consists of a HEART lying in a saclike sinus, the pericardium, ARTERIES, VEINS, and an elaborate system of blood spaces, or SINUSES. In general, it does not differ essentially from that of the snail which has already been described.

Other anatomical details may best be studied in the laboratory.

D. Other Mollusca

There are five classes of mollusks:—

CLASS I. AMPHINEURA—chitons, a group of primitive mollusks not unlike the snails, but differing from the latter in being bilaterally symmetrical. They usually possess a compound dorsal shell composed of eight transverse calcareous plates overlapping like shingles. Although obviously degenerate in some respects, they appear to be more nearly like the ancestral mollusks than any other group of the present day.

CLASS II. GASTROPODA—land snails, sea snails, whelks, etc. This group, although bilaterally symmetrical as to head and foot, shows pronounced asymmetry of the mantle, shell, and visceral mass. The other characters of this class have already been described.

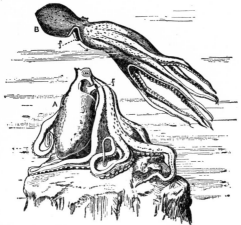

CLASS III. SCAPHOPODA—toothshells. This is a small group of degenerate mollusks with tubular shell and mantle, boring foot, and bilateral symmetry.

CLASS IV. PELECYPODA—clams, oysters, scallops, etc. This group is characterized by bilateral symmetry, a shell composed of two hinged valves, a two-lobed mantle, sheetlike gills, a plowshare foot, and practically no head.

FIG. 100. The octopus, *Octopus vulgaris*. **A,** at rest; **B,** in motion. *f*, funnel; the arrow shows direction of propelling current of water. (From the Cambridge Natural History, after Merculiano.)

CLASS V. CEPHALOPODA—squids, cuttlefishes, octopi (Fig. 100), and nautili. They are bilaterally symmetrical. The head and foot combine to make a secondary head armed with tentacles and provided with eyes that are superficially like those of fishes. The various pairs of ganglia are closely fused together to form a rather large, compact brain. These animals are apparently as advanced in their organization and as capable in every way as are fishes; in some respects they seem to be superior.

CHAPTER XIX

THE GREAT PHYLUM ARTHROPODA

THE name, ARTHROPODA, is derived from two Greek words: *arthron*, a hinge, and *pous*, a foot. Thus all animals with jointed or hinged appendages, except the vertebrates, are placed in this phylum. In numbers of species and of individuals the arthropods outnumber all the other phyla combined. Nearly five hundred thousand species of arthropods have been described, and there is reason to believe that at least that many more are still unidentified.

The phylum is one of immense antiquity, having representatives in the Cambrian rocks, whose age is estimated as between thirty and three hundred millions of years. The earliest arthropods were marine forms known as TRILOBITES, which must have been very numerous, judging by the abundance of their fossil remains. Like the mollusks, they serve as important time markers for the geologist.

It is customary to divide the arthropods into two great series, the first of which is adapted to aquatic life and usually possesses gills, and the second of which is adapted to terrestrial life and possesses a variety of air-breathing organs. The first division includes only the CLASS CRUSTACEA; the second comprises the CLASSES ARACHNIDA, ONYCHOPHORA, MYRIAPODA, and HEXAPODA (the insects). Any detailed survey of the above groups will show that the criterion used in defining the two series is only valid in a broad way; for there are terrestrial crustaceans and there are aquatic arachnids and insects.

A. GENERAL CHARACTERISTICS

a. Adaptive Radiation.—As in the case in all large and successful groups of animals, the Crustacea, Arachnida, and the insects have developed a very wide range of adaptations enabling them to occupy a multiplicity of habitats. Thus the Crustacea, the most successful of which are marine, have also invaded the fresh waters; while many of them, such as wood lice and pill bugs, have succeeded in adapting themselves for life in the air, but are limited to damp places. Similarly, the insects, which are preëminently terrestrial, not uncommonly live on the surface of or beneath the surface of water. In addition to this, they have most successfully invaded the air and are rivals of the birds and the bats in this domain. Many of the insects have also adapted themselves to subterranean life; witness the seventeen-year locust (Cicada) that lives for sixteen years as a grublike larva, burrowing underground and feeding upon the roots of plants and trees, emerging as a full-fledged winged adult only during the summer of the seventeenth year (Fig. 101).

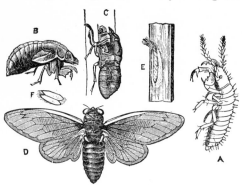

Fig. 101. Seventeen-year locust, *Cicada septendecim.* **A,** larva. **B,** nymph. **C,** nymph skin after emergence of adult. **D,** adult. **E,** section of tree showing how eggs are laid. **F,** two eggs enlarged. (From Sedgwick's Zoölogy, after Riley.)

Many insects, too, live parasitically on or in the bodies of other animals or plants, and it is this parasitic tendency that lends the group a very special economic importance. The Arachnida do not fall far short of the insects in the range of their adaptive radiation. Their particular specialties are those that are associated with the capture of prey. Thus the spiders build many sorts of snares and traps, that appear to be most ingenious. Some of the spiders also have succeeded in living under water, notably those that build miniature diving bells out of silk, which they anchor to the bottom and fill with air by carrying air bubbles trapped amidst the thick hair of the abdomen. These and many other instances serve to illustrate the almost universal application of the principle of adaptive radiation.

b. Metamerism.—One of the most general features of the Arthropoda is that they, like the annelids and the vertebrates, are built on the segmental or metameric plan (Fig. 102). In contrast with the annelids, the number of segments is small, and in the higher groups is strictly limited to nineteen (twenty, according to some authorities). The various metameres, or segments, are much

more highly specialized and diversified than is the case in the annelids, and in many of the arthropods secondary fusions of groups of
adjacent segments have taken place in such a way as to leave the
original metameric arrangements rather obscure. As a rule, each
metamere is provided with a pair of jointed appendages; these are
modified in all sorts of ways and for all sorts of purposes. Thus
some are used as sense organs, others as mouth parts for holding
or masticating food, others for walking, swimming, or even as copulatory organs. No better material for the study of the principle

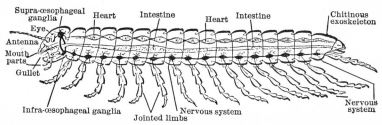

FIG. 102.   Diagrammatic representation of the structure of an Arthropod.
(From Schmeil.)

of homology, and especially of serial homology, could well be found
than is afforded by the arthropods. This subject is to be dealt
with in detail in the next chapter.

c. **Exoskeleton.**—The arthropods have no bones nor any true
internal skeleton; but they are, as a rule, covered with a hard external armor secreted by the skin and composed of a horny material
known as CHITIN. This exoskeleton is molded to the body and fits
its every contour. It is, however, not equally hard all over, for
this would render the animals entirely rigid; instead, it is soft at
those regions where flexibility is necessary, namely, at the limb
joints and between segments of the body armor.

d. **Ecdysis.**—An animal with an unyielding casing over the body
cannot, of course, grow as other animals grow. The arthropods
solve the problem of growth in a curious way. At intervals the
armor is shed, and rapid expansion takes place during the period
before another coat of armor is acquired and while the body surface is soft. The process of shedding the armor, ecdysis, is a strenuous and precarious one. The animal has first of all to loosen itself
from all contact with the armor by a process of shrinking; then,
by muscular expansion it splits the investment at certain definite
weaker points; and finally, with a great effort it withdraws each

appendage from its individual casing, parts of large dimensions sometimes being pulled through comparatively small openings. This is hard and dangerous work and not infrequently involves the loss of life or at least of limbs. Moreover, the period during which the shell is soft is one when there is great danger from predaceous enemies. It should be said that the above description of ecdysis applies particularly to the higher crustacea, but that the process in some form is characteristic of all groups of arthropods.

e. Nervous System.—The central nervous system of the arthropods follows the same structural lines as that of the annelids, but is regionally modified and specialized to a much greater extent, just as are other metameric systems. The brain, CEREBRAL GANGLIA, as in annelids and mollusks, is above the œsophagus and is connected by paired commissures, one on each side of the œsophagus, with a pair of SUBŒSOPHAGEAL GANGLIA. Behind this there are the PAIRED NERVE CORDS with PAIRED SEGMENTAL GANGLIA, which are at intervals fused together into larger nervous masses that serve as secondary brains.

f. Sense Organs.—The eyes of arthropods are either simple or compound. In the more primitive members of the phylum very simple eyes, derived from the ectoderm, are found. Such an eye consists of a simple lens-shaped, transparent thickening of the cuticle, a number of retinal sensory cells, and a nerve running to the brain. In the case of the compound eyes groups of visual cells are separated from each other by wall-like boundaries, and each has a lenticular thickening of the cuticle. Each of the facets of such an eye receives a separate miniature image of the visual field within its focus. Photographs have been taken, using the eyes of insects for camera lenses, and the result has been a group of very small isolated pictures, each one like the rest.

g. Circulatory System and the Cœlom.—In most animals the circulatory system consists of a closed system of tubes, varying in caliber from large arterial trunks to the minutest capillaries, which carry the blood from the heart to all the tissues of the body and back again to the heart without allowing it to escape the confines of walls except by processes of diffusion. In the arthropods, however, as we have already said for the mollusks, there are few veins or capillaries. The place of these vessels is taken by an extensive and all pervasive system of blood sinuses. Sooner or later, the blood which has been poured from the arteries into the various sinuses finds its way back to the large HÆMOCŒLE, or PERICARDIAL SINUS, in which lies the heart. When the heart expands, the blood occupying the hæmocœle enters through ostia in its sides; and when the heart contracts, the blood, controlled by means of valves, is forced out into the arteries, and thence all over the body.

h. Other Organs and Systems.—The respiratory organs of the arthropods are gills (BRANCHIÆ) in the Crustacea; GILL BOOKS, LUNG BOOKS, or TRACHEÆ (air tubes) in the Arachnida; and, usually, TRACHEÆ in the Myriapoda and Hexapoda (insects). Gills are usually leaflike or feathery outgrowths of the body wall that are well provided with blood sinuses and have very thin walls. Gill books and lung books, as the names imply, consist of closely packed sheets of the body surface bound together like the leaves of a book. They may be either exposed on the surface to the surrounding water, as in Limulus; or they may be inclosed in pockets but exposed to indrawn air currents, as in the scorpions and spiders.

The EXCRETORY ORGANS of the arthropods are relatively simple. They consist of a single pair of kidneylike organs situated in a variety of places, ranging from the front of the head in some Crustacea to a point near the end of the abdomen in insects and myriapods.

B. REPRESENTATIVE ARTHROPODA

In this place it is proposed merely to present a brief synopsis of the arthropod groups with characterizations of and illustrations of a few representative types. The phylum we are surveying is so immense in numbers and so diversified in structure and habitat that we are able to indicate its range only by the method of sampling.

It is customary to divide the phylum Arthropoda into two major sections on the basis of whether they are aquatic or terrestrial in their respiratory adaptations. Whether this is a valid criterion of affinities is an open question; at least it furnishes a convenient basis for classification. These two sections are: (*a*) BRANCHIATA (breathing by means of gills or branchiæ), including but one class, Crustacea; (*b*) TRACHEATA (breathing by means of tracheæ or equivalent air breathing organs), including the classes Onychophora, Myriapoda, Insecta, and Arachnida. These five classes will be dealt with in the order mentioned.

Class I. Crustacea

This class is primarily aquatic in habitat, though there are not a few terrestrial or semiterrestrial representatives. Whether they live in water or on land they all breathe with gills. The body is composed of three divisions, the head, the thorax, the abdomen. Sometimes thorax and head are fused into a cephalothorax. The head bears five pairs of appendages: two pairs of antennæ, one pair of mandibles, and two pairs of maxillæ. The rest of the body bears a highly variable assortment of appendages, differing in number, form, and function.

Five subclasses of Crustacea are distinguished:—

Subclass 1. Branchiapoda. This is believed to be the most primitive group of modern Arthropoda. In general, there is less specialization of the body regions and their appendages than in any other group. A very common type of this subclass is Daphnia, a water flea (Fig. 103, A), which though primitive in some ways is highly specialized in others. Daphnia occurs in enormous numbers in our lakes and streams. It has been estimated that in one cubic meter of lake water in some regions there are 40,000 specimens of Daphnia and other small crustaceans. These tiny forms furnish an indispensable food supply for young fishes and other small fry.

Subclass 2. Ostracoda. This group of minute crustaceans is also abundant in ponds and streams and plays much the same rôle as do the Branchiapoda. They are characterized by having the body very short and laterally compressed, covered by a bivalve shell.

Subclass 3. Copepoda. This group plays about the same rôle in the oceans as do the two previous subclasses in the fresh waters. These tiny forms lack a covering shell and have no appendages on the abdomen except on the terminal segment.

Subclass 4. Cirripedia. This is a group of degenerate sessile crustaceans, some of them being intensely parasitic. The barnacles (Fig. 103, B) are the typical representatives of the group and are characterized by being fixed during the adult period upon rocks, piles, or ship bottoms. The body is entirely inclosed in a shell that often has the consistency and appearance of a somewhat complex mollusk shell. The head parts of the animal are almost entirely wanting and the appendages are used merely in creating a current for purposes of food gathering. Sacculina, a parasitic cirripede, is discussed in detail in another connection (pp. 422, 423) and its life history is shown in Figure 186.

Subclass 5. Malacostracha. This division includes all of the higher crustacea, such as crayfishes, lobsters, crabs, shrimps, amphipods, isopods. There are at least ten orders of Malacostracha,

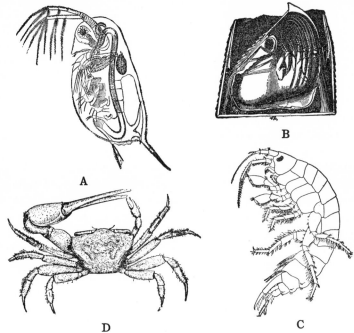

Fɪɢ. 103. Representative Crustacea. **A,** *Daphnia,* a water-flea. **B,** *Balanus tintinnabulum,* a barnacle, with one-half of shell removed to show the animal itself. **C,** *Gammarus fasciatus,* a fresh-water amphipod. **D,** *Gelasimus minax,* fiddler or soldier crab. (**A,** from Parker and Haswell; **B,** from Sedgwick, after Claus; **C, D,** from Paulmier.)

some familiar, such as the three discussed below, others relatively little known to the layman.

The order *Isopoda* consists of a vast assemblage of medium sized marine, fresh-water, and land crustaceans. Some are parasitic and very degenerate. The sow bug, Oniscus, and the pill bug, Armadillium, are familiar isopods found under logs, stones, or boards, and are generally thought of by the layman as insects. These terrestrial crustaceans breathe by means of abdominal gills and are confined to moist places.

The order *Amphipoda* comprises many species of marine and a few species of terrestrial crustaceans, such as sand hoppers or beach fleas. The so called fresh-water shrimp, Gammarus (Fig. 103, C), is one of the best known of the amphipods.

The order *Decapoda* contains most of the large crustaceans that are of economic importance because of their food value. The lobsters are the most valuable; crabs come next; and shrimps are not far behind. An interesting example of the most highly specialized group of this order is the sprightly fiddler crab, Gelasimus (Fig. 103, D).

Class II. Onychophora

Although some authors place these animals within the class Myriapoda, there is good reason for granting them class value. It is a concise and compact assemblage of some fifty species belonging to several genera, the best known being Peripatus (Fig. 101, A). These are very widely distributed over the world, but their range is extremely interrupted, for they are present in Africa, Australia, New Zealand, Tasmania, South and Central America, Mexico, West Indies, and Malaya. The most interesting point about Peripatus is that it is a classic connecting link type, having characters of the phylum Annelida and of the phylum Arthropoda; and thus the group tends to prove what is generally believed on other grounds, that the arthropods have had an annelidan ancestry. The annelid features of Peripatus are: annelid-like nephridia segmentally arranged; cilia in reproductive organs; general annelid arrangement of the chief systems. The arthropod characters are: the cœlom is filled with blood and blood sinuses; appendages are somewhat jointed and some are modified as mouth parts; tracheæ are present.

Class III. Myriapoda

These are the centipedes and wireworms. They are characteristically elongated forms, with a distinct head possessing one pair of antennæ and one pair of mandibles, and with a multiplicity of more or less insect-like paired appendages showing little regional specialization. There are four orders:

The order *Diplopoda* comprises such typical millipedes as that shown in Figure 104, B. These commonly have a cylindrical body covered with chitinous armor, and they have the habit of rolling up into a close spiral when disturbed.

The order *Chilopoda* consists of the more typical centipedes such as Lithobius (Fig. 104, C). They are dorsoventrally flattened and have longer though fewer appendages than the Diplopoda.

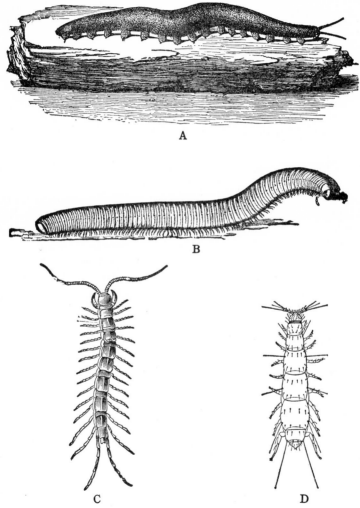

Fig. 104. Representative Myriapoda and Onychophora. **A,** *Peripatus capensis,* an arthropod with several annelid characters. **B,** a millipede; **C,** a centipede, *Lithobius forficatus.* **D,** *Pauropodus huxleyi,* a centipede with only nine pairs of legs, and having the general appearance of an insect. (**A,** from Sedgwick; **B,** from Shipley and MacBride, after Koch; **C,** from Sedgwick, after Koch; **D,** from Sedgwick, after Latzel.)

The *Pauropoda* (Fig. 104, D) are very minute degenerate myriapods, with relatively few appendages.

The order *Symphyla* are small myriapods with twelve pairs of appendages. They are interesting mainly on account of the fact that they resemble certain of the more primitive wingless insects in general appearance and in habits. This suggests that the insects may have arisen from some now extinct myriapod stock.

Class IV. Insecta

The following classification of insects recognizes nineteen orders. These orders may be distinguished from one another on the basis of their differences with respect to three characteristics: *a*, the presence or absence of wings, or the form of the wings; *b*, the structure and function of the mouth parts; *c*, the relative completeness or incompleteness of the metamorphosis.

The following is a condensed list of the orders of insects, with the common names of the representative types:—

Order 1, *Aptera* . . . . . Springtails, fish moths.

Order 2, *Ephimerida* . . . . May flies.

Order 3, *Odonata* . . . . . Dragon flies.

Order 4, *Plecoptera* . . . . Stone flies.

Order 5, *Isoptera* . . . . . Termites, or white ants.

Order 6, *Corrodentia* . . . . Book lice, bark lice.

Order 7, *Mallophaga* . . . . Biting bird lice.

Order 8, *Thysanoptera* . . . Thrips.

Order 9, *Euplexoptera* . . . Earwigs.

Order 10, *Orthoptera* . . . . Cockroaches, grasshoppers, crickets.

Order 11, *Hemiptera* . . . . True bugs, lice, plant lice or aphids.

Order 12, *Neuroptera* . . . . Ant lions, hellgramites.

Order 13, *Mecoptera* . . . . Scorpion flies.

Order 14, *Trichoptera* . . . Caddice flies.

Order 15, *Lepidoptera* . . . Butterflies, moths.

Order 16, *Diptera* . . . . Flies, mosquitoes, gnats, sheep ticks.

Order 17, *Siphonaptera* . . . Fleas.

Order 18, *Coleoptera* . . . . Beetles.

Order 19, *Hymenoptera* . . . Ants, bees, wasps, sawflies, ichneumon flies.

Of these orders the best known and most important economically and in other ways are Orders 10, 11, 15, 16, 18, and 19. All of these orders are vast assemblages of successful and highly diversified species.

The order *Orthoptera* consists of some of the most numerous and destructive species, whose ravages upon crops are proverbial as far back as history goes. A relatively harmless representative of the order is the rather attractive katydid (Fig. 105, A).

The order *Odonata*, though not so abundant as some orders, and of no great economic importance, is among the most interesting of insect orders because of the large size, conspicuous form, curious predaceous habits both of larvæ and of adults, and their remarkably abrupt metamorphosis. The dragon fly, Libellula (Fig. 105, B), is a good example of the order.

The *Hemiptera* are numerous and of great economic importance. The common chinch-bug is at once one of the best known and the most dreaded of agricultural pests (Fig. 105, D).

The *Lepidoptera* are perhaps the most attractive as well as the most destructive of insects. The butterflies and moths do their chief damage in the caterpillar, or larval, state. After metamorphosis into the "angel form" they behave in a way that is appropriate to the angel state, feeding chiefly upon the nectar of flowers and doing no harm. The cabbage butterfly, *Pieris rapæ* (Fig. 105, C), is perhaps the commonest of butterflies in the world.

The *Diptera* might receive the distinction of being pests *par excellence.* If man could select one order of animals to be rid of he would do well to select the Diptera. Think what a relative paradise the world might be without the flies, mosquitoes, gnats, and all that pesky tribe. Moreover, we would incidentally get rid of many of our worst insect transmitted diseases, as is borne out in a subsequent chapter (pp. 364–369). Of all the flies the most familiar is *Musca domestica,* our constant household companion (Fig. 105, E).

The *Coleoptera* (beetles) are among the largest and most successful of the insect orders. While less annoying to man's person and health than the Diptera, they are far more destructive of his crops and other property. One need only mention in this connection one example, the Colorado potato beetle (Fig. 105, F).

The *Hymenoptera* are the most important from almost any point of view of the insect orders. They represent a truly dominant

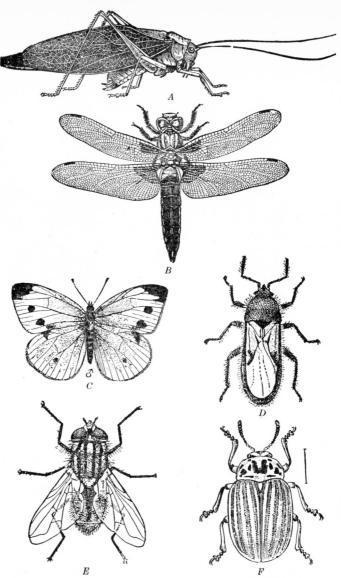

Fig. 105.   Representative Insecta. *A*, katydid, *Microcentrum retinerve*. *B*, a dragon-fly, *Libellula depressa*. *C*, cabbage butterfly, *Pieris rapæ*. *D*, chinch-bug, *Blissus leucopterus*. *E*, house-fly, *Musca domestica*. *F*, potato-beetle, *Leptinotarsa decemlineata*. (*A*, from Sedgwick, after Riley; *B*, from Miall, after Charpentier; *C*, after Webster; *D*, from Osborn, after Riley; *E*, from Howard; *F*, from the Cambridge Natural History.)

group. Little need be said here about the ants, bees, and wasps, for they are made the subject of special discussion in Chapter XXII.

Class V. Arachnida

This large and diversified group includes the king crabs, the scorpions, the spiders, the harvestmen, the ticks, the mites, and

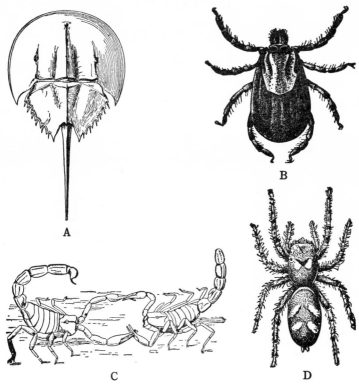

FIG. 106. Representative Arachnida. **A,** dorsal view of the King crab, *Limulus*, a marine arachnid. **B,** cattle tick, *Boöphilus annulatus*. **C,** a pair of scorpions (*Buthus occitans*) engaged in the "*promenade à deux*" or mating act. **D,** jumping spider, *Attus*. (**A,** from Shipley and MacBride; **B,** after Packard; **C,** after Fabre; **D,** from Davenport, after Emerton.)

several less familiar orders. They are characterized by the absence of antennæ, the absence of true jaws, and the division of the body into three regions (prosoma, mesosoma, and metasoma). All but the king crabs are fundamentally terrestrial and breathe by means of lung books or tracheæ. Of the eleven orders we need mention only four.

The order *Xiphosura* (king-crabs) constitutes an interesting relic of the very remote past that has come on through the ages little changed from the ancestral state. The genus Limulus (Fig. 106, A) consists of large marine arachnids, with a tough horseshoe shaped carapace covering the body so completely that they seem to be immune to almost any attack. They possess large numbers of sheetlike branchiæ bound together like the leaves of a book, and hence called gill books.

The order *Scorpionida* are predaceous arachnids that may reach a considerable size and are noted for their poison sting on the end of the whiplike tail, or metasoma, by means of which they paralyze their prey and protect themselves from their enemies. Their mating behavior is especially interesting and curious. After some strange antics while facing each other, the male seizes the chelæ of the female and the two engage in a curious formal dance or, as Fabre calls it, a *promenade à deux* (Fig. 106, C), after which mating ensues.

The order *Araneida* consists of the spiders, a highly specialized and fascinating group from the naturalistic standpoint. They are especially noteworthy because of their spinning habits and their poison fangs. They construct snares of the most elaborate architecture for capturing prey and also use their silky threads for the construction of all sorts of shelters and abodes, as well as cocoons for the protection of their eggs and young. They show very little external evidence of their segmental structure, have eight walking legs, and usually many small eyes, which give them clear vision only at very short range. Among the liveliest of the spiders are the jumping spiders, one of which is shown in Figure 106, D.

The order *Acarina* consists of the ticks and mites, an immense assemblage of rather small forms, many of them characterized by their ectoparasitic habits. Some of them merely suck the blood of the host, others burrow beneath the skin and cause severe irritation. Perhaps they are most significant on account of their propensity for transmitting diseases from one host to another. The cattle tick (Fig. 106, B) is responsible for the dreaded Texas fever, the loss from which runs up to about $100,000,000 a year in the United States. The majority of mites are free-living, occurring in leaf mold, under stones, and in water.

In our further discussion of this large and important phylum our plan is to deal with a number of typical representatives of the group in such a way that each will serve to illustrate some important biological phenomenon or principle. Thus, when discussing the crayfish, we shall emphasize chiefly the principle of homology, especially that of serial homology; in dealing with grasshoppers, emphasis is laid on crop damage done by these insects and methods of control; in dealing with ants, our chief aim is to give the facts about communal life in this most interesting group and to develop some of its implications; while flies, mosquitoes, fleas, are dealt with chiefly as agents in the transmissal of disease. In the subsequent chapter dealing with adaptations a good many other interesting facts about arthropods are given. It has been our purpose in this place merely to outline the chief characteristics of the phylum.

CHAPTER XX

THE CRAYFISH AND THE PRINCIPLE OF HOMOLOGY

(PHYLUM ARTHROPODA)

CRAYFISHES of the genus Cambarus are favorite laboratory types, and are here introduced especially to illustrate the important principle of SERIAL HOMOLOGY. A short account of their activities and of their habitat, together with a brief consideration of their general morphology, precedes the discussion of the main point at issue.

A. HABITS AND HABITAT

Crayfishes have often been called fresh-water lobsters because of their close resemblance to the latter and because they are believed to have been derived as an offshoot from the lobster tribe. One usually finds crayfishes hiding under stones or other cover during the day, but they are quite active at night. Their habit is to lie in wait behind shelters and to dart out upon unwary fishes or insects that pass within their reach, seizing them with their powerful pinchers (CHELIPEDS) and rending them to pieces. Though preferring living animal food they are not averse to dead and decaying flesh, and they even resort to plant food in times of food scarcity. The crayfish is well protected, owing to the fact that its color closely matches that of the background, making it inconspicuous both to prey and to enemies. Its characteristic backward method of locomotion is especially well adapted for avoiding enemies.

B. GENERAL MORPHOLOGY

The crayfishes belong to the PHYLUM ARTHROPODA and the CLASS CRUSTACEA. Like the annelids, the arthropods are metameric, but they exhibit a rather profound modification of the primitive segmental plan. Externally, the evidences of segmentation are quite obvious in connection with the exoskeletal rings and in the paired appendages (Fig. 107). Internally, however, one sees only rather vague indications of metamerism, for there

246

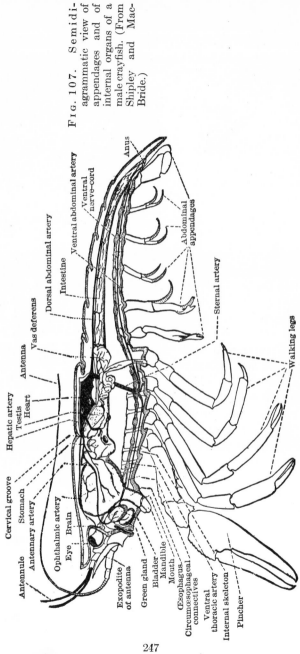

Fig. 107. Semidiagrammatic view of appendages and of internal organs of a male crayfish. (From Shipley and MacBride.)

247

are no septa dividing the cœlom into compartments, no series of paired nephridia and gonads, no obvious segmental arrangement of blood vessels or alimentary organs.   The nervous system is, of all the internal systems, the most strikingly metameric; it consists of a series of paired segmental ganglia connected by paired nerve cords—an arrangement not unlike that of the annelids.   The crayfish, like other arthropods, has no open cœlom, but the spaces between the viscera and the body wall are filled up with BLOOD SINUSES.   The body and the appendages are covered with a tough chitinous CUTICLE, which in some regions is thick and impregnated with calcium salts.   In the abdominal region each metamere is covered with a distinct ring of chitin, but the rings of the head and those of the thorax are all fused into one solid mass of armor, the CEPHALOTHORAX, which has two lateral flaps that serve as a covering for the gills, the space between them and the body forming BRANCHIAL CHAMBERS.   The other systems of organs are in no essential respects greatly different from those hitherto dealt with.

C. APPENDAGES AND SERIAL HOMOLOGY

It has already been pointed out that the metameric organization of the crayfish is indicated most clearly by the appendages. *There is a pair of appendages of some sort to each somite, or metamere.*   In the regions of the body where the somites have retained their primitive free segmental character the appendages are also found in a relatively generalized condition; but in the regions where the somites are firmly fused and closely packed together the appendages are the only external parts that give a clue as to the number of metameres represented.   In these packed regions of the head and in the anterior somites of the thorax the appendages are variously specialized for different functions.   All told, there are 19 (or 20) pairs of appendages: 5 (or 6) in the head, 8 in the thorax, and 6 in the abdomen.   There is some divergence of opinion as to whether the stalked eyes, the first appendages of the head, are to be counted as true appendages, homologous with others.   The prevailing opinion seems to be that the eyes are not strictly homologous with the other appendages, but are special appendages of the prostomium.   If, however, an eyestalk is removed, an antenna-like appendage sometimes regenerates from the eye-stalk stump. This seems to suggest that the eyes are true appendages.   Counting the eyes, there are 20 pairs of appendages, which are distributed as follows:—

Head
- Stalked eyes ⎫
- Antennules   ⎬ sensory
- Antennæ   ⎭
- Mandibles   ⎫
- First maxillæ ⎬ feeding
- Second maxillæ ⎭

Thorax
- First maxillipeds   ⎫
- Second maxillipeds ⎬ feeding
- Third maxillipeds   ⎭
- Chelipeds (grasping and defensive)
- First ambulatory   ⎫
- Second ambulatory   ⎬ walking
- Third ambulatory   ⎪
- Fourth ambulatory   ⎭

Abdomen
- First swimmerets (much reduced in female; in male modified as copulatory organs)
- Second swimmerets (typical in female; copulatory in male)
- Third swimmerets   ⎫
- Fourth swimmerets ⎬ generalized function
- Fifth swimmerets   ⎭
- Caudal appendages (swimming)

The SWIMMERETS, especially those of the female, are considered as the least specialized of the appendages, belonging as they do to the most generalized of the body somites. Each appendage is made up of three fundamental parts: the basal part, which is attached to the body, is called the PROTOPODITE; the two distal parts are named according to their position with reference to the median line of the body, the inner one being called the ENDOPODITE, the outer, the EXOPODITE (Fig. 108). In the first abdominal appendages of the male, the copulatory organs, the exopodites are lost, while the two remaining parts unite to act as a sort of semitubular channel for the transfer of sperm into the annulus, or seminal receptacle, of the female. The last abdominal appendages have all three parts present in a broadly expanded condition so that they furnish the chief paddle surface for backward swimming.

All of the WALKING APPENDAGES have lost the exopodites and

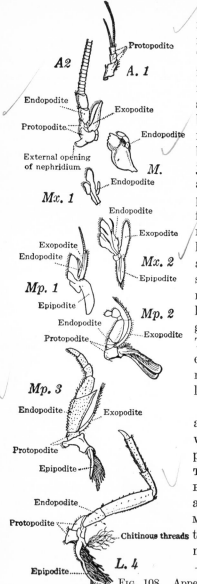

consist mainly of the enlarged, many jointed endopodite, which may or may not end in pincers. The protopodite gives off from its base a GILL and a membranous EPIPODITE, or BRACT, which serves to close off the gill chamber from the outside. A CHELIPED is merely an enlarged ambulatory organ with its terminal joint enormously overgrown into a powerful CHELA, or claw. The pairs of MAXILLIPEDS differ each from the others. The THIRD MAXILLIPED resembles a walking leg, but has a small gill and an antennalike exopodite. The SECOND MAXILLIPED has a much reduced endopodite, an antennalike exopodite, a rudimentary gill, a well developed bract. The FIRST MAXILLIPED has both exopodite and endopodite much reduced, no gills, and relatively large protopodite with large bract.

In the head the first appendages are the STALKED EYES, which probably represent the protopodite alone. In the ANTENNULES and jaws (MANDIBLES), the exopodites have disappeared. In the two pairs of MAXILLÆ, we can recognize all of the typical parts only slightly modified.

FIG. 108.   Appendages of Crayfish as seen from ventral side. *A. 1*, antennules; *A. 2*, antennæ; *L. 4*, fourth walking leg; *M*, mandible; *Mp. 1*, first maxilliped; *Mp. 2*, second maxilliped; *Mp. 3*, third maxilliped; *Mx. 1*, first maxilla; *Mx. 2*, second maxilla. (From Kerr.)

All of these appendages, with the possible exception of the eyes, have equivalent embryonic rudiments and, at an early stage, appear to be essentially alike. As they grow, they modify in different ways and come to subserve a great variety of functions, some being only sensory, others only ambulatory, others gustatory, copulatory, or swimming. Some play a mixed rôle, as has already been shown. In the process of specialization from the generalized embryonic type some parts start to grow, then cease, and either become resorbed or remain as vestiges. We have here a fine example of the specialization of similar structures for different functions. ***Organs that have a similar embryonic origin and similar morphological relations are said to be homologous,*** and those that are homologous, but in different metameres of the same animal, are termed ***serially homologous.*** These structures, specialized as they are for different functions, are classed as ***adaptations.*** One of the greatest of our unsolved biological problems is to account for the origin of adaptations. A consideration of this problem will be found in Chapter XLI.

While we cannot take the time to deal in any detail with homologies that exist between structures of the crayfish and those of other Crustacea, we must at least indicate some of the facts. We find that one whole group of Crustacea, the Malacostracha, has the same number of appendages as has the crayfish, five (or six) in the head, eight in the thorax, and six in the abdomen. But beyond this there is considerable diversity. In one group only three of the thoracic appendages are used for walking, the rest being employed in feeding; in another group all eight thoracic appendages are in a rudimentary state; in still another group seven thoracic appendages are ambulatory and only one is used in feeding.

The general conclusion that is usually drawn from these facts is that all of these different types of Crustacea, because of their fundamental similarities, must be more or less closely related, and must have descended from common ancestors. Today homologies are interpreted as among the most reliable evidences of the blood relationship of diverse groups and, indirectly, of descent with modification.

CHAPTER XXI

THE NATURAL HISTORY OF THE GRASSHOPPER

(PHYLUM ARTHROPODA)

A. Habits and Habitat

1. *Introduction*

In choosing one out of many thousands of kinds of insects for especial attention we are not guided by favoritism. Personally, the writer would rather consider the butterfly or the bee, were physical attractiveness to guide his choice. There are reasons for selecting the quaint and ubiquitous grasshopper. It is a representative insect, not too primitive nor yet too specialized; it is of convenient size for laboratory work; it is extremely widespread and abundant; and it is of unusual economic importance.

There are many kinds of grasshoppers (Fig. 109). Some kinds are called locusts, but there is no well-defined scientific distinction between locusts and grasshoppers. Our account of grasshopper natural history will not confine itself to any one species, but will serve as a representative account for a considerable group of similar forms.

The grasshopper, using the term broadly, is a typical representative of the insect order Orthoptera, which includes crickets, katydids, cockroaches, walkingstick insects and some other less familiar forms. They are characterized by having biting, or mandibulate, mouth parts; two pairs of wings, the anterior pair usually somewhat thickened; incomplete metamorphosis, a type of development in which the transition from larva to adult is through several larval stages and not all at once.

2. *Habitat and Distribution*

As the name indicates, grasshoppers are grass dwellers in the broad sense, in that they inhabit mainly meadows. Some species prefer the dry dusty fields, other species prefer damp, lush meadows and lowlands. Wherever you may go about the open fields of the

252

world, there you will find grasshoppers. Some species have a very narrow range, others have a continent wide distribution. Some forms have a migratory habit, swarming over hundreds of miles of territory in countless hordes, eating up all green vegetation in their path, leaving a wake of desolation.

The warrior grasshopper, *Camnula pellucida*, is one of the most serious insect pests of the Middle Western states. They are re-

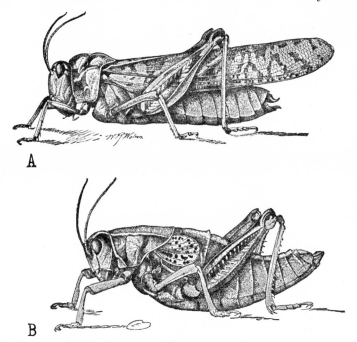

FIG. 109. Typical Locusts (Grasshoppers). **A**, *Dissosteira longipennis;* **B**, *Brachystola magna*. Both females. (From Farmers' Bulletin, No. 747, U. S. Dept. Agric.)

sponsible for "plagues" which are doubtless of the same sort as the biblical "plague of locusts" that tormented the Egyptians. In a plague year, owing to relative lack of enemies or favorable developmental conditions, a large percentage of the eggs laid develop and hatch. They hatch in May or June, and in the course of a few hours enormous numbers emerge and begin to migrate. They jump and crawl toward the sun. At this stage they have no wings and cannot fly. Since in most regions the rains come mainly in the afternoon, the grasshoppers follow the morning sun and hence move mainly in a southeasterly direction. When an army of these insects crosses a cultivated field they denude it of all green vegetation, leaving it utterly desolate. After the last larval molt the wings are ready for flight and the migration is then sometimes carried on through the air, dense clouds of grasshoppers traveling *en masse* and dropping down upon the cultivated fields.

3. *Control of Grasshoppers*

There are various kinds of natural checks upon the overproduction of grasshoppers. The eggs are easily killed in the ground during the winter if exposed to frequent freezing and thawing. Enormous numbers are killed off at various stages by insect and other enemies. Grasshopper eggs are relished as food by various types of ground-burrowing animals, such as field mice, gophers, and moles; while the young and adults are devoured in enormous numbers by birds, lizards, and skunks. Even the despised snakes of our fields take heavy toll of grasshopper life and thereby help to justify their existence in a world turned against them.

Among the insect enemies of grasshoppers are other insects that lay their eggs among grasshopper eggs, so that their young larvæ may feed upon the handy larvæ of their prey. Even plants may be parasitic on grasshoppers, as is evidenced by the large numbers found dead of a fungus disease.

Internal parasites of various sorts, including worms and bacteria, are ever present, as in all other animals, and help in the destruction of grasshoppers. Thus there is a continual conflict between the tremendous forces of reproduction and the complex forces of destruction. The result is that under ordinary conditions the various species are kept down to reasonable numbers. Under exceptionally favorable conditions the forces of reproduction gain the ascendancy and we have a "plague year." Greater success of the grasshopper increases the number of parasites and other enemies and the next year the species is back to normal or below it.

No better example could well be cited to illustrate the idea of the "Web of Life" by which is meant that no species lives to itself alone, but exists in the midst of a whole community of interdependent species. There is thus a balance in nature that is self regulatory. This is an ecological consideration of the highest significance.

B. Physiology of the Grasshopper

1. *Feeding Habits and Digestion*

In feeding, the grasshopper nips off with the mandibles small bits of grass or leaves. The LABRUM is used as an upper lip and the LABIUM as a lower lip. These act as aids in food ingestion and as tactile organs. Glands of the mouth secrete a SALIVARY JUICE that helps to lubricate the food and probably serves as a digestive fluid that acts upon the food after it reaches the CROP, an enlarged region of the alimentary tract used primarily for storage. The food passes from the crop into the STOMACH, composed of a PROVENTRICULUS and a VENTRICULUS, where the main digestive changes occur. The GASTRIC CÆCÆ pour their abundant juices into the stomach. It is this material, colloquially called "molasses" or "tobacco juice", that exudes from the mouth of a grasshopper when caught and handled. The process of digestion continues in the intestine and absorption of the diffusable products of digestion takes place in this region.

2. *Sense Organs in Relation to Behavior*

The principal senses of the grasshopper are the same as in most other animals: touch, taste, smell, hearing, and vision. The SENSE OF TOUCH is rather generally distributed over the body, but especially centered in the antennæ, mouth parts, and abdominal cerci. The SENSE OF TASTE is largely confined to the median portion of the labium. The SENSE OF SMELL appears to be situated in the basal portions of the antennæ. The SENSE ORGANS OF HEARING are the so-called TYMPANIC MEMBRANES, situated on the sides of the abdomen on the first abdominal somite. These organs are believed to have a most important relation to the sound producing STRIDULATION APPARATUS so characteristic of the grasshoppers and their allies. In some of the grasshoppers the sound is produced by rasping the hind legs across the hard anterior wings, or by rubbing the wings and wing covers together in flight so as to produce the well-known "clacking" sound. In some of the allies of the grasshoppers such as the crickets and katydids, the sound is described as chirping. These sounds are sex calls and serve to guide the female to the male. The SENSE ORGANS OF SIGHT are the COMPOUND EYES and the OCELLI. An ocellus is a simple eye consisting of a transparent lens-shaped thickening of the exoskeleton with a visual sense area beneath, which is connected with the central nervous system. Probably these eyes form only the vaguest of images and serve largely as light perceptive organs. The compound eyes are much more complex, being made up of numerous OMMA-TIDIA, each of which is a simple eye. The prevailing theory of the functioning of these eyes is that each visual unit forms a separate image. The curvature of the whole eye is such that only those ommatidia perpendicular to the rays cast by a given object form a clear image. Thus when an object moves, a series of shifting

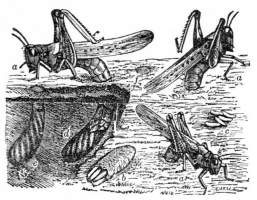

FIG. 110. Rocky mountain locust, showing *a, a, a,* females in different positions laying eggs; *b,* egg pod removed from ground; *c,* eggs lying loose on ground; *d,* and *e,* burrows in ground for deposit of eggs. (From Hegner, after Riley.)

images is formed. This gives the animal definite information about objects in movement in the immediate surroundings; how fast and in what direction the object is moving. Nothing could be more important than this information in the life of a creature so much preyed upon as is the grasshopper.

C. REPRODUCTION AND THE LIFE CYCLE

During the mating season males and females clasp each other by means of special copulatory organs at the end of the abdomen. The eggs are fertilized internally and are then laid by the female by means of the ovipositor, an organ on the end of the abdomen that enables the latter to thrust itself some distance into the ground (Fig. 110). Masses of eggs, held together by a sticky secretion, are deposited and, when the abdomen is withdrawn, are buried beneath a layer of loose earth. In order to develop and hatch, the eggs must lie just beneath the surface. If the surface be plowed under, the eggs and embryos are killed. The embryonic development proper takes place within the egg, and the young hatches out as a small larva that looks a good deal like a grasshopper, except that it seems to be mostly head and has no wings. The young develops through a series of molts, each successive larval stage being more like an adult grasshopper. The last molt is followed by the adult type, technically called the IMAGO, which spends the rest of its life in this form, neither growing nor molting. Some of the larval, or nymph, stages are shown in Figure 111.

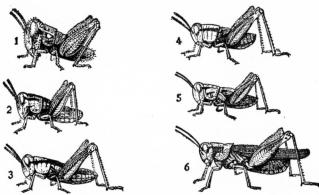

FIG. 111. Some of the stages of metamorphosis in the grasshopper. 1 to 5 are nymph stages; 6 is a young imago. (From Packard, after Emerton.)

This brief account of the natural history of the grasshopper is intended to supplement a laboratory study of its anatomy. No general account of the anatomical details is given in this place, because it is much better for the student to work them out at first hand. The points brought out here are chiefly those that cannot be brought out through a laboratory study.

CHAPTER XXII

ANTS AND SOCIAL ORGANIZATION

(PHYLUM ARTHROPODA)

Ants have for a long time attracted the attention of naturalists because of their social organization. For ages they have occupied a dominant place in the economy of nature because they are so highly adapted to the conditions of life. Their success in the world is attested by their extraordinary abundance and wide distribution. Three factors, more important perhaps than any others, have made for success: their exquisite subterranean life, their polymorphism, and their social habits.

A. Subterranean Life

Every one has seen ants in process of excavating their subterranean galleries. Processions of ants may be seen emerging from a hole in the ground, each individual carrying in its mandibles a grain of sand or a small lump of soil. Coöperative and incessant labor on their part results in the excavation of elaborate systems of tunnels and galleries, with here and there enlarged chambers used as nurseries and storehouses. The advantages of subterranean life are fairly obvious. It offers protection from both diurnal and seasonal changes of temperature; for the temperature a few feet below the surface remains relatively constant and rarely goes to extremes of heat or cold. It offers a retreat from the chief insectivorous animals, such as birds and reptiles. It furnishes storehouses for food that may be used to tide them over long periods of famine, drought, or cold, thus making it possible for most species of ants greatly to prolong individual life, some individuals living a decade or more. This is quite in contrast with the duration of life of most insects, in which a generation lasts for only a few months or a year.

B. Polymorphism

Polymorphism is a term designating the existence of several different forms, or castes, of individual in a species. We speak of the differences between the sexes as examples of sex dimorphism, but in the ants there are always at least three and frequently five or six distinctly different forms, some sexual and others functionally sexless. There are always the fertile females or queens, functional males, and workers of at least one kind, the latter zygotically female but sexually quite immature. In a number of species there is a caste called soldiers, characterized by enormous heads and mandibles (Fig. 112). The duties of the different castes are diverse and quite well defined. Queens and males are merely and solely parents. Workers are, as the name implies, generalized laborers and do all of the necessary work of the colony. Soldiers are specialists in warfare and rapine.

C. Social Life

Ant communities are somewhat like the more primitive human communities in that they are essentially family groups that hold together and coöperate for the common good. Sometimes, as we shall see later, mixed communities are formed as the result of slavery. The history of an ant colony will serve to reveal the nature of their social organization. At some season of the year, depending on the locality of the species in question, certain of the larvæ develop into functional males and females. These are winged types and tend to fly away from the nest and to rise high into the air to mate. After large numbers of them have been killed and eaten by birds a few return to earth, never to fly again, for the males die and the females hunt for a hole in the ground where her eggs may be laid. The queen breaks off her wings and becomes much like other ants except for her larger size. The eggs hatch out as grubs, which are fed by a secretion produced by the mother. She starves herself sometimes for months while feeding her young, but as soon as these young reach the IMAGO state they take over the duty of feeding the exhausted mother. When well fed, she lays other batches of eggs that are cared for and reared by the workers. Lazy, and doing nothing but feed and lay eggs, she may live this sort of life for fifteen years. As time goes on, the colony becomes large and prosperous; the greater their population, the more extensive becomes the system of galleries. How long a given community may last is unknown, but one may assume that only in case of some cataclysm does a colony come to an end; for when a queen dies, new queens take her place and a single dynasty may continue for centuries.

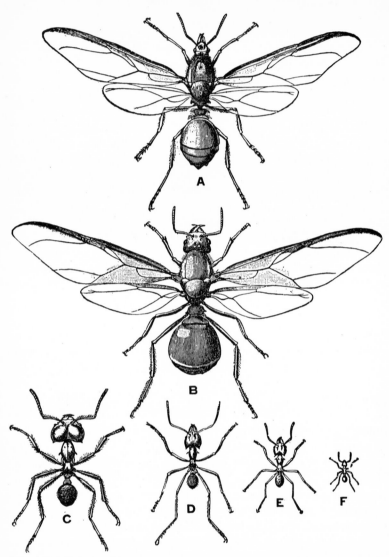

FIG. 112.   Polymorphism in ants as illustrated by the adult forms of *Atta*
(*Œcodoma*) *cephalotes* taken from a single nest.   **A,** male; **B,** winged female; **C–F,** various form unwinged: **C,** so-called soldier; **D,** large worker;
E, smaller worker; **F,** smallest nurse worker.   All equally magnified one
and a half times.   (From the Cambridge Natural History.)

D. Commensalism

Many other animals besides ants live in ant galleries. Ants have their domesticated pets of various kinds, some of which are doubtless more of a nuisance than anything else. These ant associates are usually called MYRMECOPHILES (meaning literally "ant lovers"). They share with ants all of their advantages. Some of these act a useful rôle as scavengers, others are mere camp followers, and some are actual thieves and parasites. Interesting types of commensals not infrequently found associated with ants are mealy bugs and plant lice. Ants actually domesticate these creatures much as man has domesticated cattle, and for similar purposes. Thus the corn-root aphids feed upon the juices of tender roots and excrete as a by-product drops of sweet fluid known as honeydew. This the ants eagerly lap up. So attached to aphids are ants that they capture them aboveground and carry them to their galleries. Thus the aphids are protected from their enemies and breed prolifically within the domain of the ants.

E. Slavery

Some species of ants, as the result of overspecialization, have come to produce only the soldier type of worker. These become wonderfully efficient as fighters and raiders, but cannot do the ordinary duties of the colony. To supply this very obvious deficiency, the soldiers raid the colonies of less specialized species of ants, capture, and carry home their pupæ. When the latter emerge as workers, they play the same rôle in their captors' home as they would in their own, not only feeding the young of the slave makers but feeding also their queen and the soldiers. When these workers diminish in numbers through natural or accidental death, a new supply is obtained by raiding another colony. The slave makers are utterly dependent upon slaves, and in a sense are parasites on the enslaved species. Certain other types of slave makers are less highly specialized in that they can carry on without slaves, but rarely do so.

F. Peculiar Feeding Habits Among Ants

One of the most interesting of the feeding habits of ants is that exhibited by LEAF-CUTTING ANTS (Fig. 113, 2). These industrious denizens of tropical America cut off the leaves and flowers of succulent plants, carry them to their underground chambers, where they chew them up to furnish culture beds for certain kinds of fungi. The fungus is perpetuated by means of spores carried in a specialized head fold, or pouch, and is passed on to new colonies by queens or founders. A pure culture of edible fungus is thus kept up by a given species, while different species of leaf-cutter ants rear different species of fungi.

Another very odd feeding adaptation is that found among HONEY ANTS, common in Mexico and our own Southwest (Fig. 113, 1). Certain of the workers make of themselves veritable honey

FIG. 113. Honey ants and leaf-cutting ants. (From Brehm.)

sacs. These specialized individuals feed gluttonously upon honey until their abdomens become swollen up into globular sacs many times as large as the rest of the body. In Mexico these honey glutted ants are prized as a confection. The value of this habit for the ants is that it enables them to store up for general colony use large amounts of a favorite food during periods when it is normally unobtainable. The honey filled individuals remain in a state of dormancy and do nothing but act as storage vessels.

G. Ant Societies and Human Societies Compared

W. M. Wheeler, from whose classic work, *Ants: Their Structure, Development, and Behavior,* these facts are gleaned, interestingly compares ant societies with human societies. He notes that ant societies are conducted by the female sex; while the males are merely the short lived mates of the queen, live a lazy life, and have no influence in the management of the community. The guiding spirits of the whole colony are the workers—sterile females; they constitute a society of amazons. In contrast with this situation, human society, until recently at any rate, has been conducted chiefly for and by the males. Human communities of the modern sort are artificial aggregations of unrelated individuals, each of which has a capacity for a considerable range of activities, but usually become specialized, either of his own accord or through economic pressure, along some one line of communal service. The fact that man's lot in life is so often artificially determined gives rise to unrest and discontent. In the case of ants, however, affairs are quite different: each individual is born with certain morphological characters and a certain instinctive equipment that settles once for all its status in life. Thus all is harmony and coöperation. A revolution in an ant community is inconceivable, for each ant is her own ruler and there are no regulations imposed from without or by a centralized authority. An ant community may be looked upon as a sort of socialistic anarchy.

CHAPTER XXIII

INSECTS AND DISEASE

(PHYLUM ARTHROPODA)

A. WARFARE BETWEEN INSECTS AND MAN

In all the world of life the insects seem to be preëminent for numbers of species, over 300,000 species having been named and probably as many more being still unidentified. It would be strange, then, were all of these favorable to human welfare. As a matter of fact, man and the insects are rivals for dominance in the modern world; they compete for the same food materials and the same "place in the sun." There is warfare between them: man battles the insects and the insects attack man, his domestic animals, and his crops. Perhaps the most serious modes of attack of the insects upon man are carried on by various types of disease carriers—mosquitoes, flies, bugs, lice, and fleas.

B. MODES OF DISEASE TRANSMISSAL

Some insects either in the adult state or during the larval period actually invade and feed upon human tissues. Thus, certain fleas of tropical countries burrow beneath the skin and breed there, causing sores and destroying tissue. Strictly speaking, this is a case of parasitism rather than disease, though the distinction between the two is by no means clearly defined. By far the most important relation of insects to disease has to do with their rôle as carriers of pathogenic bacteria and Protozoa. The insect itself is often diseased and transmits the germs of disease by biting human beings or by contaminating their food. A few of the best known instances of the rôle of insects as disease carriers will now be discussed.

C. MOSQUITOES AND MALARIA

One of the greatest achievements of modern medical science had to do with the discovery of the rôle played by the mosquito in the transmissal of malaria. Formerly, malaria was supposed to be the result of bad air or bad water; now, it is known to be the result of the invasion of a minute protozoan parasite—somewhat like a small Amœba—that invades and destroys the red blood corpuscles. A single organism enters a red blood cell, feeds upon its protoplasm, and multiplies. After the whole blood cell is consumed the numerous progeny escape into the blood stream and attack other blood cells. On the rupture of the dead corpuscle metabolic by-products, toxic in character, escape into the blood and cause the symptoms of chills and fever.

If a human being infested with malarial organisms is bitten by a certain kind of mosquito belonging to the genus Anopheles (Fig.

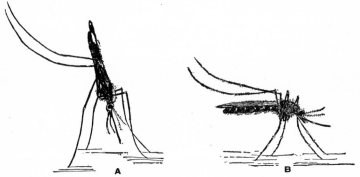

Fig. 114. **A,** position of malaria mosquito (*Anopheles*) when at rest. **B,** position of common house mosquito (*Culex*) when at rest. (After Howard.)

114), the latter draws into its stomach a small amount of human blood together with its contained malarial organisms. These go on living in the mosquito, passing through certain phases of their complicated life cycle, which is described and illustrated in Figure 115. The mosquito thus becomes diseased, and when it bites another human being, it first injects a little infected saliva into the wound. This serves to prevent the coagulation of the blood and at the same time infects the blood of the new host. Malaria can be prevented by breaking the train of transmissal, and this may be accomplished by preventing the breeding of mosquitoes or by screening houses so as to exclude mosquitoes. In cases where rabbits or other mammals act as an intermediate host alternative to man, it is much more difficult to break the train of transmissal.

Quinine is a specific remedy for malaria. When taken in suffi-

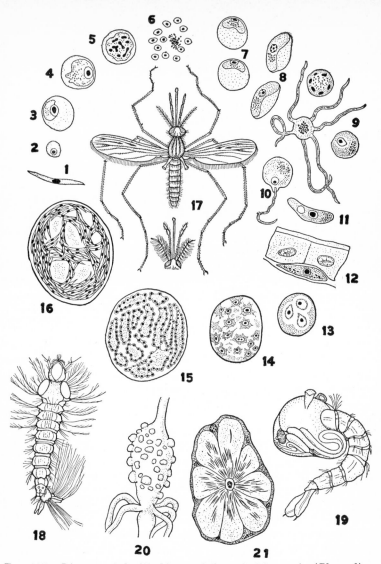

FIG. 115. *Diagram of the life history of the malarial parasite (Plasmodium falciparum).* The life cycle may be divided into (*a*) *schizogony*, the formation of self-infective spores in the human blood (stages **1–6**), (*b*) *sexual generation* or the formation and conjugation of the male and female gametes (stages **7–10**). During the early part of this phase of the life cycle the parasite is transferred to the mosquito, (*c*) *sporogony*, the formation of cross-infective spores in the invertebrate host, the Anopheles mosquito (stages **11–16**). **1,** Sporozoite, a spore introduced into the blood stream of man by the bite of the mosquito.

cient doses at the time when young parasites are free in the blood, these may be killed without injuring human tissues.

D. Mosquitoes and Yellow Fever

Much more deadly than malaria is the disease yellow fever, formerly one of the most dreaded of human plagues, now almost entirely eradicated. While the American troops were in Cuba a plague of yellow fever struck them so severely that a Yellow Fever Commission, headed by **Dr. Carroll,** was appointed to investigate the situation. It was found that the fever was transmitted by one species of mosquito and in no other way; that, as in the case of malaria, the bite of the mosquito serves both to pick up the disease and to inject it into a second person. The commission then proceeded to drain marshes or to pour crude oil on stagnant ponds where mosquitoes were wont to breed. In this way yellow fever was practically eradicated. If similar precautions were to be taken in the numerous malaria infested parts of our country, this less dreaded, but none the less serious and often fatal, disease could be entirely wiped out. A few millions of dollars would be sufficient to accomplish this; and it will be done when public opinion becomes sufficiently aroused. The total eradication of malaria from the United States would be one of the greatest accomplishments the Federal Government might boast.

E. Fleas and the Plague

The history of ancient and of modern times is punctuated by the recurrence of a terrible affliction known as PLAGUE, sometimes called the "black death." One epidemic of this disease during the fourteenth century spread over nearly the whole world and caused the death of as many as 25,000,000 people—a very large percentage of the whole population. In those days nothing was known as to the cause of the disease and less about its treatment or cure. Now it is known to be due to a minute germ and to be transmitted from rats, mice, and other small rodents, through the intermediary aid of fleas (Fig. 116). The diseased rats are bitten by fleas and the same fleas then bite human beings, injecting disease germs into their blood. Plague may be checked by destroying rats and other flea infested animals and by isolating plague stricken human beings to prevent the passage of fleas from them to other subjects.

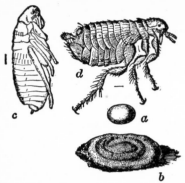

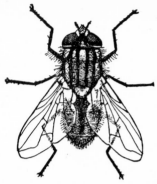

FIG. 116. Cat and dog flea, *Cteno-cephalus canis. a,* egg; *b,* larva in cocoon; *c,* pupa; *d,* adult. (From Howard, Circ. 108, Bur. Ent., U. S. Dep't. Agric.)

FIG. 117. House fly, *Musca domestica.* (From Howard, Circ. 71, Bur. Ent., U. S. Dep't. Agric.)

F. LICE AND TYPHUS

The discovery of the rôle of lice in the transmissal of typhus was made by **Dr. Henry Taylor Ricketts,** who died a martyr's death while engaged in studying this dread disease in Mexico. The situation is much like that in the case of plague. Trench fever—somewhat similar to typhus—is known to have a similar etiology.

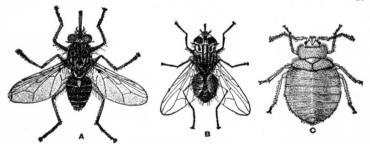

FIG. 118. Sucking insects that carry disease germs. **A,** tsetse fly, which carries the germs of sleeping sickness; **B,** stable fly; **C,** bedbug. (After Howard.)

Mites and ticks, while not insects, are responsible for various other diseases such as itch, mange, relapsing and Rocky Mountain fever.

G. FLIES AND TYPHOID FEVER

The common house fly (Fig. 117) is one of the greatest nuisances with which man has to contend. This insect has very filthy habits, feeding upon and breeding in all sorts of decomposing organic matter. When they alight upon the excreta of typhoid patients, they pick up upon their padded feet countless typhoid germs, which they leave upon exposed food or cooking utensils. Thus they serve as the most effective disseminators of typhoid. The "swat the fly" campaign is therefore one of great importance. Proper sanitation, such as adequate sewage disposal, screening of houses, and covering of garbage, are known to be important prophylactic measures.

H. FLIES AND SLEEPING SICKNESS

One of the most terrible of tropical diseases—the so-called sleeping sickness—is known to result from the bite of a blood-sucking insect, the tsetse fly (Fig. 118). The organism directly responsible for the disease is a flagellate protozoan—a trypanosome which lives in the blood. Horses, mules, and camels are infected with this disease, and it is transmitted from these animals to man or from man to man through the bite of the fly. The fly lives in marshy thickets and it is possible to render any limited region comparatively safe by cutting down all neighboring thickets, especially those near the haunts of horses.

The future history of mankind will doubtless be marked by his conquest of insects and, incidentally, of the diseases that are associated with insects and allied forms. It is not too much to hope that the next hundred years will see this war carried to a successful issue.

CHAPTER XXIV

ROUNDWORM PARASITES IN MAN

(PHYLUM NEMATHELMINTHES)

A. PARASITISM IN GENERAL

IF one were to list all free-living animals in the world in one column and all the parasites in another, the parasite list would be much longer than that of the independents. That this is true is readily deducible from the fact that practically every organism has upon it or within it at least one, and usually several, species of parasites. Even the parasites themselves have parasites within them. Thus there is a hidden, ugly world of parasites which doubtless outnumbers that of the host species.

The usual effects of extreme parasitism upon the parasite are that those organs and systems associated with a free life and the earning of an independent living tend to degenerate or to be entirely lost, and instead, there appear various kinds of suckers, hooks and other holdfasts by means of which the parasite clings to the host. Associated with the fact that parasites are so commonly fixed in position and cut off from association with members of their kind, they are very commonly HERMAPHRODITES (male and female in one). Again, because they very frequently occupy two or more species of hosts, the vicissitudes of life are so great that it is necessary to produce very large numbers of offspring. As a result of this the relative bulk of reproductive tissues as compared with that of the body as a whole is greatly increased.

Of all the animal phyla, three stand out preëminently as parasitic phyla: Protozoa, Nemathelminthes, Platyhelminthes. By no means all members of these phyla are parasitic, but undoubtedly over ninety percent of all animal parasites are to be found in these three phyla. Among other phyla that exhibit parasitism should be mentioned especially Arthropoda, Mollusca, and Annelida.

Of the three phyla of animals that are outstandingly parasitic,

270

the Nemathelminthes seem to show less difference between the parasitic and free-living species than do the others. They show little degeneration, only occasional hermaphroditism, and but few specialized organs of attachment; yet they are blind, have no special organs of locomotion and produce very large numbers of offspring, as many as 60,000,000 eggs having been estimated as the product of a single nematode.

The Nemathelminthes are important to man chiefly because they invade the human body and produce various morbid symptoms that are called diseases.

B. The Abundance of Roundworms

In a previous chapter, under the caption, "The Inhabitants of Two Square Feet of Soil," a paragraph (p. 92) was quoted from N. A. Cobb, a world's authority on nematodes. This paragraph would bear reading again in this place.

There are thousands of species of parasitic nematodes and other roundworms and still larger numbers of free-living species. It has been estimated that there are more than 80,000 nematode species parasitic on vertebrates alone, to say nothing of those infesting other invertebrates. "Numerous as the parasitic species are," says Cobb, "it is certain the number of species of nematodes living free in soil and in water far outnumber them. . . . There must be hundreds of thousands of species." A group so widespread and numerous deserves attention even in a general course.

C. Characteristics of the Phylum Nemathelminthes

As the name indicates, these are long, slender worms with the body cylindrical instead of being flattened as it is in the flatworms. They differ from the flatworms also in the following ways: The intestinal tract has two openings, mouth and anus, at opposite ends of the body; there is a dorsal as well as a ventral nerve cord, the two cords being united by several commissures; they are nearly all diœcious (have separate male and female individuals); there is a total absence of cilia. They resemble the flatworms in having no specialized circulatory or respiratory systems.

The roundworms differ from the annelids in the following respects: They are unsegmented; they have no true cœlom, but merely a space between the mesoderm cells of the body wall and

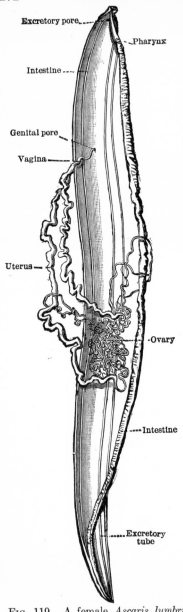

Fig. 119. A female *Ascaris lumbricoides* cut open and internal organs spread out to view. (From Shipley and MacBride.)

the endoderm cells of the intestine; they have no special organs of circulation and respiration; they have a dorsal as well as a ventral nerve cord; and they have no locomotor appendages.

The method of cleavage in most of the roundworms is decidedly determinate, which makes them in that respect more like the annelid-arthropod group; the mesoderm is set apart as early as the eight-cell stage, a fact that further seems to link the Nemathelminthes with the annelid-arthropod series. These two characteristics, together with the lack of any true cœlom, seem to prohibit the alignment of this phylum with either main series. We obtain, however, a suggestion from a group of primitive wormlike forms known as Chætognatha (the arrow worms), which resembles the Nemathelminthes more closely than any other group. These forms give rise to the cœlom in a fashion characteristic of the echinoderm-chordate series, *i.e.*, by cutting off pouches from the archenteron. It seems probable therefore that the cœlomless Nemathelminthes of today may have originally had an enterocœlic cœlom, but have lost it through degeneration.

Out of the many thousands

of species of roundworms we shall choose, for reasons that will
be obvious, two of the best known species: *Ascaris lumbricoides*
and *Trichinella spiralis*.

D. Ascaris Lumbricoides

Various species of the genus Ascaris are parasites in the intestines of mammals. *A. megalocephala* infests the horse, *A.
suiela* occurs in the pig, while *A. lumbricoides* lives in the intestines of man. Because of the bearing of the last species upon the
practice of medicine we shall confine our account to it alone.

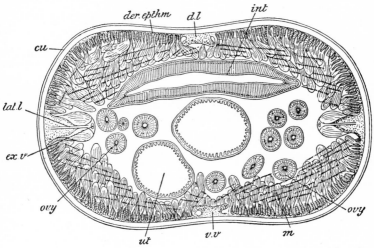

Fig. 120. Transverse section of *Ascaris lumbricoides*. *cu*, cuticle; *der.
epthm*, dermal epithelium; *d.l*, dorsal line; *ex.v*, excretory tube; *int*,
intestine; *lat.l*, lateral line; *m*, muscular layer; *ovy*, ovary; *ut*, uterus;
v.v, ventral line. (From Parker and Haswell.)

Ascaris lumbricoides (Fig. 119) is a slender worm, the females
of which are about 8 to 16 inches long and about one-fourth inch
in diameter. The male is much smaller. The mouth is at the
anterior end and has three liplike lobes, one median-dorsal and
two ventrolateral (Fig. 121, *b* and *c*). The anus is at the posterior
end and opens by a transverse slit bounded by lips. This opening is also the opening for the reproductive ducts.

The body wall (Fig. 120) consists of a delicate, transparent
cuticle (*cu*), a protoplasmic layer (*der. epthm*) containing scattered nuclei and fibers imbedded in a continuous substratum. This

is, of course, a SYNCYTIAL ECTODERM. The next layer is a single layer of very peculiar muscle cells, or fibers. The contractile part of each cell is spindleshaped, but from the side of each fiber comes off a sort of bladderlike enlargement with a nucleus extending into the false cœlom. The muscle layer is divided into four separate ribbons by means of four thickenings of the ectoderm known as DORSAL, VENTRAL, and LATERAL LINES.

a. The Digestive Organs.—These consist of the MOUTH, PHARYNX (or STOMODÆUM), the INTESTINE, the short RECTUM, and the ANUS. The food consists of the partially digested semifluid contents of the intestine of the human host, which is sucked up by the muscular movements of the pharynx.

There is a very distinct space, the FALSE CŒLOM, between the body wall and the intestine. The viscera lie very loosely in this, not slung by mesenteries or supported by septa.

b. Excretory System.—Two longitudinal canals comprise this system. They are separate posteriorly but unite anteriorly into

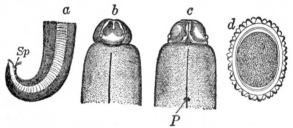

FIG. 121. Parts of *Ascaris lumbricoides. a,* hind part of male with two penial setæ (*Sp*); *b,* anterior end from dorsal side showing dorsal lip and two papillæ; *c,* same from ventral side showing two lateral ventral lips; *d,* egg with external membrane; *P,* excretory pore. (From Sedgwick.)

a single short canal that opens on the ventral side near the mouth by a single opening (EXCRETORY PORE). This system differs from that of the flatworms in having no cilia or flame cells.

c. Nervous System.—The nervous system consists of a flat nervous ring about the pharynx from which there are six branches forward and six branches backward. Two backward branches, one dorsal and one ventral, are larger than the others and run from end to end of the worm, being connected at intervals by transverse commissures.

d. The Reproductive Organs.—In the males (Fig. 121), the TESTIS is a long, coiled tube, about the diameter of fine sewing

thread. This passes into the vas deferens which in turn en-
larges into a distended seminal vesicle. This opens into the
rectum near the anus. Near this opening are paired muscular
sacs, containing penial setæ, organs of copulation. In the
females (Fig. 119), the ovaries are paired, each ovary being long
and coiled and passing into a long enlarged duct, the uterus.
The two uteri unite into a short muscular vagina, that opens on
the ventral side about one-third way back from the head.

The eggs are fertilized in the uterus of the worm in enormous
numbers. Each egg becomes coated with a layer of chitin (Fig.

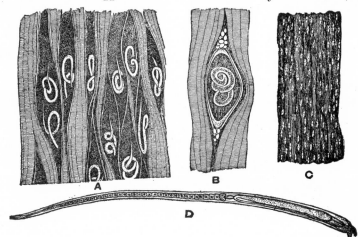

Fig. 122. *Trichinella.* **A,** larvæ among muscle fibers, not yet encysted; **B,**
a single larva encysted; **C,** piece of pork natural size containing many
encysted worms; **D,** adult, much enlarged. (After Leuckart.)

121, *d*), which prevents it from being injured by the digestive
fluids of the host and allows it to pass unharmed out of the
body with the fæces. It is transmitted directly to other hosts by
means of contaminated drinking water or through soil adhering
to food. The eggs hatch in the intestine of the new host, and
there the worms grow to a large size at the expense of the host.
A person infested with a considerable number of Ascaris is likely
to exhibit extreme emaciation, which may end in death.

E. Trichinella Spiralis

Trichinella is one of the most dreaded of human parasites. It
is responsible for the terrible disease, trichinosis, which is so often

fatal. The worms are very tiny, hardly more than an eighth of an inch long in the female (Fig. 122, B) and much smaller in the male (Fig. 122, D). In the adult condition this worm lives in the intestinal canal of man, the pig, and other mammals. The adult females, which give birth to living young, burrow out through the wall of the intestine and enter various lymphatic vessels, where they release their broods of young. Thousands of these become distributed passively about the body in lymph and blood. When they reach their favorite region, the voluntary muscles, they burrow in, each minute worm penetrating a single muscle fiber, where it coils up (Fig. 122, A). The irritation causes the muscle fiber to degenerate and form a cyst about the coiled up worm larva. The host then shows various severe morbid symptoms upon which we need not dwell. In severe cases there may be as many as 100,000,000 encysted worms in a single subject.

F. Other Roundworm Parasites in Man

Among many other roundworms that are of economic importance because they are the cause of human disease and suffering, are *Filaria bancrofti*, which produces the disease ELEPHANTIASIS, and *Necator americanus*, the cause of the disease called HOOKWORM, that has affected millions of human beings and has caused the death of many and a markedly lowered efficiency in all who are afflicted with it.

Research in connection with various educational institutions and medical organizations has served to reveal the life histories of these pests and has shown us how the disease may be wiped out. Much good has been done already and we have every reason to hope that at no very distant time man will free himself from these enemies within his body.

CHAPTER XXV

THE STARFISH

(PHYLUM ECHINODERMATA)

A. STATUS OF THE PHYLUM ECHINODERMATA

THIS phylum is at present, and has been since early Palæozoic times, a successful group. There exists a high degree of diversity of form, habit, and habitat among the echinoderms, and they are very abundant and widespread. From the first they have been exclusively marine forms of moderate size. They are most strikingly distinguished from most other groups of animals by their star-shaped, or radiate, body form, a condition especially plainly seen in the starfishes, brittle stars, and crinoids, but less obvious in the sea urchins and sea cucumbers.

The radial symmetry of the starfish and its relatives is not in any true sense equivalent to the radial symmetry of the Cœlenterates, but is merely a secondary distortion of bilateral symmetry, as is shown in a subsequent section of the present chapter.

The adults, largely on account of their secondarily developed radial form, bear scarcely any resemblance to any other animals. Hence the group seems to stand apart as though unrelated to any other phylum. Their embryonic and larval history, however, bears many fundamental resemblances to that of some of the lower members of the phylum Chordata, notably Balanoglossus and its relatives.

The echinoderms and the lower chordates are similar in the following respects:—They are characteristically indeterminate in cleavage; the mesoderm is derived from a proliferation of cells around the lip of the blastopore; the cœlom is derived from paired out pouchings of the archenteron; the blastopore remains the functional anus and a new mouth is established secondarily near the anterior end of the archenteron; and the larvæ of some of the echinoderms and those of some of the chordates are extremely similar.

It is because of these fundamental homologies that some leading zoölogists feel justified in placing the echinoderms and the chordates together in the same main branch of the diphyletic tree. This is also why in this book the echinoderms are placed next to the chordates.

B. GENERAL MORPHOLOGY OF THE STARFISH

1. *External Characters*

The visitor to the seashore finds the starfishes among the most interesting of the novelties encountered. They are found in considerable numbers along nearly all of the world's seacoasts, being especially abundant wherever the coast is rocky; for starfishes are fond of rocky bottoms.

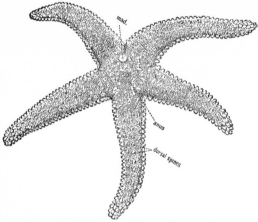

Two main divisions of the body are to be distinguished, the CENTRAL DISK and the ARMS, or RAYS, which are usually five in number (species with six, seven, or even twenty or more rays are known).

FIG. 123. The starfish, *Asterias rubens*, seen from the aboral surface. *mad*, madreporite. (From the Cambridge Natural History.)

Starfishes are usually seen with the mouth side (ORAL, or ACTINAL SURFACE) in contact with the substratum, and the anal side (ABORAL, or ABACTINAL SURFACE) chiefly in view.

The ABORAL SURFACE (Fig. 123) has a spiny or rugose appearance, owing to the presence of numerous SPINES, BRANCHIAL PAPILLÆ, and PEDICELLARIÆ. On the central disk and situated near the angle made by two of the rays is a porous plate, the MADREPORIC PLATE, which acts as a filter for the water-vascular system.

The ORAL SURFACE (Fig. 124) is quite different in appearance. The mouth is situated at its center and is surrounded by a soft membrane, the PERISTOME. Running from the mouth out to the ends of the five arms are the AMBULACRAL GROOVES, so called because they are largely filled with tube feet, the chief locomotor organs of the group.

2. *The Skeleton*

The skeleton of the starfish, unlike that of most animals with an external armor, is developed in the dermis, or deeper skin, and

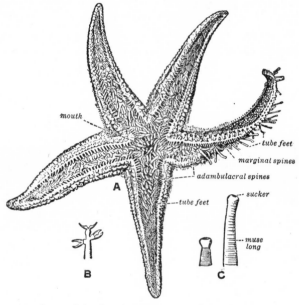

FIG. 124. **A,** the starfish, *Asterias rubens*, seen from the oral surface; **B,** an adambulacral spine, showing three straight pedicellariæ; **C,** a tube foot expanded and contracted. (From the Cambridge Natural History.)

is covered over by a thin EPIDERMIS, or outer skin. It is composed of numerous small calcareous plates bound together by means of connective tissue so as to form an intricate basketwork. The spines are quite short as compared with those of the sea urchins (distant cousins of the starfishes); and often they have rounded or knobbed ends.

Around the bases of the spines there are numerous tiny modified spines, called PEDICELLARIÆ, that have a structure and mechanical operation like pliers or pinchers (Fig. 124, B). These little organs function in a variety of ways, their chief duties being to protect the delicate branchial papillæ from being browsed upon by small carnivorous crustaceans and the like, to aid in the capture of food, and to keep the delicate skin free from dirt and débris. Each pedicellaria is an automatic weapon of offense or defense and is set into action by definite stimuli. When, for example, a small crustacean walks over the surface of the starfish, its legs come in contact with several groups of pedicellariæ. These reach forth their snapping pinchers and many of them succeed in grasping hairs on the invader's appendages. If a struggle ensues, many more pedicellariæ come to the rescue until the struggle ceases because the captive is held rigid by myriads of tiny clamps, for once they have closed upon their prey they are like bulldogs for tenacity. When all struggle ceases, the pedicellariæ release their holds and the tubefeet take over the duty of seizing and passing the prospective luncheon from hand to hand, or rather from foot to foot, over the edge and down to the mouth.

While the skeleton renders the starfish rather stiff and unyielding to the touch, it is not entirely rigid. In fact, numerous muscles which are attached to the inner surfaces of the plates are capable of moving the whole body, or any part of it, slowly and deliberately into any position demanded by the exigencies of life.

3. *Internal Organization*

a. The Cœlom.—If one cuts through the skeleton, he will note that the internal organs (viscera) lie rather loosely in a capacious body cavity, the cœlom. This large cavity is lined with a smooth PERITONEAL MEMBRANE and is filled with CŒLOMIC FLUID, which, except for a small quantity of suspended albuminous matter, has about the consistency and chemical content of sea water. The cœlomic fluid plays the rôle of blood, for there is no true system of blood vessels. Oxygen is taken into the blood and carbon dioxide eliminated into the sea water through the thin walls of the BRANCHIAL PAPILLÆ, which consist of fine processes of the cœlom thrust through the interstices of the skeleton and protruding on the outside. Certain AMŒBOID CELLS, which appear to function quite like the leucocytes, or white blood cells, of our own blood, are rather abundant in the cœlomic fluid. Their duty seems to be that of ingesting and digesting waste matters that cannot be eliminated in liquid form. When old or exhausted, these cœlomic corpuscles work their way through the thin walls of the branchial papillæ and undergo dissolution in the sea water.

b. Water-vascular System.—This important and unique system (Fig. 125) takes its origin from one of the larval cœlomic cavities known as the HYDROCŒLE, and differentiates into an extremely intricate system of water tubes and sacs, the like of which is not found anywhere else in the animal kingdom. Water from the sea enters this system through a stony sieve, the MADREPORIC PLATE; it passes through a pressure tube with stone lined walls (the STONE CANAL) to a ringlike tube around the mouth (the CIRCUMORAL CANAL), which in turn gives off the five RADIAL CANALS, one to each arm, and is provided with bulbs (POLIAN VESICLES) which lie between the radial canals and doubtless act as pumps to force the water out into the canals. Each radial canal is

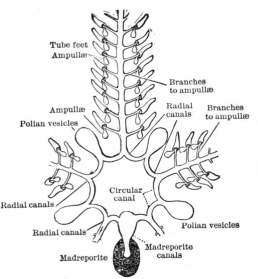

FIG. 125. Water-vascular system of a starfish. (From Parker and Haswell, after Gegenbaur.)

provided with numerous short, lateral branches that occur in pairs and terminate each in a TUBE FOOT with its AMPULLA, a sort of syringelike bulb. Sea water is taken into the water-vascular system by means of pressure created by the inward beat of the cilia lining the water canals.

A large part of the cœlom is filled with the much folded STOMACH and the large HEPATIC CÆCA, or liver glands. Also, during the breeding season the gonads (OVARIES and TESTES) become voluminous and occupy most of the otherwise open space of the cavity.

C. ACTIVITIES OF THE STARFISH

Locomotion.—The main efforts of the starfish, like those of so many other animals, are concerned with the search for and the capture of food. In moving about, the tube feet (Fig. 124, C) and the arm musculature together constitute the locomotor mechanism. The operation of the tube foot is simple: it is extended partly by contraction of its circular muscles and partly by the pressure exerted by the contracting muscular bulb, the ampulla. The flat end of the tube foot is pressed so firmly against some smooth surface that it acts like a vacuum cup and adheres tenaciously. Then, through the contraction of the longitudinal muscles, the tube foot shortens and in doing so exerts a pull. The combined pull of many coördinated tube feet serves to drag the body of the animal in whatever direction the tube feet may determine. Thus the feet operate the animal, not the animal the feet.

Food and Feeding Habits.—The food of the starfish consists mainly of oysters, clams, mussels, fish, crabs, and barnacles. When a starfish finds a suitable mussel, it proceeds, according to **MacBride,** in the following way:—

"Their mode of seizing their prey is very curious. If they are attacking a bivalve, they bend all their arms down around it, thus

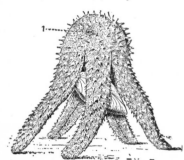

arching up the central portion of the body (Fig. 126). The stomach is pushed out—this being rendered possible by the turning inside out of its edges, which are loose and baggy— and wrapped round the fated mollusk. The pushing out is effected by the contraction of some muscle fibers in the body wall: these tend to diminish the space which the cœlom occupies, and as this is filled with incompressible fluid, the

Fig. 126. View of starfish (*Echinaster*) devouring a mussel. *1*, madreporite. (From the Cambridge Natural History.)

stomach must be pressed out. After some time has elapsed the starfish relaxes its hold and it is then seen that the shell of the mollusk is completely empty and as clean as if it had been scraped with a knife. It was long a puzzle how the starfish succeeded in forcing its victim to relax its muscles and allow its valves to open. It was supposed that the stomach secreted a paralyzing poison, but it has been conclusively proved that this is not the case, but that the starfish drags the valves of its victim apart by main force, often actually breaking the adductor muscles. The pull exercised by the suckers is not nearly strong enough to open the valves at once, but the starfish has staying power and eventually the mussel is slowly forced open." The secret of the unusual endurance of the starfish is that its tube feet work in relays, some resting while the others work. This the mussel cannot do, for it has only one set of adductor muscles and these in the course of time become fatigued and relax. The shell once open, the abundant digestive juices of the hepatic cæcæ pour out upon the soft flesh and complete digestion takes place.

The Starfish a Brainless Automaton.—It may seem strange to speak of any animal so highly organized as a starfish as brainless, but the statement is literally true. The starfish, in fact, has no head, for the true head—the preoral lobe of the larva—is entirely lost in the process of metamorphosis and a new mouth breaks through into the side of the stomach. Morphologically, then, the starfish is a creature consisting of the posterior end of an organism. One would not expect much of a brain in an animal so constituted. The nearest approach to a central nervous system consists of a slender NERVE RING around the mouth. This ring gives off five RADIAL NERVE CORDS, one above each ambulacral groove. There is nothing equivalent to a central ganglionic mass, but many small ganglia are present, especially throughout the skin, and are associated with the activities of tube feet, pedicellariæ, branchiæ, and body muscles. Each of these organs is at least semiautomatic, each being provided with its own nerve cell or ganglion. The chief sense organs are the pads of the tube feet, the delicate branchiæ, and the five EYE SPOTS, one at the tip of each arm. At best, the nerve ring and the five radial nerve bands act as coördinating organs, bringing some harmony of action out of a multiplicity of minor activities. In last analysis, however, it appears that the starfish is managed by its numerous movable parts. Speaking of the sea urchin, whose mental status is equivalent to that of the starfish, *Von Uexkull* explains in picturesque fashion the difference between the activities of an animal with a brain and one without: "In a dog," he says, "the animal moves the legs: in a sea-urchin the legs move the animal."

The Question of Intelligence.—After accusing the starfish of being a brainless automaton, the question naturally arises as to whether or not the animal shows any symptoms of having intelligence. Several investigators have interested themselves in this problem. *Professor Jennings,* for example, endeavored to teach the California starfish some new tricks, with what success we shall presently relate. Each starfish has its own individuality, for no two of them behave just alike when they are turned upside down and have to right themselves. One uses a given pair of arms to roll over upon; another uses quite a different combination. A chosen individual is first allowed a number of 'trials in order that he may demonstrate his peculiar habitual method of righting himself. Then the experiment begins. The animal is turned over, and when it attempts to right itself in the preferred way, it is prevented from so doing by detaching the tube feet as fast as they reach out to gain a foothold. Only when it resorts to the use of an unfamiliar method is it allowed to proceed. After a considerable number of trials, it is then allowed to right itself several times without interference. According to Jennings, the animal has learned its lesson, for it now uses the new method in preference to the old for a number of trials, although in a few days it goes back to its original preference. The experiment seems to show that the animal has the elements of memory and a slight degree of ability to learn or to profit by experience; but various critics point out that the experiment is far from conclusive, for the constant loosening of the feet by means of a glass rod merely injures these organs for a short time so that they are not so strong or so active as the tube feet of other arms. The question of the intelligence of the starfish and its kin is still unsettled and probably will remain so until the experts can agree upon a definition of what constitutes intelligence.

D. The Development and Metamorphosis of the Starfish

The early development is quite like that of several other groups of invertebrates. Cleavage ends in the production of a typical hollow BLASTULA (Fig. 127, 1) which is capable of swimming about by means of its cilia. This blastula is a larva, for it is capable of leading an independent life, though as yet it has no mouth and therefore cannot feed. The gastrula stage is attained by means of an inturning or invagination of the cells at the lower or vegetal pole of the blastula (Fig. 127, 2). These cells extend up into the BLASTOCŒLE, or hollow of the blastula, as a cylindrical tube with an opening to the outside (the BLASTOPORE) and a blind end directed toward the apical end of the larva. This inner layer of cells is known as the ARCHENTERON, or primitive intestine. The GAS-

TRULA larva (Fig. 127, 3) now elongates; the blind end of the archenteron expands into a thin walled vesicle, one part of which

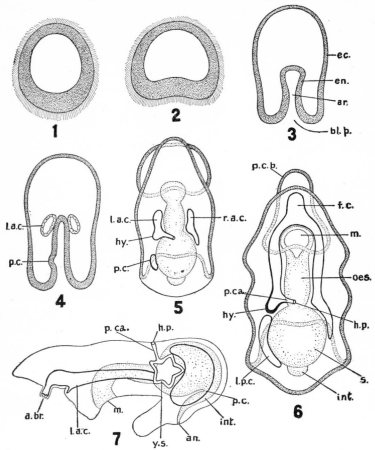

FIG. 127.   Stages in the development of the starfish, *Patiria miniata* showing especially the changes from the bilaterally symmetrical larva to the radially symmetrical adult. **1,** blastula; **2,** early gastrula; **3,** late gastrula; **4,** early bilaterally symmetrical Bipennaria larva; **5,** first appearance of asymmetry, hydropore and water pore appearing on the left side; **6,** late Bipennaria larva; **7,** Brachiolaria larva showing radial symmetry established by the fanning out into radial order of the radial branches of the hydrocœle. (Original.)

grows toward the ventral surface and fuses with an ingrowth of the ectoderm (STOMODÆUM) to form the mouth, the blastopore being the larval anus. The remaining parts of the thin walled vesicle just referred to spread out laterally to form the paired right and left COELOMIC POUCHES. Up to this stage the larva (Fig. 127, 4) is strictly bilaterally symmetrical, but soon there appear signs of asymmetry, or inequality between the two sides. The left coelom grows much more rapidly than the right and sends to the surface a tube, called the PORE CANAL, destined to become the stone canal of the adult. Subsequently this left coelom gives off a lateral pouch known as the HYDROCOELE (Fig. 127, 5 and 6). This body

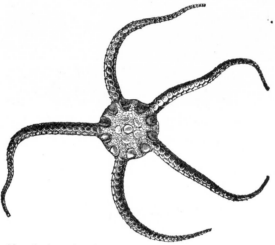

FIG. 128.   Aboral view of *Ophioglypha bullata,* a brittle star.   (From Shipley and MacBride, after Thompson.)

lies on the left side of the larval stomach and has typically no counterpart on the right side. From the hydrocoele there are given off the five radial canals, which are at first serially arranged but soon undergo a twisting that results in the formation of the water ring and the radiating arrangement of the water-vascular system (Fig. 127, 7). It is this series of changes that determines the adult symmetry of the starfish, for all the other organs come to group themselves about the hydrocoele and the radial canals. A new mouth forms on the side of the stomach in the middle of the water ring; a new anus forms on the opposite side; and an entirely new axis and a new symmetry are thus attained.

E. RELATIVES OF THE STARFISH

· The Phylum Echinodermata is made up of five living and several extinct classes. The living classes are:—

CLASS I. ASTEROIDEA—the starfishes, of which there is a great variety.

CLASS II. OPHIUROIDEA—the brittle stars (Fig. 128), basket stars, serpent stars. These are characterized by having a set of five simple or branched arms that are well supplied with muscles and are used for locomotor purposes much after the fashion of oars. These arms are sharply separated from the central disk

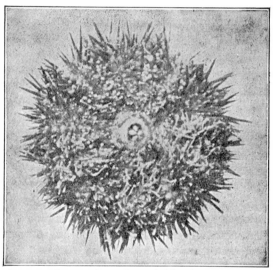

FIG. 129. A sea urchin, seen from the oral side, showing mouth and teeth of the Aristotle's lantern projecting from it. (From Clark.)

and contain no portions of the cœlom except the radial water canals. In contrast with the Echinoidea, the aboral surface is much more highly developed than the oral, so that the true oral surface of the central disk is practically wanting. The animals are chiefly mud feeders.

CLASS III. ECHINOIDEA—the sea urchins (Fig. 129), heart urchins, and sand dollars. These echinoderms differ from the two previous classes in having the aboral surface reduced to a mere vestige, so that the ambulacral rays run nearly all the way from the mouth to the anus like meridians around a globe. Hence the tube feet are present on both lower and upper surfaces. All of the structures typical of the aboral surface are aggregated in a small area around the anus. There we find the madreporic plate, the genital openings, and the optic plates, the homologues of which are found in the starfish at the tips of the arms. The skeleton is a closely knit system of tilelike plates perforated by numerous holes for the tube feet. There is a highly specialized masticatory apparatus, the ARISTOTLE'S LANTERN, named after its first describer. The whole body surface, with the exception of the soft peristome around the mouth, is covered with spines,

FIG. 130.   A sea cucumber, seen from the side showing the specialized tube feet used as tentacles. (From Clark.)

usually long and hollow, with ball-and-socket joints, and provided with muscles by means of which they may be moved about. These spines, in many species, are the chief organs of locomotion, and are used after the manner of stilts. The food of the sea urchins is chiefly seaweed, which they grind up in their food mills. There are many varieties of pedicellariæ, which are used for various purposes, some of them being provided with poison fangs.

CLASS IV. HOLOTHUROIDEA—sea cucumbers (Fig. 130).   These are like the Echinoidea in having the aboral surface reduced to a rudiment or entirely lacking, but unlike them in that they have merest vestiges of a skeleton composed of microscopic plates embedded in the skin. As a rule, they live in the mud and move about in wormlike fashion by means of the highly developed muscular equipment of the body wall. Primarily, they are mud feeders, but, incidentally, they pick up a good many small mud dwelling organisms. When strongly irritated, they have the habit of eviscerating themselves, shooting out their internal organs through rupture of the body wall. This is not so serious a measure as it might seem, for they have the power of regenerating all lost parts quite readily.

CLASS V. CRINOIDEA—sea lilies, stone lilies (Fig. 131). In contrast with all other present-day echinoderms, these flowerlike forms are typically sessile, being fastened to the bottom by means of a jointed stony stalk attached to the aboral surface. Thus the oral surface is turned upward. A few species of modern

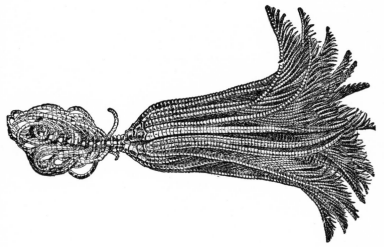

FIG. 131. A crinoid, *Pentacrinus maclearanus*, seen from the side. The arms are to the right and the stem and holdfasts to the left. (From the Cambridge Natural History.)

crinoids break free from the stalk, after passing a sessile larval period, and lead a free-swimming adult life. The skeleton is exceptionally heavy and massive, giving the impression of being carved out of stone. Crinoids feed by catching minute organisms in their ciliated ambulacral grooves and passing them down to the mouth. The group is an extremely ancient one, and their fossil remains constitute one of the commonest types found in the oldest fossil bearing strata.

PART III

THE FROG (A TYPICAL VERTEBRATE)

7/15/32

CHAPTER XXVI

THE FROG: ACTIVITIES AND GENERAL MORPHOLOGY

THE frog is used extensively the world over as a laboratory animal. The reasons for its popularity are not far to seek. Frogs are of very wide occurrence; they are of convenient size; they are easily kept alive for long periods; they stand near the middle of the vertebrate series, exhibiting both aquatic and terrestrial adaptations; their eggs are easily obtained and their embryology easily studied; and, finally, it has come to be a time honored custom to use the frog either as an introductory type or to place it at the end of an evolutionary series and to make it the object of intensive study. In one large university with which the writer was connected there was a so-called "Frog Course," which occupied the second semester of the first year course in Zoölogy. This section of the present text, dealing as it does more or less intensively with the frog, is so designed that it will be found equally available as an introduction to the study of animal types or as the last one of a series of animals representing various levels of increasing complexity of organization.

A. THE FROG'S PLACE IN NATURE

Frogs belong to the PHYLUM CHORDATA and the SUBPHYLUM CRANIATA (VERTEBRATES). There are seven classes of Vertebrates:—

CLASS 1, CYCLOSTOMATA—lampreys and hag fishes,
CLASS 2, ELASMOBRANCHII—sharks and skates,
CLASS 3, PISCES—true fishes,
CLASS 4, AMPHIBIA—newts, salamanders, and frogs,
CLASS 5, REPTILIA—lizards, snakes, turtles, alligators,
CLASS 6, AVES—birds,
CLASS 7, MAMMALIA—mammals (beasts, quadrupeds).

According to this classification, there are three thoroughly aquatic classes, three thoroughly terrestrial classes, and one amphibious class, neither fully aquatic nor fully terrestrial, the Amphibia. The Amphibia constitute a sort of transitional group, some of which are aquatic through life, though having lungs as well as gills; others are thoroughly aquatic during their embryonic and larval periods, but are more or less terrestrial in the adult stages. The frog belongs to the latter category.

The CLASS AMPHIBIA, so far as living types are concerned, is divided into three orders:—

ORDER 1, APODA—characterized by the lack of both legs and tail during the adult period. Example, cæcilians or blind worms.

ORDER 2, URODELA—characterized by the possession of both legs and tail during the adult period. Example, salamanders.

ORDER 3, ANURA—characterized by the possession of legs and by the lack of a tail during the adult period. Example, frogs.

The ORDER ANURA is divided into two suborders:—

SUBORDER 1, AGLOSSA—characterized by the absence of a tongue. This is a small group represented by the Surinam Toad (*Pipa americana*). (See Fig. 168.)

SUBORDER 2, PHANEROGLOSSA—characterized by the presence of a tongue. This group contains nearly all of the frogs and toads.

Most of the common frogs belong to the FAMILY RANIDÆ and to the genus RANA.

B. ACTIVITIES OF THE FROG

1. *Habitat*

Most of the true frogs of the genus Rana are aquatic or at least semiaquatic. One expects to find them either actually in the water, as is the case with the bullfrog (*Rana catesbiana*), or else along the shores of streams, ponds, or lakes, as in the case of the grass frog or leopard frog (*Rana pipiens*). Here they occupy a strategic position, being able to jump into the water to escape enemies on land or to climb out of water and hop away to escape aquatic enemies. Most of what we shall have to say in this section will have reference especially to *Rana pipiens*, the commonest of all North American frogs.

2. *Feeding Habits*

Frogs are carnivorous. Their favorite food consists of insects, worms, small fishes, and the young of their own or allied species.

Earthworms seem to be especially relished by frogs, a liking shared by many other animals. Frogs are greedy feeders and are not very choice in their selection of food. Like many other animals, when food is plentiful, they stuff until they can hold no more. In catching insects or other swift moving prey the frog uses its tongue in a surprisingly facile manner. The tongue is hinged at the front of the lower jaw and may be suddenly flipped out so as to bat down a fly. A sticky secretion on the end of the tongue enables the latter to hold small insects till they can be flipped back into the mouth (Fig. 132). The tongue is shot out by means of a curious mechanism: a large lymph sac beneath the tongue fills suddenly, lifting and throwing forward the free end of the tongue. Contraction of the lingual muscles flips it back into the mouth.

3. *Jumping and Swimming*

The frog is an athlete of considerable versatility: an expert broad jumper and an exceptional swimmer and diver. His chief assets in both terrestrial and aquatic locomotion are his highly developed hind legs. When resting on land, the hind legs are always flexed in readiness to jump, the forelegs acting merely to support the front end of the body and to change the direction of the leap. In swimming, both hind legs are folded forward into the shape of a Z and then straightened, the great webbed foot being shoved broadside on against the water. This is not at all like the so-called "frog stroke" used by human swimmers; for in that stroke the propulsion is secured by forcing the water backward between the thighs. The forelegs of the frog are of little use in swimming, being mainly used for guiding purposes. In diving, we distinguish two quite different operations. The first is a leap from the land into the water, a headfirst plunge executed with much neatness; the second is a vigorous swim to the bottom. Usually when jumping from the shore, the frog, even before reaching the bottom, makes a quick shoreward turn and buries himself in the mud. When the frog is resting on the surface, diving is a more compli-

F I G. 1 3 2. T h r e e stages of the movement of the tongue of a frog, *Rana esculenta*. (From the Cambridge Natural History.)

cated operation. The first step is a sudden withdrawal from the surface, accomplished by a quick forward stroke of the hind legs. The second step, as before, consists of a swim to the bottom. Frogs rest in the water by floating. The position when floating is one in which the legs are fully extended, while the nostrils and eyes are the only parts of the body above the surface. One sees here the advantage of having the eyes set high on top of the head. The extended position of the hind legs is one that spells readiness for quick withdrawal from the surface, when a fraction of a second may mean either safety or peril.

4. *How the Frog Croaks*

Some writers have attempted to spell out the syllables of the frog's spoken language, but with indifferent success. The most feasible spelling seems to be "au-au-au-auk," but even this bears not the slightest resemblance to what the frog actually says. Most people know what he says, though they are unable to spell it. The males are the chief croakers and seem to be proud of their superiority in this respect, especially during the breeding season, when the voice of the male seems to charm and captivate the female. The vocal organ of the frog consists of vocal cords. Air is forced out of the lungs over the cords into the mouth. The sound is amplified by means of vocal sacs, which are inflated portions of the mouth and pharynx. Both nostrils and mouth are kept closed so that the buccal cavity is distended. This then contracts and forces the air back over the cords into the lungs. Thus a series of croaks may be made without taking breath; and hence the frog can croak under water. The vocabulary of the frog, though limited, is sufficiently varied to express the ordinary gamut of emotions: a low grunt indicating contentment, a sharp cry or scream when in pain or peril, and various modulated croakings when engaged in courtship.

5. *Why the Frog Swells Up*

We have all heard the fable of the frog who tried to inflate himself so as to rival the ox in size. While not being able to vouch for the motive thus imputed, we do know that there are times when the frog finds it advantageous to make a balloon of himself. When seized by a snake or other enemy, he fills himself with air and thus becomes round and slippery, a difficult object to swallow.

6. *Enemies of the Frog*

Apart from their agility both on land and in the water, and their excellent protective coloration, frogs are almost entirely defenseless and fall an easy prey to many predaceous animals. Perhaps their worst enemy is man, who desires the hind legs for food and uses millions of specimens a year for laboratory purposes. Other frog eaters are snakes, herons and their kind, crows, skunks, water rats, and turtles. Various species of water bugs and leeches catch tadpoles and suck their blood. Beside this type of enemy, the frog has numerous parasites. Various species of nematodes or roundworms infest the lungs and other organs. Flukes of several kinds are inhabitants of intestines, lungs, and bladder. Protozoan parasites, chiefly belonging to the Class Sporozoa, are numerous. Especially noteworthy is the parasitic ciliate, *Opalina*, found in the frog's intestine. With all of these enemies, outside and inside, it seems a wonder that the poor frog survives at all. It is only its ability to reproduce immense numbers of offspring that saves the race from extinction, for only one in hundreds survives to adult life.

7. *Seasonal Changes*

In early SUMMER the frog is thin and hungry and spends most of his time feeding. When fat and satiated, he retires to sheltered places, spending the midsummer season in what has been called somewhat erroneously the "summer sleep"; for it is only a period of relative inactivity and easy living. In the AUTUMN of the year the frog is fat and well nourished, with much reserve food for the hard winter. Besides accumulations of fat, much reserve food is stored in the liver, in muscles, and elsewhere. In the late fall frogs go into WINTER quarters. There they hibernate. In doing so they retire below the frost line at the bottom of ponds or streams, bury themselves in the mud and remain dormant till the spring, carrying on the various functions only at their lowest possible levels. There is so little metabolic activity that oxygen enough is obtained through the mud covered skin to satisfy all requirements. The reserve food supply is used up partly for fuel to keep the spark of life smoldering and partly for elaborating the sexual products, which grow during the winter at the expense of other tissues. In the SPRING, when the frog first wakes up from the winter sleep, the most active tissues of the body are the reproductive organs, and these control the activities until their demands are satisfied. Even hunger must await its turn for satisfaction.   The breeding habits demand separate consideration.

8. *Breeding Habits*

The male frog has an uncontrollable obsession to clasp something, preferably a female frog, with its forelegs.   Once the arms are clasped about the female's body, thumbs locked together, the male is very difficult to dislodge.   He is in a sort of trance.   Even cutting him in two seems to have little effect on him, for he will continue to clasp until loss of blood weakens him and his grip is loosened.   The value of this reflex on the part of the male is that it insures fertilization of the eggs; for eggs are laid only after the male has clasped the female for some days.   When the female is ready to extrude the eggs, the pair sink together to the bottom. As the eggs emerge from the genital opening, the male discharges spermatic fluid over them, and fertilization takes place in a very high percentage of the eggs.   After the entire batch of eggs is laid and forms a gelatinous mass, the male loosens his clasp, and from then on for the rest of the summer is totally indifferent to females. Sometimes, however, a female, after laying her first batch of eggs, may be clasped by a second male, in which event she is likely to bring to maturity and lay a second batch of eggs.   The development of the frog is to be dealt with in detail in a subsequent chapter.

9. *Hypnosis*

One may readily hypnotize a frog.   If seized in the hands and held gently but firmly on its back till it ceases to struggle, it will usually remain motionless for some time.   The position taken by the limbs during hypnosis is said by **Verworn** to be equivalent to that assumed by a frog performing righting movements—movements normally performed when the animal is inverted.   The muscles are believed to be in a state of tonic contraction.   The heartbeat and breathing movements, at first more rapid than normal, soon settle down to a rhythm much slower than normal. Any sudden stimulus serves to awaken the frog from the state of hypnosis; while absolute quiet and lack of visual and tactual stimulation may induce a very protracted hypnosis, lasting for hours.

Now that we have introduced the frog as a living organism operating as a unit, we may profitably turn our attention to the details of the organic machine.

C. The Frog as a Chordate

Anyone would adjudge the frog a considerably more advanced organism than an earthworm; yet there are several important features of organization common to the two groups, Chordata and Annelida:—

(a) They are both METAMERIC.

(b) They are both CŒLOMATE.

(c) They both exhibit the same general plan of organization, having a PRIMARY AXIS (axis of polarity, or anteroposterior axis), a DORSOVENTRAL AXIS, AND BILATERAL SYMMETRY.

All of these features express themselves in a more advanced form in the vertebrates than in the annelids.

a. Metamerism.—In the frog metamerism has become greatly modified. Externally, the ringed or segmental structure is almost indistinguishable. Only in some of the more primitive relatives of the frog is external segmentation visible, and then only because the body musculature, which has retained much of its primitive segmental character, shows through the skin. Internally, the adult exhibits but few signs of metamerism. The vertebral column, the spinal nerves, the ribs, are obviously metameric; but most of the organs have lost their metameric arrangements.

b. The Cœlom.—In this part there is no trace of the original segmental arrangement. In the adult it consists of one large cavity inclosing the viscera. Septa, such as those seen in the earthworm, are entirely absent.

c. The Primary Axis.—Considerable alteration by an increase in the size and complexity and dominance of the head marks the primary axis. This process is generally spoken of as CEPHALIZATION. We can usually distinguish three regions of the primary axis —head, trunk, and tail; and these three regions appear to be independently modifiable, so that one may increase or decrease out of proportion to the others, giving rise to large-headed tail-less types and small-headed long-tailed types, etc.

D. Three Distinctive Characteristics of the Chordates

Chordates differ from all other animals in the possession of a notochord, pharyngeal clefts, and a medullary plate, groove, or tube.

a. The Notochord.—Typically an elastic rod, the notochord runs from the base of the brain to the end of the tail, lying dorsal to the alimentary tract and ventral to the nerve cord. In the majority of vertebrates the notochord is present only during embryonic and larval stages and is subsequently replaced by the VERTEBRAL COLUMN that grows up about it. A system of NEURAL ARCHES arises above the notochord, and these arch over, grow around, and ultimately surround the nerve cord.

b. Pharyngeal clefts.—These consist of a series of metameric perforations of the body wall and of the pharynx, forming passages from the latter to the exterior. Typically, the pharyngeal clefts are gill slits or branchial clefts in which lie gills, or BRANCHIÆ. The outside part of the branchial cleft is lined with ectoderm and may be provided with EXTERNAL GILLS; the inside part is lined with endoderm and may be provided with INTERNAL GILLS.

c. Dorsal Tubular Central Nervous System.—The neural tube (brain and spinal cord) is dorsal to the notochord and arises by longitudinal infolding from the ectoderm of the mid-dorsal region. The system is truly tubular, with a central canal, or NEUROCŒLE. These two features of the central nervous system sharply distinguish that of the vertebrates from those of the various invertebrates; for in the latter the nervous system is usually ventral in position and solid. The earliest embryonic condition of the vertebrate central nervous system is the MEDULLARY PLATE stage, a thickened dorsal plate of ectoderm. As development proceeds, the margins of the elongated plate rise up to form the medullary folds, with a sort of gutter or groove running lengthwise between them—the MEDULLARY GROOVE. The folds arch toward each other and gradually come together in the mid-dorsal line, fusing to form a tube—the MEDULLARY TUBE. The tube breaks away from the contiguous ectoderm, the latter closes together above, and the central nervous system thus becomes an internal one. Regional specialization of the walls of the neural tube give rise to the various specialized subdivisions of the brain. Paired cranial and spinal nerves grow out segmentally from it to all parts of the body.

We have described the three outstanding anatomical characteristics that serve to hold together the very heterogeneous group of animals constituting the Phylum Chordata. There are some additional characteristics that distinguish the Subphylum Craniata (Vertebrates).

E. Some Important Vertebrate Characteristics

There are some important respects in which the vertebrates differ from the other chordates: They have a CRANIUM, or skull; they have at least the beginnings of VERTEBRÆ; they have PAIRED LIMBS and LIMB GIRDLES (with the exception of the Cyclostomata); they have some sort of integumentary protective structures, such as SCALES, FEATHERS, HAIR (except Cyclostomata); they have HINGED JAWS developed from the first pair of GILL ARCHES (except Cyclostomata); they have three pairs of special sense organs, namely, the OLFACTORY, the OPTIC, and the AUDITORY, and these lie in capsules closely associated with the cranium.

The CYCLOSTOMATA are the lampreys and hag fishes, a group usually placed lowest among the vertebrates. They differ from the other vertebrates in so many important ways, however, that they seem to us to deserve separate subphylum value. Without the Cyclostomata, the rest of the vertebrates constitute a much more coherent group.

F. The Frog as an Amphibian

At the beginning of this chapter the classes of vertebrates were listed and the Class Amphibia was placed in a central position; for they are considered representative of the vertebrates as a whole. The principal characteristics of the Amphibia and the ways in which this class differ from other vertebrates follow:—

(1) The limbs are of the five fingered or hand type, characteristic of terrestrial as opposed to aquatic vertebrates.

(2) The heart has two auricles and one ventricle. It is three chambered, and in this way is transitional between the two chambered heart of the fishes and the four chambered heart of the birds and mammals.

(3) Functional gills are present at least during the larval period.

(4) The cranium is articulated with the ATLAS—the terminal vertebra of the neck—by means of two rounded pivots, the OCCIPITAL CONDYLES.

(5) There are no scales in modern Amphibia, except in the Apoda, where minute dermal scales are embedded in the skin.

(6) The teeth of modern Amphibia are small and inconspicuous.

(7) The eggs develop (with some exceptions) in water, and do not have an AMNION nor an ALLANTOIS, embryonic membranes of great importance in the embryonic life of terrestrial vertebrates.

CHAPTER XXVII

ANATOMY OF THE FROG

The following somewhat dry account of the anatomy of the frog may seem superfluous to those students who make a thorough laboratory study of this animal, but teachers demand the data here presented for review purposes and for other reasons.

A. Gross Anatomy

a. External Features.—The following structures are easily noted: (*a*) the paired nostrils, or EXTERNAL NARES; (*b*) the paired eyes with two eyelids, the upper almost immovable, the lower a transparent movable membrane capable of covering the eye; (*c*) the circular TYMPANIC MEMBRANES, or eardrums, just back of the eyes; (*d*) the opening of the CLOACA on the dorsal surface between the hind legs; (*e*) the two quite unequally developed pairs of limbs. The fore limb consists of UPPER ARM, FOREARM, WRIST, and HAND with but four DIGITS—the thumb being reduced to a tiny rudiment; the hind limb consists of THIGH, SHANK, and FOOT, with a long ANKLE region and five webbed digits, the shortest of which is the HALLUX, homologous with the human "great toe."

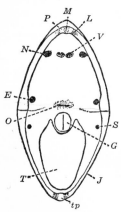

Fig. 133. Mouth of the frog widely opened. *E*, Eustachian tubes; *G*, glottis; *J*, lower jaw; *L*, lateral subrostral fossa; *M*, median subrostral fossa; *N*, posterior nares; *O*, œsophagus; *P*, pulvinar rostrale; *S*, opening of vocal sac; *T*, tongue; *V*, vomer, *tp*, tuberculum prelinguale. (From Holmes.)

b. Mouth Cavity.—A study of the mouth cavity shows a set of small teeth in the upper jaw, a set of VOMERINE TEETH in the roof of the mouth, INTERNAL NARES opening beside the latter, a pair of EUSTACHIAN TUBES near the angle of the jaws, the TONGUE hinged in front of the lower jaw, the GLOTTIS, or entrance to the lungs, and the GULLET (Fig. 133).

302

c. Body Wall.—The wall of the body is composed of the skin, body muscles, LYMPH SPACES, blood vessels, LIMB GIRDLES, and the PLEUROPERITONEUM, or lining of the body cavity. The skin is composed of a thin layer of SQUAMOUS EPITHELIUM on the outside (the EPIDERMIS) and a thicker internal layer (the DERMIS) composed of connective tissue, blood vessels, and glands. Near the surface one always sees parts of the INTERNAL SKELETON, especially the skull and the limb girdles. The lateral and ventral walls of the body are supported only by muscle layers. Several

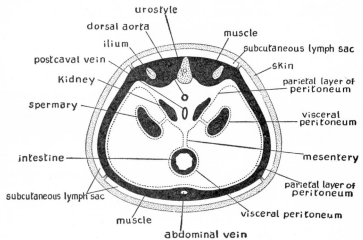

FIG. 134.   Diagram of a cross section of the body of a frog showing the course of the peritoneum by a dotted line. (Redrawn after Parker and Parker.)

layers of these muscles deserve special mention: the paired RECTUS EXTERNUS muscles on the sides, the RECTUS ABDOMINIS along the median ventral region, and the PECTORAL muscles covering the ventral side of the upper body region.

d. Cœlom and Mesenteries.—The cœlom, or body cavity, is the large space within the body wall that contains the VISCERA. The viscera consist of: the ALIMENTARY TRACT and its derivatives— lungs, liver, pancreas; the circulatory system, including the heart and the chief arteries and veins; the lymph vessels; the excretory and reproductive systems; the sympathetic nervous system and the branches of the central nervous system innervating the viscera. The PERITONEUM lines not only the body wall but is wrapped about all of the visceral organs. The whole peritoneum, however, remains a continuous sheet and extends from the body wall in the form of thin folds, the MESENTERIES, that serve to suspend and to protect the viscera. Each mesentery consists of a double layer, owing to the way in which the membrane enwraps the viscera. It is as though the wrapping of several articles were done by folding each up in a part of an elastic sheet, the edges of which were fastened to a wall. Each visceral organ thus comes to be wrapped in a sheet of tissue. The special sac of peritoneum loosely enwrapping the heart is known as the PERICARDIUM. The general relations of the body cavity and mesenteries are shown in the accompanying illustration (Fig. 134).

7/16/32

B. Special Anatomy

1. *The Skeletal System*

Most vertebrates have both an exoskeleton and an endoskeleton. The exoskeleton, sometimes known as the integument, appears in other animals in the form of scales, feathers, hair, bony plates, spines, but in the frog there is no superficial exoskeleton, the body being covered by a smooth, soft skin. Some of the ancestral integumentary elements, so-called dermal bones, have sunk beneath the surface and have become parts of the skull, limb girdles, and other parts of the internal skeleton.

The skeleton of the frog (Fig. 135) consists of an AXIAL SKELETON and an APPENDICULAR SKELETON, both made up of a complex of bones and cartilages. The axial skeleton consists of the SKULL, or CRANIUM, and the SPINAL COLUMN of vertebræ. The appendicular skeleton consists of the framework of the paired limbs and their supports, the PECTORAL and the PELVIC GIRDLES.

a. The Axial Skeleton.—The VERTEBRAL COLUMN comprises nine vertebræ and a long, slender posterior lobe, the UROSTYLE. Each vertebra is a complex bony ring (Fig. 135) surrounding a part of the spinal cord. The thickened ventral part is known as the CENTRUM; the dorsal projection is called the NEURAL SPINE; the lateral riblike processes are termed TRANSVERSE PROCESSES; the other processes are called ZYGOPOPHYSES.

The SKULL and the VISCERAL SKELETON are shown in the accompanying illustration (Fig. 136). According to a generally accepted theory, the upper and lower jaws, together with the hyoid and laryngeal cartilages, were originally branchial arches, whose main function was to support the gills. In the frog larva, or tadpole, there are six pairs of VISCERAL ARCHES, which in the course of development become profoundly modified from the original ancestral condition and are transformed into structures quite different in function. The first pair of these arches goes to form the framework of the upper and lower jaws, while the others either disappear entirely or are reduced to a relatively vestigial condition as HYOID and LARYNGEAL CARTILAGES.

The skull is at first entirely cartilaginous, and is known as the CHONDROCRANIUM. This might be characterized as a tough capsule surrounding the brain. The cartilaginous capsules of the olfactory and auditory organs become fused with the chondrocranium to form a more complex skull. The adult cranium is also reinforced by membrane, or dermal, bones. Meanwhile the original chondrocranium undergoes partial ossification, resulting in the formation or a definite complex of separate bones between which are sutures. In Figures 135 and 136 the bones of the skull are shown in such a way that the reader may readily distinguish the cartilage bones from the membrane bones, for the cartilage bones are stippled. The cartilage bones are:—SPHENETHMOIDS, EXOCCIPITALS, PROÖTICS, PTERYGOIDS, QUADRATES (still cartilaginous), and PALATINES. The membrane bones are:—NASALS, FRONTOPARIETALS, PREMAXILLARIES, MAXILLARIES, QUADRATOJUGALS, SQUAMOSALS, VOMERS, and PARASPHENOIDS. In the lower jaw there is one pair of cartilage bones, the MENTOMECKELIANS, not shown in the figures; and there are two pairs of membrane bones, the DENTARIES and the ANGULOSPLENIALS.

b. The Appendicular Skeleton (Fig. 135).—The fore and hind leg bones together with the PECTORAL and PELVIC GIRDLES comprise the appendicular skeleton. The PECTORAL GIRDLE consists of: a dorsal flat cartilage, the SUPRASCAPULA; a bone ventral to this, the SCAPULA, in which lies the cup-shaped socket into which fits the rounded head of the humerus; the CLAVICLE, or collar bone, making up the anterior, ventral part of the girdle; beneath the clavicle lies the PROCORACOID cartilage; and the CORACOID bone, forming the posterior, ventral part of the girdle. There is a chain of small bones and cartilages lying between the ventral ends of the pectoral girdle which constitute the STERNUM, or breastbone. To the pectoral girdle are attached the bones of the arms, or forelegs. The bone articulating ball-and-socket fashion with the

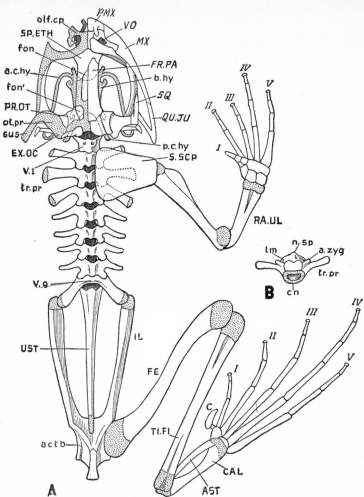

Fig. 135. A, skeleton of *Rana temporaria*. The left limbs, left shoulder girdle, and the membrane bones of the left side of the skull are removed. Cartilaginous parts dotted; names of cartilage bones in thick; those of membrane bones in italic capitals. *a.c.hy*, anterior cornu of hyoid; *actb*, acetabulum; AST, astragulus; *b.hy*, basi-hyal; C, calcar; CAL, calcaneum; EX.OC, exoccipital; *fon, fon'*, fontanelles; FR.PA, frontoparietals; HU, humerus; IL, ilium; MX, maxilla; *olf.cp*, olfactory capsule; *ot.pr*, otic process; *p.c.hy*, posterior cornu of hyoid; PMX, premaxilla; PR.OT, proötic; QU.JU, quadratojugal; RA.UL, radio-ulna; SP.ETH, sphenethmoid; *SQ*, squamosal; S.SCP, supra-scapula; *sus*, suspensorium; TI.FI, tibio-fibula; *tr.pr*, transverse process; UST, urostyle; V.1, cervical vertebra; V.9, sacral vertebra; *VO*, vomer; I-V, digits. B, the fourth vertebra seen from the front; *a.zyg*, anterior zygopophysis; *cn*, centrum; *lm*, lamina; *n.sp*, neural spine; *pd*, pedicle; *tr.pr*, transverse process. (Redrawn after Parker and Haswell.)

scapula is the HUMERUS. Next comes the composite RADIO-ULNA, made by the fusion of two separate bones, radius and ulna, that are separate in man and most other vertebrates. Then come the wrist (CARPAL) bones, of which there are six. Finally come the PHALANGES, or finger bones.

The PELVIC GIRDLE consists of a firmly united complex of three elements; the long ILIUM bones, articulating with the transverse

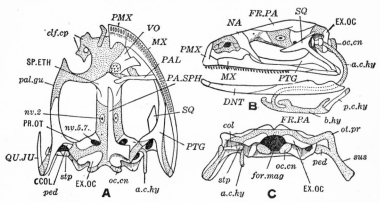

FIG. 136. Skull of *Rana temporaria*. **A,** from beneath with membrane bones removed from the right side (left of figure); **B,** from the left side showing the lower jaw and hyoid; **C,** from behind. Names of cartilage bones in thick; those of membrane bones in italic capitals. Only those parts not already explained in legend of Fig. 135 explained here. *b.hy,* body of hyoid; **COL,** columella; *DNT,* dentary; *for. mag,* foramen magnum; *NA,* nasal; *nv, 2,* optic foramen; *nv, 5, 7,* foramina of the fifth and seventh nerves; *oc.cn,* occipital condyle; *PAL,* palatine; *pal.qu,* palato-quadrate; *PA.SPH,* parasphenoid; *ped,* pedicle; *PTG,* pterygoid; **QU.JU,** quadratojugal; *stp,* stapes. (Redrawn after Parker and Haswell.)

processes of the last sacral vertebra; the PUBIS, a cartilaginous element comprizing the anterior, ventral part of the girdle; and the ISCHIUM, making up the posterior, ventral portion of the crest of the girdle. The socket, or ACETABULUM, occurs at a meeting place of all three bones. Into this socket fits the head of the FEMUR, or thigh bone. Next to the femur comes a compound bone, the TIBIO-FIBULA, made up by the fusion of the originally separate tibia and fibula. Next to these are the TARSAL, or ankle bones, two of which, CALCANEUM and ASTRAGULUS are much enlarged and the others correspondingly reduced, or absent. The terminal, or distal, bones are the posterior phalanges, or toe bones.

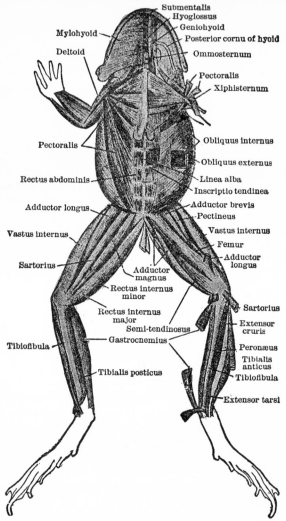

FIG. 137.   Muscles of the frog, ventral view.   (From Parker and Haswell.)

2. *The Muscular System*

The muscles of the body wall have already been referred to.   The remaining voluntary muscular system consists of the muscles of the limbs (Fig. 137).   A typical voluntary muscle, such as the GASTROCNEMIUS, has the following parts: the TENDON, a tough cordlike portion attaching the muscle to a bone or to another muscle; the FASCIA, the glistening membrane surrounding the muscle; the BELLY, or fleshy part of the muscle. We call the more fixed attachment point of the muscle the ORIGIN, and the less fixed point the INSERTION. With this introduction the student should be in a position to gain a concrete idea of the muscular complex of the frog by making a laboratory dissection of one or more systems, such as that of the hind leg. One may find in any good laboratory

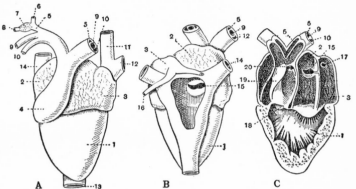

FIG. 138. Heart of the frog. **A,** ventral view. **B,** dorsal view. **C,** ventral wall removed. *1,* ventricle; *2,* right auricle; *3,* left auricle; *4,* truncus arteriosus; *5,* carotid arch; *6,* lingual artery; *7,* carotid gland; *8,* carotid artery; *9,* systemic arch; *10,* pulmocutaneous arch; *11,* innominate vein; *12,* subclavian vein; *13,* vena cava inferior; *14,* vena cava superior; *15,* opening of sinus venosus into right auricle; *16,* pulmonary vein; *17,* aperture of entry of pulmonary vein; *18,* semilunar valves; *19,* longitudinal valve; *20,* point of origin of pulmocutaneous arch. (From Shipley and MacBride, after Howes.)

manual directions for this valuable exercise. It seems well in this place to refrain from any attempt to describe in detail the muscular system of the frog.

An extensive system of INVOLUNTARY MUSCLES is found in connection with the movable vital organs, such as the heart, the alimentary tract, the bladder, etc. The histology of muscular tissues is dealt with in a subsequent chapter.

3. *The Circulatory System*

This system consists of the heart, the veins, the arteries, and the capillaries.

a. The Heart.—The heart consists of four main parts: the sinus venosus, the right and left auricles, and the ventricle (Fig. 138).

Such a heart is known as three chambered in contrast with that of birds and mammals, which have four chambers, two auricles and two ventricles. The SINUS VENOSUS is a large, thin walled vessel formed by the union of the three venæ cavæ. It enters the RIGHT AURICLE, which is also thin walled and larger than the left auricle. The right auricle opens into the ventricle through a valve, the auriculo-ventricular valve. The VENTRICLE acts as a force pump, driving the blood out through the TRUNCUS ARTERIOSUS into the AORTIC ARCHES and thence all over the body. The truncus is provided with a SPIRAL VALVE, sometimes called the longitudinal valve. Between the truncus and the ventricle there are two SEMI-LUNAR VALVES whose function it is to prevent back flow of the blood when the ventricle expands. The truncus divides into two main right and left trunks, each of which subdivides into the three aortic arches described later.

b. The Venous System.—This comprizes all vessels carrying blood toward the heart (Fig. 139). It may be subdivided into four main sections: SYSTEMIC, HEPATIC PORTAL, RENAL PORTAL, and PULMONARY.

The SYSTEMIC SYSTEM consists of the large single postcaval and the paired precaval veins. Each precaval receives blood from several large vessels, the external jugular, the internal jugular, and the subclavian veins, the latter in turn receiving blood from the branchial and the musculocutaneous veins. The postcaval receives blood from the paired hepatic veins, from six pairs of renal veins, and from either spermatic or ovarian veins, depending on the sex of the individual.

The HEPATIC PORTAL SECTION consists of a number of veins that, instead of carrying blood directly to the heart, divert it to the liver, where it is chemically altered in various ways before it is returned to the systemic section through the hepatic veins that connect directly with the postcavals.

The RENAL PORTAL SECTION comprizes several large veins that divert a considerable part of the blood returning from the hind legs and visceral organs through the kidneys, where it is purified of some of its waste products before it escapes from the kidneys through the renal veins. These empty into the postcaval vein, which in turn carries the blood for further purification to the liver before returning it to the postcaval.

The PULMONARY VEINS are rather small in the frog, carrying

blood from the lungs to the heart. Here we have the unusual situation of a vein carrying purified, or oxygenated, blood.

c. The Arterial System.—All vessels carrying blood away from the heart comprise the arterial system (Fig. 140). The three

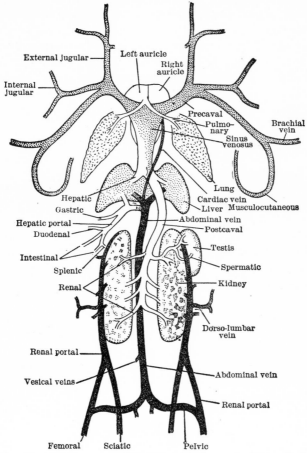

Fig. 139. The venous system of the frog, dorsal aspect. (From Parker and Haswell.)

most anterior arterial trunks are the vestiges of three of the ancestral branchial arches. These are the carotid, the pulmocutaneous, and the systemic arches. The CAROTID ARCH divides into internal and external carotids, both carrying blood to the head; the PULMO-

CUTANEOUS is chiefly respiratory in significance as it carries blood to the lungs and the skin; the SYSTEMIC ARCH supplies purified blood to the viscera and the limbs. The two systemic arches are known as AORTÆ. These unite back of the heart into the single dorsal aorta. Before this union, however, each aortic arch gives rise to an occipitovertebral artery that in turn divides into an

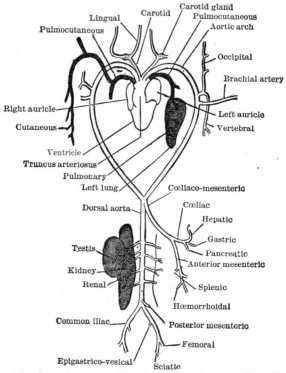

FIG. 140. The arterial system of the frog, ventral view. (From Parker and Haswell.)

occipital and a vertebral. The DORSAL AORTA branches into the following vessels in the order given: cœliacomesenteric, which soon divides into many branches supplying stomach, pancreas, liver, spleen, etc.; the several pairs of renal, or urogenital, arteries; the posterior mesenteric artery; and finally the aorta bifurcates to form the paired common iliac arteries, the branches of which go mainly to the hind legs.

4. *The Respiratory System*

One commonly thinks that only such organs as lungs or gills are entitled to be designated respiratory organs, but the frog is able to survive for months after its lungs are removed, provided that the surrounding temperature be kept reasonably low. The explanation of this is that the soft, moist SKIN of the frog is an accessory respiratory organ of great importance. That is the reason why a frog can stay under water so long, for it respires through the skin at all times. The LUNGS, however, are definitely differentiated respiratory organs. They consist of a pair of rather simple sacs communicating with the mouth cavity by means of the GLOTTIS, an opening at the base of the tongue, which leads to the LARYNX. The mechanism of inspiration and expiration differs radically from our own. In our own case air is sucked in by enlarging the chest cavity by means of diaphragm and ribs; but in the frog the air is pumped in by muscular contractions of the mouth cavity. When the pressure in the mouth cavity is lowered the air comes back from the lungs to the mouth because of the elasticity of lungs and body wall. The frog has no windpipe, or trachea, a structure adapted especially to the suction type of inspiration, for it prevents collapse of the intake tube.

5. *The Digestive System*

Little need be said about the general morphology of the digestive system. It is a relatively short food tube, for the frog is carnivorous in the adult state. In Figure 141 one can readily trace the tube from mouth to anus. Note the very short GULLET, or ŒSOPHAGUS; the STOMACH, seen as a spindleshaped enlargement; the slender SMALL INTESTINE, somewhat coiled; the LARGE INTESTINE, or RECTUM; and the CLOACA into which also open the ureters, the bladder, and the genital ducts. An integral part of the digestive tract are the digestive glands, LIVER and PANCREAS. These are derived embryonically as diverticula of the digestive tract and are connected with the latter by means of ducts, the BILE DUCT leading from the liver into the small intestine, and the PANCREATIC DUCT emptying into the small intestine a little closer to the stomach. The whole alimentary tract is slung to the dorsal body wall by sheets of tissue, or MESENTERIES, that serve also as a bridge over which the blood vessels of the viscera may connect with the main arterial and venous trunks.

6. *The Urogenital System*

As in other vertebrates, there is in the frog a sort of amalgamation of the excretory and the reproductive systems. The amount and kind of combination of the two systems differs in the two sexes.

a. The Male Urogenital System (Fig. 142).—Each of the paired oval TESTES is slung from the wall of the body cavity by means of

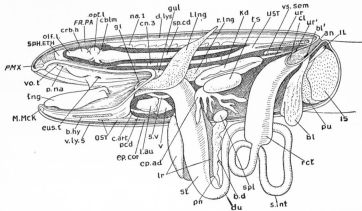

FIG. 141.   General internal anatomy of male frog seen from the left side, the viscera somewhat displaced. *an*, anus; *b.d*, bile duct; *b.hy*, body of hyoid; *bl*, bladder; *bl′*, its opening into cloaca; *c.art*, conus arteriosus; *cblm*, cerebellum; *cl*, cloaca; *cn. 3*, centrum of third vertebra; *cp.ad*, corpus adiposum; *crb.h*, cerebral hemisphere; *d.ly.s*, dorsal lymph sinus; *du*, duodenum; *ep.cor*, epicoracoid; *eus.t*, eustachian tube; **FR.PA**, fronto-parietal; *gl*, glottis; *gul*, gullet; **IL**, ilium; **IS**, ischium; *kd*, kidney; *l.au*, left auricle; *l.lng*, left lung; *lr*, liver; **M.MCK**, mento-meckelian; *n.a.l*, neural arch of the first vertebra; *olf.l*, olfactory lobe; *opt.l*, optic lobe; **O.ST**, omo- and epi-sternum; *pcd*, pericardium; **PMX**, premaxilla; *pn*, pancreas; *p.na*, posterior naris; *pu*, pubis; *rct*, rectum; *r.lng*, right lung; *s.int*, small intestine; *sp.cd*, spinal cord; **SPH.ETH**, sphenethmoid; *spl*, spleen; *st*, stomach; *s.v.*; sinus venosus; *tng*, tongue; *ts*, testis; *ur*, ureter; *ur′*, its opening into the cloaca; **UST**, urostyle; *v*, ventricle; *v.ly.s*, ventral lymph sinus; *vo.t*, vomerine teeth; *vs.sem*, seminal vesicle.   (Redrawn after Holmes.)

a mesentery, or MESORCHIUM.   Leading from each testis are several small sperm ducts, the VASA EFFERENTIA, that penetrate the kidney.   These little ducts are modified nephric tubules that have ceased to play an excretory rôle and are now genital ducts until they unite in the kidney to form a common duct for both urine and spermatic fluid.   This common duct is the URETER and empties into the cloaca.   A storage sac for spermatozoa, the SEMINAL VESICLE, opens into the ureter.

b. The Female Urogenital System.—The OVARIES (Fig. 143) are large and conspicuous, especially during the breeding season when they are more massive than the remaining viscera. Each ovary is slung from the dorsal wall of the body cavity, by a mesentery, the MESORCHIUM. The OVIDUCTS are large convoluted tubes, one on each side of the body cavity. The free anterior end of each oviduct is in direct communication with the cœlomic cavity by means of an opening, the OSTIUM, which is ciliated and sweeps the eggs from the body cavity into the oviduct. The main part of the oviduct is glandular and secretes the gelatinous envelope that covers the eggs. The lower part of the oviduct is enlarged into a thin walled distensible chamber, the UTERUS, which in turn opens into the cloaca. The KIDNEYS and URETERS are much the same as in the male, but in the female there is no need to use the ureter as a genital duct, for the oviduct serves this function. Attached to both ovaries and testes are conspicu-

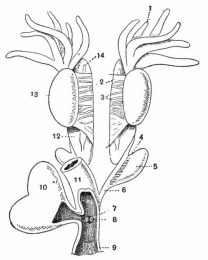

FIG. 142. The urino-genital organs of the male frog, dissected from the front after removal from the body. 1, fat body; 2, fold of peritoneum supporting the testis; 3, efferent ducts of testis; 4, ducts of vesicula seminalis; 5, vesicula seminalis; 6, archinephric duct; 7, cloaca; 8, orifice of ureter; 9, proctodæum; 10, allantoic bladder; 11, rectum; 12, kidney; 13, testis; 14, adrenal body. (From Shipley and MacBride, after Howes.)

ous orange colored FAT BODIES, which though seemingly parts of the urogenital system, are merely organs of food storage.

7. *The Nervous System*

This may be divided into three parts: the central, the peripheral, and the sympathetic nervous systems. The CENTRAL NERVOUS SYSTEM consists of the BRAIN and the SPINAL CORD; the PERIPHERAL NERVOUS SYSTEM consists of the CRANIAL and SPINAL NERVES that run to all parts of the body; and the SYMPATHETIC NERVOUS

SYSTEM consists of a group of nerve masses or GANGLIA, together with their connectives, and are associated with the control of the involuntary activities, such as digestion and circulation.

The BRAIN (Fig. 144) is enveloped in a darkly pigmented membrane, the PIA MATER. The chief sections of the brain are the fore-

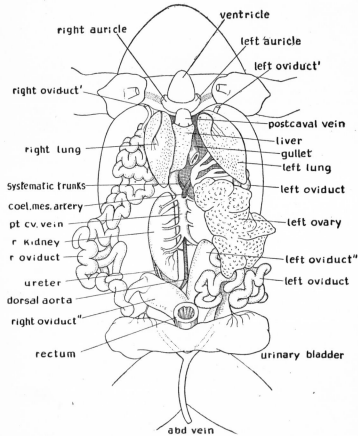

FIG. 143. Organs of a female frog. The alimentary canal has been cut off at the gullet and rectum and most of the liver has been removed. The right ovary and fat body are also removed and the ventricle of the heart turned forward. (Redrawn after Parker and Haswell.)

brain, the midbrain, and the hindbrain. The FOREBRAIN consists mainly of a pair of elongated OLFACTORY LOBES separated by a longitudinal shallow groove, and a pair of small, poorly developed

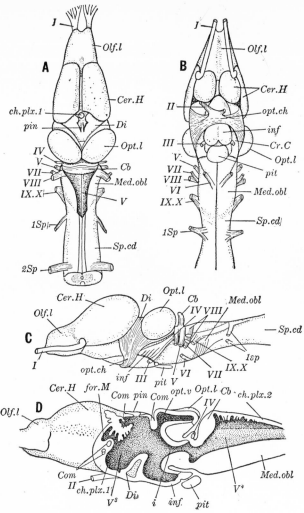

Fig. 144. Brain of the frog. **A,** dorsal side; **B,** ventral side; **C,** left side; **D,** in vertical longitudinal section through the middle. *Cb,* cerebellum; *Cer.H,* cerebral hemispheres; *ch.plx.1,* anterior, and *ch.plx.2,* posterior choroid plexus; *Com.* commissures connecting right and left halves of the brain; *Cr.C,* crura cerebri; *Di,* diencephalon or thalamencephalon; *for.M,* foramen of Monroe; *i,* iter, or aqueduct of Sylvius; *inf,* infundibulum; *Med.obl,* medulla oblongata; *Olf.l,* olfactory lobe; *opt.ch,* optic chiasmus; *Opt.l,* optic lobe; *opt.v,* optic vesicle; *pin,* pineal body; *pit,* pituitary body; *Sp. cd,* spinal cord; V^3, third ventricle; V^4, fourth ventricle; *I-X,* cranial nerves; *1Sp, 2Sp,* first and second spinal nerves. (Redrawn after Parker and Haswell.)

CEREBRAL HEMISPHERES. The MIDBRAIN is made up chiefly of the THALAMENCEPHALON and the OPTIC LOBES. The HINDBRAIN comprizes the very small CEREBELLUM and the large MEDULLA OBLONGATA.

Ten pairs of CRANIAL NERVES (Fig. 144) come off in serial order and run to various regions as follows:—The first nerves are olfactory, running to the organ of smell; the second pair, optic nerves, run to the retina of the eyes; third, fourth, and sixth nerves are very small and innervate the muscles of the eyeball; the fifth pair of nerves come off from the anterior part of the medulla and are among the largest of the cranial nerves, innervating upper jaws, lips, and other parts of the head; the seventh pair has many branches running to various parts of the head including the lower jaw, lining of mouth, etc.; the eighth, or auditory nerves, innervates the inner ear exclusively; the ninth innervates the mucous membranes of the tongue and the pharynx; the tenth, or vagus, has two branches, one running to the eardrum, the other to the heart, the stomach, lungs, œsophagus, and larynx.

CHAPTER XXVIII

GENERAL PHYSIOLOGY OF THE FROG

ALTHOUGH this chapter deals specifically with the physiology of one animal, the frog, it will also serve as an introduction to physiology in general; for essentially the same functional phenomena as are here to be dealt with appear in man and in most other highly organized animals. No attempt will be made to present in detail the whole physiology of the frog; rather, an effort will be made to make clear the essential features of a few of the most important processes, such as digestion, respiration, circulation, excretion, and some phases of the physiology of the nervous system.

A. PHYSIOLOGY OF DIGESTION

The purpose of digestion is to break down complex food materials, such as proteins, fats, carbohydrates, into simpler compounds capable of being assimilated by the cells of the organism and elaborated into new protoplasm. The proteins are the most essential of these three types of food. In addition to carbon, oxygen, and hydrogen, which they possess in common with carbohydrates and fats, they contain also nitrogen, without which life seems to be impossible. In the process of digestion the various kinds of food materials are acted upon by specific ferments, ENZYMES, which hasten the conversion of insoluble substances into soluble ones capable of passing through the membranes of the digestive tract and thus reaching the blood stream.

Let us now trace the food through the alimentary tract, noting the various changes it undergoes at various stages of its course.

Since the frog does not masticate its food, but swallows it whole, there is no mouth digestion such as is to be found in man and other mammals with salivary glands—glands that secrete digestive ferments which take the initiative in breaking down foods.

a. Glands of the Stomach.—The frog's digestion begins in the stomach. There are two kinds of stomach glands: those situated at the CARDIAC end, which are longer and rather deep-set; and those at the PYLORIC end, which are shorter and less deep. These glands secrete GASTRIC JUICE, a fluid containing about 0.4 per cent hydrochloric acid, a ferment, or enzyme, called PEPSIN, and a number of inorganic salts. Pepsin acts directly upon the proteins, converting them into soluble substances known as PEPTONES. Stomach digestion is a relatively slow process in the frog. It requires fully twenty-four hours completely to digest a small earthworm, and much longer if several worms are eaten at once.

b. The Pancreas.—The partially digested food passes out of the stomach through the PYLORIC VALVE and enters the DUODENUM. While in this part of the intestine a secretion from a large irregular gland, the PANCREAS, is mixed with the food. PANCREATIC JUICE is alkaline, owing to the presence of sodium carbonate (Na_2CO_3). It contains three ferments, or enzymes: STEAPSIN, whose action splits fats into glycerin and fatty acids; AMYLOPSIN, by means of which starch is converted into sugar; and TRYPSIN, which completes the conversion of peptones and undigested proteins into amino acids. Trypsin differs from pepsin in that it acts in an alkaline instead of an acid medium.

c. The Liver.—This is a large gland whose secretion is a greenish fluid, termed BILE. This fluid is mixed with pancreatic juice in the bile duct before it enters the duodenum. Bile is stored in the GALL BLADDER until needed. The functional cells of the liver, HEPATIC CELLS, are arranged so as to form a branching system of tubular glands communicating with BILE CAPILLARIES; these in turn unite into larger vessels, these into still larger, till the largest branches unite to form the BILE DUCT. The action of the bile is not fully understood. Some of its constituents are believed to be no more than waste products; others almost certainly aid in digestion, having much to do with the conversion of fats into a soapy emulsion capable of passing through the intestinal membranes and reaching the blood. Another important function of the liver is that of elaborating GLYCOGEN, a carbohydrate material having the same empirical formula as starch ($C_6H_{10}O_5)_n$, and hence called "animal starch." The quantity of glycogen in the liver varies greatly with the season of the year, being lowest in the spring and highest in the early fall. This seems to indicate that the liver is an important storehouse of reserve food.

d. Absorption of Food in the Intestine.—When the food leaves the stomach and passes into the intestine, it is strongly acid, due to the hydrochloric acid of the gastric juice. While in the duodenum the acidity is neutralized by the alkaline elements of the bile and of the pancreatic juice. Food still undigested is further broken down in the intestines. After digestion is complete the dissolved foods of various kinds are absorbed by the intestinal cells and passed by osmosis into the blood and lymph.

e. Disposal and Use of Food in the Body.—Foods are used to build up tissues and to furnish energy for bodily activities. The proteins are the only foods that can build up living substance, for only they possess the necessary ingredients. Fats are, for the most part, stored in cells as droplets. Some fat in adipose tissue is a by-product of the breakdown of carbohydrates and proteins. Fats and carbohydrates function chiefly as fuels. They are combusted by being combined with oxygen and converted mainly into CO_2 and water. Proteins are also constantly being broken down for energy production. There is no sharp distinction between tissue building and energy producing foods; for even fats and carbohydrates go to form certain parts of the tissues. After the food materials have been broken down in the process of energy production there are various waste products that must be eliminated through the organs of respiration and excretion.

B. Physiology of Respiration

a. Chief Respiratory Organs.—In the frog the chief respiratory organs are the lungs and the skin, and these share about equally in this important duty.

The lungs are rather simple structures as compared with the lungs of man, and are considerably less efficient. They are thin walled sacs, ovoid in form and capable of great distension. The inner surface is subdivided by means of septa into a number of small compartments, ALVEOLI, which serve to increase the amount of surface exposed to the air. An intricate network of capillaries lines the whole surface and affords a ready means of exchange between the air and the blood.

b. Respiratory Movements.—Inhalation is largely a matter of swallowing air into the lungs by means of contractions of the buccal cavity. Air comes into the buccal cavity through the nostrils. These are closed by a sort of valve and the glottis is opened, so that when the buccal cavity is contracted, air is forced into the lungs. Exhalation is due partly to the contraction of the muscles of the body wall and partly to the elasticity of the lungs. The frog does not have movable ribs nor a diaphragm, as has man, and hence has a totally different respiratory mechanism.

c. Changes in the Blood during Respiration.—In the main, it may be said that the blood receives oxygen from the air and gives off CO_2 and water into the lungs. Oxygen is taken up and carried mainly by the red blood corpuscles, whose color is due to the presence of a chemical substance known as HÆMOGLOBIN, which has the property of readily uniting with oxygen to become OXYHÆMOGLOBIN. This substance, in turn, holds its oxygen loosely and readily gives it up when in contact with tissues that need oxygen. It is thus an ideal medium for the transfer of external oxygen to internal tissues. The whole process of respiration includes also the exchange of gases in the lungs and the actual oxidation or combustion of various substances in the protoplasm. The latter is perhaps the fundamental respiratory process; the other steps are merely accessory to respiration proper. Oxidation of foods and protoplasmic materials results in the formation of various by-products, some of which are eliminated through the lungs and some through the skin and kidneys.

d. The Skin as a Respiratory Organ.—Important as are the lungs, they are hardly as important in the frog as is the skin. During hibernation the lungs do not function at all, and the whole burden of respiration is thrown upon the skin. Moreover, it is important to realize that, when for long periods frogs are submerged in the water, the skin acts as a sort of gill, for it can respire even better in water than in air. Even if the nostrils are plugged with wax, a frog can live for days in a moist atmosphere, thus using only the skin in respiration. Experiments have shown that the skin gives off more CO_2 than the lungs. Between its two systems the frog is provided against all respiratory emergencies.

C. Physiology of Circulation

a. General.—The circulatory system is mainly a medium of exchange. It serves as a distributing agent, carrying substances from the outside to internal regions and transporting products elaborated in one tissue to various parts that require the stimulus of such products for their normal functioning. Thus it may be said that the circulatory system is also a coördinating factor of great importance.

The circulatory system consists of many specialized parts, each serving a different function. The main functions may be listed under five heads: pumping, carrying food and oxygen to the tissues, distributing these to the ultimate consumers, or individual cells, carrying waste products to their appropriate points of exit, and distributing hormones throughout the body. These various functions are performed by the heart, the arteries, the capillaries, and the veins. Let us consider these separately.

b. The Functions of the Heart.—The heart (Fig. 138) is essentially an automatic muscular force pump. It arises as a specialized region of the venous system and is therefore essentially a tube. In the heart rhythm the contraction begins in the sinus venosus; then the auricles, ventricle, and conus follow in that order. The heart possesses a system of valves between these sections, preventing the backward flow of blood. In the frog there is not a complete separation, as there is in man, between the systemic and the pulmonary circuits, but the blood from the lungs and that from the veins (pure and impure blood) mingles somewhat in the single ventricle, though the outlets are so placed as to reduce such admixture to a minimum.

So automatic in its action is the frog's heart that it will continue to beat for hours or even days after it has been removed from the body, provided only that it be kept in an appropriate medium. Various experiments have proved that the sinus venosus is the pace setter for the heart rhythm. If the sinus be removed or paralyzed, the other regions of the heart beat more slowly than normal and with a less regular rhythm; while an isolated sinus maintains its normal rate of beat. A heart that has ceased to beat spontaneously may be stimulated into renewed activity by electrical or other means.

c. The Arteries.—The main function of the arteries (Fig. 140) is that of conduits, but they also regulate the flow of the blood through the elasticity and contractility of their muscular walls.

d. The Capillaries.—These are extremely fine, thin walled vessels of such small caliber that blood cells sometimes have to roll up or become elongated in order to force a passage through some of the finer branches. Dissolved food substances diffuse out through the capillaries and pass into the tissue cells. White blood corpuscles (leucocytes) are able to pass bodily through capillary walls, going in or out as the occasion demands.

e. The Veins (Fig. 139).—The veins are merely thin walled non-muscular conduits, leading from the capillaries back to the heart. They also pick up foods and waste products as they pass through various important organs.

f. The Blood.—In the frog the blood is composed of a fluid, the PLASMA, with free cells or corpuscles suspended in it. Three kinds of corpuscles are distinguished: red corpuscles, white corpuscles, and spindle cells. The red corpuscles, ERYTHROCYTES, are elliptical in form, with a well defined nucleus. Seen edgewise, they are rather flat, with a bulge near the center where lies the nucleus. The cytoplasm is stained with hæmoglobin. The white corpuscles, LEUCOCYTES, are much like tiny Amœbæ in form, changing shape and moving about among other cells by means of their pseudopodia. By this mode of locomotion they are able to pass through the capillary membranes with ease, pushing aside the thin endothelial cells as they go through, the latter closing up behind them. The most important function of the leucocytes is the result of their ability to engulf and digest foreign bodies. Thus, invading bacteria that are parasitic on the organism and sometimes cause disease are constantly being destroyed. If the attack of these invaders be too long sustained or be carried on with overwhelming numbers, the leucocytes may not be able to cope with it and the organism may succumb. The presence of invading bacteria at any point sets up an inflammation, and this attracts leucocytes from all sides. Usually the battle between the invaders and the defenders results in favor of the latter. Another function of the leucocytes is that of removing by feeding upon them the inevitable fragments of dead and dying cells that have worn themselves out in the performance of some arduous duty. A third type of cellular blood element consists of spindle cells. These cells are not well understood. They seem to partake of the properties of both red and white corpuscles, being able to transform themselves at times into either of these types.

D. Physiology of Excretion

a. General.—The combustion of the various energy forming foodstuffs and the breaking down of living matter gives rise to various products that are of no value to the organism, but, like ashes and smoke of a furnace, must be gotten rid of in order that the metabolic process may go on unhindered. Carbon dioxide is one of the most abundant of the by-products, but there are many others that are in solution and cannot be eliminated directly through the lungs or through the skin. These dissolved waste products are removed by a special mechanism or system of mechanisms known as the excretory organs. The chief organs of excretion in most animals are the kidneys and the skin. Little is known about skin excretion in the frog, but in the higher forms such as the mammals the sweat glands of the skin perform some share of the excretory duties. The liver also rids the blood of various waste products. We shall, in this account, confine our attention to the function of the kidneys.

b. The Kidneys.—These are two elongated, flattened, dark red organs, lying far back in the body cavity, one on each side of the

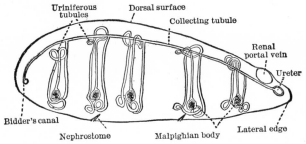

FIG. 145. Diagram of a cross section of the kidney of the frog.

vertebral column. A kidney consists of a complex system of convoluted URINIFEROUS TUBULES packed in connected tissue. The distal end of each tubule consists of a bulbous enlargement, the MALPIGHIAN BODY, composed of the inflated end of the tubule, called BOWMAN'S CAPSULE, into which is invaginated a bulbous mass of capillaries, the GLOMERULUS. The liquid wastes pass out through the walls of the capillaries into the lumen of the Bowman's capsule and flow successively through the uriniferous tubule, the collecting tubule, the ureter, the cloaca, and finally collect in the bladder. Ciliated funnels, NEPHROSTOMES, occur on the ventral side. These in the larva open into tubules, but in the adult they open directly into veins. The main functions of the kidneys are those of ridding the blood of liquid waste products of metabolism and of assisting in the maintenance of the chemical neutrality of the blood.

The kidney secretion, URINE, is a compound of various substances in solution, the chief of which is UREA, $(NH)_2CO$, which in the dry state is a white crystalline solid. In addition, the kidney excretes excess salts, principally soluble chlorides of Sodium, Potassium, Calcium, and Magnesium.

c. The Bladder (Fig. 146).—This organ is a storage sac for urine. It is thin walled, bilobed, and opens near the cloaca. It is capable of great distension. The filling of the bladder is effected through the closing of the sphincter muscles of the cloaca, which prevents the escape of the urine and thus causes it to collect in the bladder, whence it may suddenly be expelled by a quick

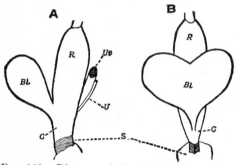

Fig. 146.   Diagram of the bladder and rectum of the frog; **A,** from the side; **B,** from below; *Bl*, bladder; *C*, cloaca; *R*, rectum; *S*, sphincter muscle; *U*, ureter; *Ut*, uterus. (Modified from Gaupp.)

contraction of the body muscles and a corresponding relaxation of the cloacal muscles.

E. Physiology of the Nervous System

a. General.—The main functions of the nervous system are those of irritability and conductivity: those of changing in response to stimuli and of transmitting stimuli to other parts. A good example of the simplest phase of nervous activity is seen in the so-called REFLEX ACTION. If one places a small bit of filter paper, dipped in dilute acetic acid, upon one side of the frog's body, the hind leg will be brought forward and the paper wiped off. How promptly the wiping action takes place depends upon the strength of the stimulus. The same reaction will be repeated with almost machine like precision every time the particular stimulus is applied. It is a simple mechanical response. Such an action is termed a reflex action because it calls to mind the way in which light striking a mirror is reflected back upon its original source. The mechanism of the reflex action is thought to be as follows: A sensory nerve-ending in the skin is stimulated by the acid; afferent nerve fibers running inward from the skin conduct the stimulus through the dorsal root of the spinal cord to certain cells in the cord; then the stimulus is carried up or down the cord to the place where lie the motor nerve cells of the leg muscles used in performing the wiping reflex; an impulse is sent along the motor, or efferent, fibers of these cells to the appropriate muscles; and the muscles contract in the manner described.

We have spoken of two kinds of nerve fibers and nerve cells: the SENSORY, or AFFERENT, cells and their fibers, and the MOTOR, or EFFERENT, cells and fibers. A reflex arc is composed of at least two nerve cells and their extended fiberlike processes, together with shorter processes, DENDRITES, by means of which two cells come into contact. Other reflexes in the frog are the croaking reflex and the clasping reflex. The latter has already been discussed. The croaking reflex may be stimulated by rubbing the frog's side with a finger. A complex habit may often be resolved into a series of reflexes, the first of which sets off the next, and so on to the end of the series.

b. The Functions of the Brain.—The brain (Fig. 144) is something like a telephone exchange, where communication is established between numerous parts of the organism. Coördinations between various complexes of stimuli are made in the brain and a selected appropriate response given.

The CEREBRAL HEMISPHERES seem to have no very highly specialized function in the frog. In the higher organisms, however, it is certain that this region of the brain is the chief seat of the intelligence. What limited intelligence the frog possesses may be located in the hemispheres, but we have little certain knowledge on this point. The THALAMENCEPHALON seems to be the chief seat of spontaneous movement in the frog. Removal of this organ causes the frog to be completely inert to stimuli from without. The OPTIC NERVES enter the thalamencephalon, and, as we might expect, extirpation of this part of the brain causes blindness. The OPTIC LOBES seem to act as inhibitors of reflex activity. They serve to tone down the irritability of the cord. The CEREBELLUM is a small organ in the frog and its function uncertain, though it probably has some coördinating action. The MEDULLA OBLONGATA is an extremely important part of the frog's brain, for it is the seat of many indispensable involuntary activities, such as shooting out the tongue, swallowing, breathing, and many bodily movements.

The nervous system of the frog is distinctly segmental or metameric. Even in the brain there is a linear series of centers that differ qualitatively and quantitatively; while the different levels of the cord control limited portions of the musculature and other active parts. We have here one of the best evidences of the essentially segmental organization of the vertebrates.

CHAPTER XXIX

HISTOLOGY OF THE FROG

HISTOLOGY may be defined as that branch of biology treating of the minute (microscopic) structure of tissues. In subdividing an organism into its constituent parts, we find that the largest subdivisions are systems, such as the circulatory system, the muscular system, the reproductive system. A system may consist of several well defined, specialized parts, each performing some particular function of its own. Such parts are known as organs—typical organs being heart, stomach, liver. Most organs consist of two or more kinds of tissue, so arranged as to work harmoniously together in the performance of a special function. Thus a heart, though composed chiefly of muscular tissue, is made up partly of epithelial tissues, circulatory tissues, nervous tissues, and connective tissues.

A TISSUE may be defined as "a group of cells of similar structure forming a continuous mass or layer." Histology is concerned with the typical arrangements of these tissue cells and with the finer structures of the individual cells.

In the body of the frog, as in those of other animals, we are able to distinguish four main classes of tissues: (1) EPITHELIAL, (2) CONNECTIVE, (3) MUSCULAR, (4) NERVOUS.

Some authorities add a fifth class: BLOOD AND LYMPH TISSUES. These differ in some important respects from other tissues, for they are not groups of cells bound together into membranes or masses, but consist of loose cells floating in the plasma. Whether or not they are to be classified as tissues in the strict sense, they are extremely important ingredients of the organism and will be dealt with at the end of the present chapter. The four main categories of tissues listed above include a manifold variety of cellular associations and each is to receive separate attention.

A. EPITHELIAL TISSUES

These tissues consist of layers of cells with very little intercellular substance. The commonest function of the epithelial

329

tissues is that of furnishing coverings for various surfaces, both interior and exterior. Thus, the skin of the frog is an EPITHELIUM, as are also the linings of the body cavities, glands, ducts, and blood vessels. It is customary to classify epithelial cells according to the shapes of the constituent cells. In the outermost skin of the frog (Fig. 147), which is cast off in molting, we have a typical example of flattened or SQUAMOUS EPITHELIUM. The cells are somewhat like flat tiles, slightly bulging at the middle where the nucleus lies and much thinned out at the edges. The cells of the peritoneum are also of this type. In COLUMNAR EPITHELIUM each cell is an elongated column, standing perpendicular to the surface. When these cells are packed tightly side by side they commonly assume the form of hexagonal prisms. Good examples of columnar epithelia are to be seen in the mucous lining of the intestine. Sometimes epithelial tissues are composed of several layers and may contain more than one type of epithelial cells. Such tissues are known as STRATIFIED EPITHELIA. Another type of epithelium very common in the frog is CILIATED EPITHELIUM, a modified form of columnar epithelium in which each cell is provided with cilia at its free end. Such cells are found in the lining of the mouth cavity, the throat, the trachea, the genital and urinary ducts. The synchronous beat of the cilia in one direction creates a current that serves to transport small objects or fluids into or out of a duct, or passage.

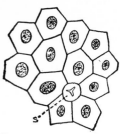

FIG. 147. A portion of the epidermis of *Rana pipiens. s*, stoma cell. (From Holmes.)

B. CONNECTIVE TISSUES

This category of tissues includes all sorts of cellular structures that have to do with supporting the body or uniting its various parts solidly into organs. The most striking feature of these tissues is the relatively large amount of intercellular material involved. Some connective tissues are characterized by the presence of one kind of intercellular material, others by that of another. In some, as in bone, the intercellular material becomes hard, owing to the deposit of mineral substances such as calcium carbonate and calcium phosphate. In other tissues, as in cartilage, the intercellular matrix remains relatively soft and elastic. Four principal kinds of connective tissues are distinguished: (*a*) white, fibrous connective tissue; (*b*) cartilage; (*c*) bone; (*d*) adipose tissue.

a. White, Fibrous Connective Tissue (Fig. 148).—Such tissue is very abundant in the frog's body. It is most frequently found in membranes that serve to attach the skin to the deeper layers of the body wall. Microscopically, we note that these tissues are composed of numerous unbranched, wavy fibers, often in bundles, embedded in a clear, homogeneous matrix. Closely associated with the above tissues are often found YELLOW ELASTIC CONNECTIVE TISSUE FIBERS, which are straight and branched. All three ingredients just mentioned belong to the intercellular part of the tissue. The living cellular ingredients consist of scattered cells, rather

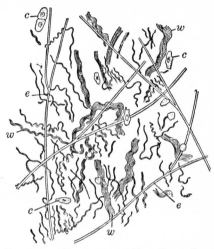

FIG. 148. Fibrous connective tissue from the frog. *c*, connective tissue corpuscles; *e*, elastic fibers; *w*, white fibers. (From Holmes, after Parker and Parker.)

small in size and without any particular morphological peculiarities. One finds other types of fibrous connective tissue in the TENDONS and LIGAMENTS and in the muscle sheaths, or FASCIA. ADENOID TISSUE contains also a variety of loose, soft fibrous connective tissue.

b. Cartilage (Fig. 149).—Cartilaginous tissue is characterized by its massiveness and its density. As a rule it is hyaline or semitransparent. The main bulk of cartilage is the semitransparent intercellular matrix, in which are embedded at intervals single ovoid cells or groups of such cells probably derived from one divided cell. The cells lie in small rounded cavities within the matrix, known as LACUNÆ. Each cell secretes about itself, layer after layer, a mass of MATRIX material, which in old cartilage forces the individual cells far apart. HYALINE CARTILAGE is found at the ends of the long bones, between the vertebræ, in the skull, in the limb girdles and in various other regions. Most bone originates through the ossification of cartilage. The skull, for example, is at first a continuous cartilaginous capsule (CHONDROCRANIUM) containing the brain.   Various centers of ossification arise and build

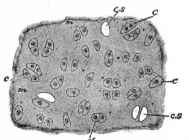

FIG. 149. Cartilage from the head of the femur. *c*, cells; *c'*, cells in process of division; *c.s*, empty cell space; *m*, matrix. (After Parker and Parker.)

up the separate bones.   CALCIFIED CARTILAGE is a kind of hard cartilage with lime salts in the matrix.

c. Bone (Fig. 150). — Bone commonly has cartilage as a precursor and resembles the latter in general structure.   There is the same abundant matrix, here rendered hard through the deposit of lime salts.   The bone cells, too, lie in lacunæ.   Two types of bone may be distinguished: compact bone and spongy, or cancellous, bone.   The former is strong and resistant, the latter relatively weak and loose in texture.   A typical bone is the femur of the frog.   If a transverse section of it be examined, it is seen to be a hollow tube filled with marrow, a complex tissue composed of adipose, connective, and blood cells.   The outer surface of the bone is covered with a membrane (PERIOSTEUM) which consists of cells known as OSTEOBLASTS that are engaged in the manufacture of new bone cells. The main body of the bone is seen to be composed of concentric layers (LAMELLÆ) of hard material in which are embedded many bone

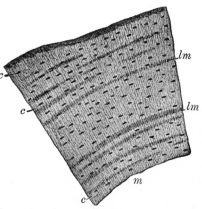

FIG. 150.   A part of a cross section of the femur of the frog.   *c*, canaliculi; *lm*, lamellæ; *m*, marrow cavity.   (From Holmes, after Parker and Parker.)

cells, each lying in a separate LACUNA.   Fine canals (CANALICULI) connect all adjacent lacunæ one with another, so that all of the living bone cells are in communication.

d. Adipose Tissue.—We may define adipose tissue as storage or packing tissue.   The individual cells are gorged with fat and

are greatly enlarged. On account of the accumulation of fat in
the cytoplasm, the nucleus is crowded to one side of the cell and is
flattened against the cell membrane. Sometimes a fat cell seems
to be no more than a ball of fat surrounded by a thin film of protoplasm. The fat is secreted by the cytoplasm in the form of small
droplets and these droplets enlarge and fuse together so as to form
a solid mass.

C. MUSCULAR TISSUES

The cells of muscle are called muscle fibers on account of their
slender, elongated form. There are two main types of muscle:
striated or voluntary, and unstriated or
involuntary.

a. Unstriated Muscle Fibers (Fig. 151).
—These are relatively simple in structure.
They are spindleshaped, with the nucleus
near the middle. In some organs, notably
the bladder, these fibers are very much
elongated; while in other organs, notably
the walls of the blood vessels, they are relatively short and thick. The longitudinal
lines or stripes are due to the presence of
slender contractile elements in the cytoplasm, known as FIBRILLÆ. The cell wall
of an unstriated muscle fiber is very thin
and transparent. These cells are relatively
slow and sluggish in their action and are
therefore found in organs with slow and
regular movements, such as the intestines,
the blood vessels, ducts, the bladder, and
the ciliary muscles of the iris.

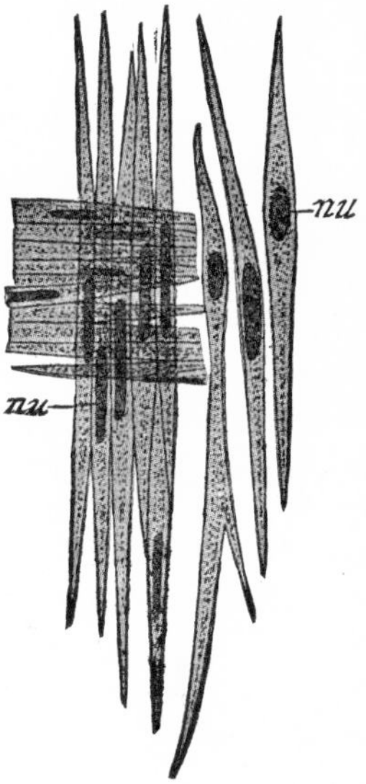

b. Striated Muscle Fibers (Fig. 152).—
Fibers of this nature have a more elaborate

FIG. 151. Unstriated mus-
cle fibers from the intestine of the frog. *nu*, nucleus. (From Holmes,
after Howes.)

structure, due to the fact that the cytoplasm is practically all
specialized and consists of complex contractile elements. A thin
membrane, SARCOLEMMA, surrounds each fiber. In a sense a
muscle fiber is a SYNCYTIUM rather than a single cell, for there are
numerous nuclei within the bounds of a single cell membrane.
The distinctive feature of these cells is that they are, in addition
to being longitudinally striped, transversely striated. The length-

wise striping is due to the presence of numerous closely-packed FIBRILLÆ that run from one end of the cell to the other. A small amount of unmodified cytoplasm, SARCOPLASM, separates the

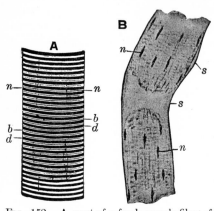

FIG. 152. **A,** part of a fresh muscle fiber of a frog; **B,** the same after treatment with distilled water followed by methyl green. *b,* light bands; *d,* dark bands; *n,* nuclei; *s,* sarcolemma showing more clearly where the fiber is broken. (From Holmes, after Parker and Parker.)

fibrillæ from one another. Transverse striation is due to the fact that each fibrilla is divided into a long series of segments, SARCOMERES, separated from each other by thin dark disks of another consistency, known as KRAUSE'S MEMBRANES, which extend not only across each fibrilla but from fibrilla to fibrilla, uniting these into one mass. Several minor elements, the meaning of which is little understood, may also be made out under high powers of the microscope. The mechanism of muscular contractility is still an unsolved problem, though several theories have been proposed to explain it.

c. The Muscle Fibers of the Heart.—Such fibers differ in several respects from those of any other organ. Though they are involuntary, they are striated. Each of the short, thick muscle cells has a single nucleus, and each cell branches so as to join with branches of adjacent muscle cells and thus to form an elaborate network.

D. NERVOUS TISSUES

The cellular elements of the nervous tissues (Fig. 153) consist of nerve cells or NEURONES, which are characterized by the possession of long, slender branches. Two kinds of projections or branches are to be distinguished: those bringing impulses to the nerve cell body, DENDRITES; and those conducting impulses from the cell body, AXONS.

The body of the neurone (Fig. 153, D) is stellate, owing to its branching habit, and has but one nucleus. One neurone may be in contact with another neurone by means of its dendrites or by means

Cicada – locust – come every year

of its axon; or it may have both contacts at once, th
an intermediary between two other neurones. The poi
is known as a SYNAPSE.

A single nerve fiber (Fig. 153, A) consists of: (*a*) a central strand,
the AXIS CYLINDER; (*b*) an insulating sheath of fatty material, the
MEDULLARY SHEATH; (*c*) a delicate surface membrane, or NEURI-
LEMMA. The medullary substance is interrupted at intervals, giving rise to constrictions known as NODES of RANVIER. The nuclei,
of which there may be many in a long fiber, lie just beneath the
neurilemma. Though the axis cylinder is merely a prolonged outgrowth of a single cell, the
medullary sheath is com-
posed of numerous cells,
which during growth seek
out the extending nerve
processes and surround
them. These cells are not
of nervous origin, but are
simply modified mesoderm
cells.

When a nerve fiber is
cut, the part of the fiber
that is separated from the
cell degenerates, and the
axis cylinder grows out
again, following the path
of the disintegrating part
of the fiber.

Neurones are usually ag-
gregated into masses known
as GANGLIA. The brain is a
compact mass of ganglia,
together with certain other
non-nervous tissues. Other
ganglia occur in the spinal

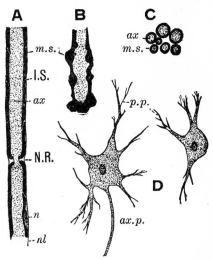

FIG. 153. Nerve cells and fibers of the frog.
A, fresh nerve fiber. **B**, nerve fiber with
the myelin swollen through the absorption
of water. **C**, cross section of nerve fibers.
D, ganglion cells. *ax*, axis cylinder; *ax.p*,
axis cylinder process of ganglion cell; I.S,
incisure of Schmidt; *m.s*, medullary sheath;
n, nucleus; *nl*, neurilemma; N.R, node of
Ranvier; *p.p*, protoplasmic process of ganglion cell. (From Holmes.)

cord and in connection with the sympathetic nervous system. In
the brain, as well as in other ganglionic masses, the neurones are
connected up in various ways so as to form conduction paths. A
typical conduction path is that known as the REFLEX ARC, which
consists of a SENSORY NEURONE with its dendrites in contact with

a tactile cell on the surface of the skin and its axon forming a SYN-
APSE with the dendrites of a MOTOR NEURONE in the spinal cord,
the latter in turn having its axon in contact with a muscle fiber.
An irritation of the skin is imparted to the dendrites of the sensory
neurone, conducted over the axon of the latter to the spinal cord, is
then passed to the dendrites of a motor neurone, conducted over the
motor axon to the muscle cell, which is stimulated to contract. It
is believed that even the most elaborate of mental processes are
reducible to series of such arcs as this.

CHAPTER XXX

THE DEVELOPMENT OF THE FROG

ONE of the marvels of nature is the development of a complex organism out of a single cell, an egg. We are even more in the dark as to the underlying cause of individual development (ON-TOGENY) than we are about racial development (PHYLOGENY or EVOLUTION); yet we may witness either with the unaided eye or with the enlarging eye of the microscope every event in the developmental history of an individual. With the help of the compound microscope we can watch the process of cell division and multiplication; we can catch the changes that lead to differentiation of tissues and division of labor among them; we can observe the beginnings of organs and of systems and follow the various steps in their development up to the definitive condition. We can even follow out the smallest details in the gradual making of an eye out of a collection of diverse tissues. We can see the first heart beat, the first appearance of gills, the origin of blood, the formation of the mouth. In fact, we can see the whole moving picture of development; but we do not yet know what makes it develop. Even to the expert embryologist the development of any organism is a sort of miracle, for he knows not the motive power that drives the machine.

The problem as to the mechanism of development is unsolved, but not because of any lack of effort on the part of biologists to solve it. Much thought has been taken and many experiments have been performed in the search after a satisfactory understanding of the causes of development.

A. THEORIES OF DEVELOPMENT

Two opposed theories, or types of theory, have been held for many years and by many thinkers: PREFORMATION THEORIES and EPIGENESIS THEORIES.

a. Preformation Theories.—Some of the older writers evaded the issue of explaining the origin of an individual from the egg by predicating that the adult organism is already preformed in the egg or in the spermatozoön. The miniature organism was supposed to be present in an extremely condensed form within the confines of one of the germ cells, needing only to take up water and food in order to expand or unfold itself into the complete organism. This crude form of the preformation doctrine has given way in recent times to the much more refined conception that all of the characters of the adult are represented by appropriate determiners or genes, which lie in the germ cells and either singly or in groups take part in the realization of the specific characters of the mature organism.

b. Epigenesis Theories.—Other early writers held a view directly opposite to that of preformation; namely, that the germ cell is structureless and homogeneous at the beginning of development and that it acquires organization and complexity largely through the molding influence of the environment and that of one part upon another. Views essentially epigenetic are held today by prominent biologists, but few would accept this theory in its extreme form.

Modern biologists, as a rule, are inclined to strike some sort of compromise between these opposed theories and to hold that much of the type of organization of an individual is predetermined in the fertilized germ cell, but that the environment exercises a profound influence in shaping the course of ontogeny. It will be noted that neither of these theories has anything to say about the motive power of development. Doubtless the motive power may be spelled l-i-f-e, but we have been unable to say what that is.

B. Development of the Frog

Amphibian embryology, and that of the frog in particular, occupies a very central place in the system of comparative embryology. It will therefore well serve the purpose of illustrating the important steps in ontogeny (the origin of a new individual) and the principles that underlie the science of embryology in general. No better type could well be selected for such a purpose.

1. *The Germ Cells of the Frog*

The frog's EGG is a comparatively large cell, about the size of a buckshot. The upper hemisphere of the egg is black, owing to the presence of many pigment granules. The dark color is believed to be an adaptation for absorbing and retaining heat; for the eggs are laid in early spring when the ponds and streams are very cold, and the egg needs to conserve all of the sun's heat that it can. The egg is surrounded by three layers of transparent JELLY (Fig. 154): a thin layer lying tightly against the cell membrane, a thick layer of somewhat fluid consistency, and a thick outer layer somewhat less fluid. The jelly is be-lieved to have a protective function, warding off at-tacks of bacteria; and it also helps to retain heat, for it has the property of letting in heat rays from the sun more readily than it lets them out. The up-per, pigmented part of the egg marks the hemisphere characterized by the pres-ence of the ANIMAL POLE, that region of the proto-plasm which is most ac-tive and near which lies

FIG. 154. Egg in jelly. (From Holmes, after Schultze.)

the nucleus, or GERMINAL VESICLE; the unpigmented hemisphere is the site of the VEGETAL POLE, or yolk pole, the least active region of the egg. The whole egg is surrounded by a delicate cell wall, or VITELLINE MEMBRANE. The arrangement of the pigment and the position of the nucleus are somewhat eccentric and on this account furnish useful landmarks for determining the bilateral symmetry of the undivided egg.

The SPERMATOZOÖN of the frog (Fig. 155) is also a single cell, highly specialized for the one function of fertilizing the egg. It is composed of a spindleshaped head, a short middle piece, and a long slender tail. The head consists largely of a condensed mass of chromatin.

2. *Maturation of the Germ Cells*

Before maturation each male and female cell contains a double set of chromosomes. They occur in pairs, one of each pair having been derived from each parent of the previous generation.

a. The Origin of the Spermatozoön.—We shall describe the origin of the spermatozoön first as it is a little simpler than that of the mature egg. The chromosomes pair off, uniting two and two according to kinds, for only homologous, or equivalent, chromosomes pair. Then a mitotic spindle forms and the paired chromosomes line up in the equatorial plate of the spindle. After a pause, one chromosome of each pair begins to travel toward each pole of the spindle. Soon two groups of chromosomes are formed, one at one pole and one at the other. The result is that each cell that arises from this division has but a single set of chromosomes, consisting of one of each kind, and therefore has only one half the number of chromosomes that were present in the original sperm cell, or SPERMATOCYTE. This division is known as the REDUCTION DIVISION and the pairing of chromosomes that paved the way for reduction is known as SYNAPSIS. A second maturation division quickly follows, but it is just like any ordinary mitotic division in that each chromosome is longitudinally split into two half chromosomes and no reduction in the number of chromosomes is involved. Thus, as the result of two cell divisions, four SPERMATIDS, each with the HAPLOID (reduced to one half) number of chromosomes, are pro-

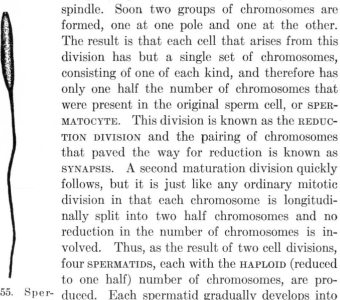

Fig. 155. Spermatozoön of *Rana esculenta.* (From Holmes, after La Valette St. George.)

duced. Each spermatid gradually develops into a mature SPERMATOZOÖN.

b. The Origin of the Egg. —The original egg, OÖGONIUM, undergoes a long, slow period of growth at the end of which it is termed an OÖCYTE of the first order. During the growth period chromosome synapsis takes place. The two maturation divisions take place, as in the origin of the spermatozoön, except that the divisions are very unequal with respect to the cytoplasm and yolk, one large cell nearly equal in size to the oöcyte and one small cell (POLAR BODY) being produced at each division. Sometimes the first polar body divides to form two small abortive eggs; and these, together with the second polar body, represent three of the four cells resulting from the maturation divisions. The fourth cell is the matured egg (OÖTID) with the haploid number of chromosomes. The polar bodies and the functional egg are alike in nuclear content, but extremely different in cytoplasmic content, for practically all of the cytoplasm that might be expected to be shared by four cells has been appropriated by one. The two kinds of maturated germ cells—spermatozoa and eggs—are known as GAMETES, a term which implies that they are cells that mate.

3. *Fertilization*

The union of two gametes—an egg and a spermatozoön—is the first event of fertilization. This union produces the fertilized egg, or ZYGOTE. The spermatozoön swims to the egg and enters it by penetrating the vitelline membrane. The entrance of one spermatozoön into an egg so alters the chemical character of the latter that no additional spermatozoa can enter. In the frog, only the head of the spermatozoön enters the egg, the tail being discarded. The head of the sperm soon rounds up into a spherical nucleus, known as the MALE PRONUCLEUS. At first this is much smaller than the nucleus of the egg, but it soon increases in size at the expense of the egg cytoplasm until male and FEMALE PRONUCLEI are equal or nearly so. Immediately the sperm enters the egg the surface membrane of the latter blisters up from the underlying protoplasm, leaving a fluid-filled space. This membrane is usually called the FERTILIZATION MEMBRANE and the space, the PERIVITELLINE SPACE.

4. *Cleavage*

Development begins with a series of mitotic cell divisions, which occur without any intervening growth. In spite of the rather large mass of yolk present, the cleavage furrows cut through the entire egg; thus cleavage here is total or HOLOBLASTIC. The first and second cleavages (Fig. 156, A, B) are from pole to pole (MERIDIONAL), giving rise to four equal BLASTOMERES. The third cleavage (Fig. 156, C) is slightly above the equator and parallel with the latter, and is said to be EQUATORIAL. This cleavage gives rise to four pigmented and slightly smaller cells of the animal pole (MICROMERES) and four unpigmented and somewhat larger cells at the vegetal pole (MACROMERES). The micromeres, having been derived from the more active region of the egg protoplasm, divide more rapidly than the macromeres; and hence the cells at the animal pole become considerably smaller and more numerous than those at the vegetal pole (Fig. 156, D). As the cells continue to divide, they form a hollow sphere, the BLASTULA (Fig. 156, E, F), with a

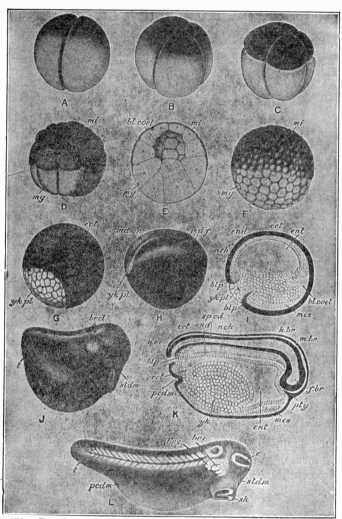

Fig. 156. Development of the Frog. **A-F**, cleavage; **G**, overgrowth of ectoderm; **H, I**, establishment of germ-layers; **J, K**, assumption of tadpole-
form and establishment of nervous system, notochord and enteric canal
(archenteron); **L**, newly-hatched tadpole. *bl. cœl*, blastocœle; *blp. blp'*,
blastopore; *br1. br2*, cutaneous gills; *br.cl*, branchial arches; *e*, eye; *ect*,
ectoderm: *end*, endoderm; *ent*, enteron; *f.br*, fore-brain; *h.br*, hind-brain;
m.br, mid-brain; *md.f*, medullary fold; *md.gr*, medullary groove; *mes*,
mesoderm; *mg*, macromeres; *mi*, micromeres; *nch*, notochord; *n.e.c*, neu-
renteric canal; *pcdm*, proctodæum; *pty*, pituitary invagination; *rct*,
commencement of rectum; *sk*, sucker; *sp.cd*, spinal cord; *stdm*, stomodæum; *t*, tail; *yk*, yolk cells; *yk.pl*, yolk plug. (From Parker and Haswell, after Ziegler and Marshall.)

342

fluid-filled cavity known as the BLASTOCŒLE, or CLEAVAGE CAVITY. The typical blastula stage in developing organisms is a one-layered stage, with all the cells exposed on the surface. In the frog, however, the large size of the cell and the accumulation of yolk have the effect of causing more or less crowding of some of the cells from the surface, giving the blastula the appearance of being several cell layers thick in some regions. Since, however, there is no difference between the superficial and the deeper cells, it may be claimed that this blastula is essentially one-layered.

5. *Gastrulation*

Typically, gastrulation consists of the folding in of the larger cells of the vegetal region to form an inner layer of cells called the ARCHENTERON, or primitive intestine. In the frog, the vegetal pole cells, the prospective ENDODERM, are so massive that a simple infolding would be very difficult. The difficulty is partly evaded by having the inpushing (INVAGINATION) of the endoderm take place at the thinnest part of the endoderm where ectoderm and endoderm meet. The archenteron is produced by a flat infolding just below the edge of the pigmented area, leaving a crescentic crease on the surface, which is the BLASTOPORE. Gastrulation is not considered complete until all of the endoderm cells are surrounded by ectoderm; so it becomes necessary for the more actively growing ectoderm cells (Fig. 156, G) to lend their aid. These fold over the exposed endoderm cells, like a cap being pulled over a head, until only a small opening, the true blastopore, is left (Fig. 156, H). The archenteron, at first quite flat, soon expands greatly and fills most of the cleavage cavity. Thus the finished gastrula, whose equivalent is found in nearly all Metazoa, is typically a two-layered stage with a layer of ectoderm outside and a layer of endoderm inside.

6. *Formation of Mesoderm*

Mesoderm formation is accomplished by the ingrowth of a sheet of cells around the margin of the blastopore, where ectoderm and endoderm meet. This zonelike layer soon splits into two sheets, an outer or SOMATIC LAYER and an inner or SPLANCHNIC LAYER, with the secondary body cavity, CŒLOM, between. Metameric cœlomic pouches arise from the dorsal lateral regions of the archenteron, and a median dorsal strip of the latter is left over to form the NOTO-CHORD.

7. *Formation of the Nervous System*

Development of the nervous system is decidedly precocious; for even in a late gastrula stage the MEDULLARY PLATE, a flattened sheet of ectoderm on the dorsal side, is clearly defined. At a time when the blastopore is nearly closed, the dorsal parts of the embryo have shaped themselves into a broad primitive furrow, flanked on both sides by two pairs of MEDULLARY FOLDS (Fig. 156, H), inner and outer. The outer ones fade away, but the inner ones arch over the groove and meet in the median dorsal line. They fuse together first in the region of the future neck, and from there fusion proceeds both forward and backward until the neural groove is converted into a NEURAL TUBE (Fig. 156, K). The anterior part of the neural tube soon becomes constricted so as to form the three primary brain vesicles, the primordia of the FORE-, MID-, and HIND-BRAINS. During these changes the embryo has been elongating, and before hatching reaches a length nearly three times as great as its breadth.

8. *Larval Period*

At the time of hatching the larva is somewhat fishlike in appearance, with a vertically flattened tail (Fig. 157, 1, 2). The mouth is ventral in position and is surrounded by a chitinous rim or scraper, a purely larval feeding organ used for scraping nutritive matter from the surfaces of aquatic plants. Two pairs of branching EXTERNAL GILLS (Fig. 157, 4), true larval organs, grow out from the sides of the head and act as the first of a series of respiratory organs. Somewhat later a fold of skin (Fig. 157, 5) appears in front of the gills and grows backward over the main part of the trunk, inclosing the gill region. This skin fold is known as the OPERCULUM. It has on the left side a single opening, the SPIRACLE (Fig. 157, 6), through which water may be passed from the gill slits to the outside. While the operculum has been growing backward, the external gills have been resorbed, and INTERNAL GILLS, much like those of adult fishes, take their place and constitute the second respiratory system of the developing frog. The frog at this stage has many anatomical features decidedly fishlike in character. Up till now no paired appendages have appeared, but this deficiency is soon made good. The hind legs are the first to develop (Fig. 157, 7–12), closely followed by the forelegs, which for some time grow

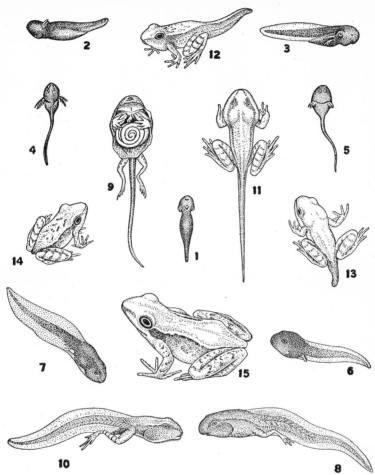

Fig. 157. Larval development of the frog and Metamorphosis. **1,** tadpole
just hatched, dorsal aspect; **2, 3,** older tadpoles, side view; **4, 5,** later
stages, dorsal views showing external gills and development of operculum; **6,** older tadpole, left side, showing single opening of operculum;
7, older stage, right side, showing hind leg and anus; **8,** and **10,** lateral
view of two later stages showing development of hind legs; **9,** dissection
of tadpole to show internal gills, spiral intestine, and anterior legs developed within operculum; **11,** advanced tadpole just before metamorphosis;
12, 13, 14, stages in metamorphosis, showing gradual resorption of tail;
15, juvenile frog after metamorphosis. (Redrawn after Leuckart-Nitsche
wall chart.)

underneath the operculum and cannot be seen from the outside. The tadpole at this stage is a strange looking object—neither fish, flesh, nor fowl; it is high time for something radical to happen.

9. *Metamorphosis*

The period of metamorphosis (Fig. 157, 12–15) is really part of the larval period and cannot be marked off sharply from the latter. One phase blends gradually into the other. Toward the close of the larval period the tail begins to be resorbed and the materials derived from its dissolution are stored up in the liver; the long spirally coiled intestine, a typical vegetarian organ, shortens up into the relatively short intestine appropriate for a carnivorous animal; the gills are resorbed and lungs appear and grow rapidly in size. At this time the polliwog comes to the surface to breathe air.

At the end of the period of metamorphosis the animal is no longer a larva, but an adolescent frog. Some species of frog go through their whole development up to adolescence in the course of a few weeks; others require several months; while the northern bullfrog (*Rana catesbiana*) sometimes takes three or four years— even longer larval periods have been reported—to reach the period of metamorphosis; and occasionally specimens remain permanently larval, steadily increasing in size until as large as some adults, but remaining polliwogs in every respect except that they become sexually mature. This interesting phenomenon, involving failure to metamorphose and sexual maturity in larvæ, is called NEOTENY or PÆDOGENESIS.

10. *The Period of Adolescence*

This is a long period, covering the time after the completion of metamorphosis up to sexual maturity. The chief changes involve alterations in the relative proportions of the parts, the head being at first relatively large and the legs relatively small. The young skeleton, largely cartilaginous at first, gradually ossifies. The most significant changes are those that are last to be initiated; namely, those that have to do with the onset of sexual maturity. Shortly before the beginning of the first breeding season, the cells of the ovaries and those of the testes begin to multiply and then to grow rapidly in size; the ducts of these gonads differentiate, and the processes of oögenesis and of spermatogenesis begin—processes that culminate in maturation, the point where we began our description of the frog's life cycle.

PART IV

DYNAMIC ASPECTS OF ZOÖLOGY

CHAPTER XXXI

BIOLOGICAL MECHANISMS

ACCORDING to the mechanistic view of life, a view well nigh universal in professional biological circles, an organism is a kind of machine. By a machine we mean a complex unit made up of many interoperating and coöperating parts, a unit that goes, and performs useful work. Parts of a machine may be appropriately called mechanisms.

A. Living and Lifeless Mechanisms Compared

A living machine resembles a lifeless machine in some important ways, but it differs in equally important ways. For convenience, let us compare a horse, a type of living machine, with an automobile, a type of lifeless machine.

Both the horse and the automobile are complex in structure and are made up of numerous parts that are connected up in definite ways with one another. In both of them every part bears a definite relation to every other part. In both of them the great majority of parts are essential to the functioning of the machine as a whole, but some parts are less essential than others. For example, the horse will go almost as well without a tail or minus an ear, while a motor car will perform as a vehicle as well without bumpers or fenders as with them. For the best functioning under all sorts of conditions, however, both machines need practically all of their parts.

Another resemblance between the horse and the automobile is seen in the fact that the motive power for running must be furnished by materials outside the machine. The automobile must have gasoline put into its tank and must take in air through its carburetor, while the horse must eat hay, oats, or other energy producing materials, must drink water and breathe air. The chief difference in the fueling of the two machines is that in the case of the car the fuel must be furnished in a highly refined form ready for immediate combustion, while in the case of the horse the fuel taken in is in a very crude state, requiring an elaborate process of refinement before it is in condition to be used for power production. If the automobile had its own refinery it would be more like a horse.

Once more, the horse and the car have certain parts that are mainly for protection against the dangers of the environment. The car has a hood over the engine, waterproof varnish over exposed parts, bumpers, springs to prevent jars, cooling and lubricating systems to prevent injury to moving parts, stop signals, horn, lights, and other mechanisms that help to prevent injury or destruction of the machine. Correspondingly, the horse has its most important working parts inside the body, well protected by the body wall and the ribs. It has a waterproof skin covered by a coating of hair to protect the surface, highly perfected temperature regulating mechanisms corresponding to a cooling system, hoofs and teeth to fend off dangerous enemies, and a host of other adaptations for maintenance and protection.

Again, both the horse and the car have centralized motivating parts. The battery and the timer, with their various accessories and connections, in some important ways corresponds to the central nervous system of the horse and its connections. By means of this centralized control both horse and motor car exhibit coördination in the operation of all moving parts. In the car centralized control enables all parts to move in harmony, any change in the speed of one part being accompanied by appropriate changes in all other parts. This is also true for the horse, for there are many synchronized functions, such as rate of respiration, rate of heart beat and circulation, and changes in body temperature, that are very closely correlated.

While there are many correspondences between the horse and the automobile, there are also many differences. You will immediately think of the fact that the horse needs no driver, but can control its own activities. It can get information about its environment and govern its movements accordingly. In contrast with this, the automobile cannot control its course without a human driver; it cannot get its own fuel or other necessities for operation.

Again, the automobile gradually wears out and needs repairs, while the horse repairs its worn parts as fast as they are in need of repair. Then the horse has the capacity of reproducing more horses like itself, a capacity unfortunately totally lacking in the automobile. The horse is able to modify itself in accord with changes in the environment, as when it grows a heavier coat of hair in cold weather, or when it increases its speed by training. Finally, the horse possesses intelligence, something totally lacking in any lifeless machine. This is hardly the place to discuss the nature and manifestations of intelligence, but we must not fail to realize that it is in this respect that we must draw the sharpest line between the living and the nonliving.

On the whole then it would seem that the differences between the living and the lifeless machine are more impressive than are the resemblances. Even if we go so far as to admit that the characteristics of the living machine that resemble those of the lifeless machine are subject to mechanistic interpretation, does this admission necessarily include those characteristics that are found only in the living? Are we in a position to assume that, because many of the activities of the organism are explained in physicochemical terms, all of the other activities may also be similarly explained? Are all vital activities expressions of mechanisms at work?

B. A Conception of Organic Mechanisms

Our answer to the above questions must depend upon our definition of mechanism. If we define a mechanism as a complex unit all the activities of which are explainable in terms of the known laws of matter and of energy as worked out for lifeless objects, it is obvious that living organisms will fall outside the scope of this definition. If, on the other hand, we define a mechanism as any complex unit in which any sort of transformations of energy and of matter are taking place, we make room for organisms in our definition. In so doing we remain in the realm of material things.

It seems obvious that the arrangement and configuration of chemical substances in life units differ from those in nonliving units, but this does not mean that anything immaterial is introduced at the life level. What it does mean is that when we pass from the lifeless level to the living level of material units there emerge as a consequence of the new order a whole set of entirely new properties that are in no sense inherent in the ingredients of which the life unit is composed. These higher expressions of energy are the product of the organization and configuration of all the component parts. They are what we term vital properties; they are essentially properties of the organism as a whole and depend upon the interaction of all the parts, for if the interrelations and interactions of parts become seriously deranged the vital properties are lost.

This view does not involve a denial of the mechanistic interpretation of life: it merely extends the definition of mechanism in a legitimate way so as to include a new level of mechanisms. It involves no concession to vitalism, for it introduces no immaterial or mystical forces presiding over the organism. The energies and the materials involved at the life level of units are to be thought of as *natural* materials and *natural* energies.

If then we realize that the most strikingly biological characteristics of organisms emerge only at the organic level of material units, we shall not expect to understand these characteristics solely in terms of the properties of nonliving units. It is our belief that the higher types of biological phenomena can be interpreted only in terms of biological facts and factors. The sooner this comes to be recognized, the sooner will real progress be made in the direction of a distinctive science of biology.

When we intimate that many of the higher vital phenomena are susceptible of analysis only in biological terms, we do not mean to imply that none of the processes going on in organisms are of the simpler sort that are explicable in purely physicochemical terms. The organism must be looked upon as living in a physicochemical environment and hence carrying on a traffic with this environment. It is to be expected that the organism will make use of all chemical or physical means that are useful in the maintenance of its relations with the environment. The fact is that a great many processes in organisms have been shown to be purely physicochemical; that many other processes have physicochemical aspects and accompaniments, though not fully understood in physicochemical terms; but there are still many biological phenomena that are as yet unintelligible in terms of the physics and chemistry of the nonliving world. It would be rash to say that these phenomena never will yield to physicochemical analysis, but the outlook at the present time is not very hopeful.

In spite of the situation just discussed, it is reasonable to think of organisms and their various integral parts as mechanisms, using the term in the broad sense in which we have defined it. In this definition we shall include all structures and activities that are regular and play a definite and useful part in the life of the organism, that are in a word adaptive.

It will be helpful in presenting the data about biological mechanisms if we are able to classify them. The two primary objectives of life, if we may use the term objective without implying any idea of purpose, are self maintenance and race maintenance. The individual must first keep itself internally adjusted and in normal relation with the environment; and it is equally important that the perpetuity of the race be maintained. We may then classify all mechanisms as those whose prime objective is self maintenance and those that are concerned chiefly with reproduction.

Mechanisms for self maintenance may be divided into two categories: those that regulate and coördinate the activities of the various parts of the organism itself, and those that serve to adjust the organism to the living and nonliving environment. Mechanisms for race maintenance include modes of reproduction, from the simplest to the most complex types. Incidental to race maintenance we shall consider all those mechanisms of racial change and racial adjustment that are included under the term "factors of organic evolution."

Following the scheme outlined above we may now consider the remaining chapters of the book as discussions of the various mechanisms involved in self maintenance and race maintenance.

CHAPTER XXXII

COÖRDINATING AND REGULATING MECHANISMS

ONE of the most fundamental characteristics of organisms is that they are units in the sense that all component parts are so correlated in their activities that they seem to be regulated by some central mechanism or mechanisms.

Two kinds of correlating mechanisms are recognized: chemical and nervous. By chemical regulation of bodily processes we mean the control of vital processes by chemical substances carried in the blood and lymph. These chemical substances are often the products of secretion of various glands in the body. Nervous regulation needs no special characterization at this juncture.

A. CHEMICAL REGULATING MECHANISMS

1. *The Maintenance of Chemical Neutrality*

One of the best regulated features of the body is the chemical neutrality of the blood. No matter how much acid or alkali enters the system in the food, the blood and lymph and even the protoplasm within the individual cells remains almost chemically neutral, at least so long as the system is in health. If the system becomes either too acid or too alkaline, serious disturbances follow, and the result is grave illness or even death. Now the fluid part of the blood consists of a complex solution of various chemical substances of which the following are the most important: various inorganic salts (chiefly the chlorides, sulphates, carbonates, and phosphates of sodium, calcium, potassium, and magnesium), proteins, carbohydrates, fats, enzymes, hormones, vitamines, and excretory products. How can such a complex mixture remain chemically neutral? The regulatory mechanism involved is very complex and involves several apparently independent agents.

The kidneys constitute one of the chief mechanisms for maintaining blood neutrality. These organs quite rapidly excrete any excess acid or alkali. The tissues of most of the other organs of the body are able to absorb and neutralize within the cells any excess acid or alkali that reaches them. The blood itself contains two important neutralizing mechanisms, one associated with blood proteins and the other with certain inorganic salts. The blood proteins are AMPHOTERIC, that is, they are able to combine equally well with either acids or alkalis and of neutralizing either one that happens to be in excess. The salts that have most to do with the maintenance of neutrality are known as BUFFERS and consist of certain carbonates and phosphates. Their mode of action may be illustrated by the following examples:—HCl (strong acid) when combined with Na_2CO_3 (weak alkali) produces NaCl (neutral) and $NaHCO_3$ (nearly neutral); again, NaOH (strong alkali) when combined with NaH_2PO_4 (weak acid) forms H_2O (neutral) and Na_2HPO_4 (more nearly neutral). All of these mechanisms, and some others not mentioned, combine forces to maintain blood and tissue neutrality and thus to preserve the health of the organism.

2. *The Clotting Mechanism of the Blood*

One of the necessary and most efficient regulatory mechanisms in the body is the clotting mechanism, an automatic emergency process. Whenever a cut or other injury causes the rupture of a blood vessel, an individual would be certain to bleed to death were it not for clotting. A blood clot is a sort of fibrous plug at the open end of a blood vessel that prevents the outpouring of blood. Clotting is the result of the quick crystallization of one of the blood proteins, FIBRINOGEN, in the form of needlelike or fibrous crystals that are able to form a tangled wad at the end of a ruptured vessel. The instigating cause of clotting is some substance produced when tissues are crushed or damaged, a substance known as THROMBIN, whose character is not fully known. The presence of this material in coöperation with the calcium in the blood causes clotting. Lest too frequent or too easy clotting take place, there is provided in the liver a substance known as ANTITHROMBIN that neutralizes thrombin if dangerous amounts are formed. Thus through the interaction of two antagonistic substances the body is protected from loss of blood.

3. *Digestion*

The actual processes of food digestion seem to be purely chemical, but the various steps in the complex series of changes are regulated partly by the nervous mechanism. The various chemical fluids involved in digestion are mainly saliva, gastric juice, pancreatic juice, and intestinal juices. The active principles of the several juices are called ENZYMES. Thus the enzyme of saliva, PTYALIN, changes insoluble starch into maltose, a soluble sugar; the enzyme of gastric juice, PEPSIN, changes proteins into soluble peptones and proteoses; the three enzymes of pancreatic juice, AMYLOPSIN, LIPASE, and TRYPSIN respectively change starch into maltose, fats into glycerin and fatty acids, and proteins into amino acids; and the enzymes of the intestinal juices, MALTASE, SUCRASE, and LACTASE, respectively change maltose, cane sugar, and milk sugar into simple sugars, while another intestinal enzyme, EREPSIN, completes the digestion of proteoses and peptones by converting them into amino acids.

This whole complex of chemical processes seems to be beautifully regulated in such a way that each earlier step sets going the next step. Thus the first stage of digestion, the secretion of saliva, is started by the smell or taste of food. This in turn starts gastric secretion. If food is forced into the stomach without permitting it to be smelled or tasted, no gastric secretion occurs; but the mere smell of highly palatable food makes the mouth water, and gastric juice is generated even if no food is forthcoming. Again, the secretion of gastric juice, especially the hydrochloric acid ingredient of it, stimulates the secretion of pancreatic juice. This acid, if introduced into the stomach without food, has the same effect. The other steps follow in definite sequence and are similarly conditioned by previous steps. There is something almost perfectly mechanical about the whole sequence, while the chemical changes can readily be duplicated in test tubes.

4. *Hormone Regulations of Growth*

In the bodies of all higher animals there are various glands of internal secretion, sometimes known as ductless or ENDOCRINE GLANDS that pour into the blood stream highly specific substances known as HORMONES, which are probably enzymes of a complex sort. Among the most important endocrine glands are the thyroids, adrenals, hypophysis, ovaries, and testes.

The THYROID GLANDS are especially important in regulating the whole metabolic rate of the body. If the thyroid be removed from a young rabbit, for example, growth is arrested, the metabolic rate is lowered, nervous activity is depressed, the growth of hair, teeth, and claws is impaired, and various degenerative processes set in. In short, the animal becomes a CRETIN. Sometimes a hereditary deficiency in thyroid secretion causes natural cretinism in both animals and man. It has been found that the active principle in the thyroid hormone is some compound of iodine, probably THYRO-GLOBULIN, and that injection of this substance into cretins, if they are not too old, will restore normal metabolic balance and enable the animal or the child to become normal.

The importance of the thyroid secretion as a regulator can hardly be overemphasized. No tissue, no cell even, in the body will function normally in the absence or deficiency of the thyroid hormone. On the other hand, excessive thyroid secretion has the opposite effect. Metabolism is speeded up far beyond the normal rate, resulting in too rapid oxidation of tissues, high excitability and irritability. If not relieved, this condition rather quickly results in death. The treatment for it consists in removing a sufficient part of the thyroid gland to reduce the amount of the hormone to normal. The mechanical nature of the thyroid regulating effect is seen clearly from the fact that the same regulation is readily duplicated by the injection or feeding of known chemical substances.

The rôle of the OVARIES and TESTES as endocrine glands, in contrast with their rôle as organs in which germ cells are produced, has received a great deal of attention during the last decade. The effects of both testicular and ovarian hormones upon the growth and differentiation of the secondary sex characters is well known. For example, the difference between the rich and elaborate plumage, head furnishings, and other features of the brown leghorn cock, and the contrastingly plain characters of the hen of the same breed, is accounted for by the difference in hormones. If the ovary of a young pullet be completely removed, the bird will develop plumage and head furnishings fully as fine as those of a cock, indicating that the ovary secretes a hormone that inhibits the development of the full specific plumage.

In mammals, such as rats, mice, guinea pigs, and others, the removal of the ovaries or testes from young animals prevents the development of the adult male or female secondary sexual characters, and the animal remains permanently juvenile or neutral. If, however, into a young animal from which the testes have been removed, a piece of ovary be introduced in such a way as to enable the latter to survive and grow, the animal will be more or less altered in a female direction. This shows that an individual genetically of one sex may be modified in the direction of the other sex by means of hormones.

A beautiful experiment conducted by Nature herself helps to make the function of the sex hormones quite clear. Professor F. R. Lillie has shown that, in cattle, twins occur in a small percentage of births and they come from two fertilized eggs, usually one egg coming from each ovary. As a rule, the two eggs develop in opposite horns of the two-branched uterus. Each embryonic vesicle grows excessively long and both extend down into the unpaired median portion of the uterus, where they come in contact and usually undergo more or less extensive fusion of their chorionic membranes. One sequel of this fusion of embryonic membranes is that the blood vessels of the two fœtuses fuse, or anastomose, and the blood streams of the two individuals become mixed. The result of this admixture of fœtal blood is as follows:—If both individuals of the pair are of the same sex no harm is done, but if they are of opposite sexes the female is always the one to suffer. She becomes profoundly modified in a male direction in all secondary sexual characters. Farmers have long known of these anomalous individuals and have called them FREEMARTINS (Fig. 158).

The explanation offered for this result is as follows:—The male gonads (testes) differentiate very early in fœtal life, while the female gonads (ovaries) differentiate much later. At the time when the blood streams of the two individuals mingle, the only sex hormone in circulation is the male hormone. The prospective female individual then comes under the controlling influence of the male hormone and is acted upon in such a way that the whole future differentiation of the individual is in a male direction. The change in sex trend takes place too late to result in the complete transformation of a prospective female into a typical male, for some female characteristics had already been fixed before blood admixture took place; but sometimes the transformation of sexes is nearly complete.

Nature furnishes a neat control experiment that strongly confirms the hormone theory of sex differentiation. Occasionally the fusion between the membranes of a male and of a female fœtus is less extensive than usual, and as a result there is no anastomosis of blood vessels, and hence no crossing over of male blood into the

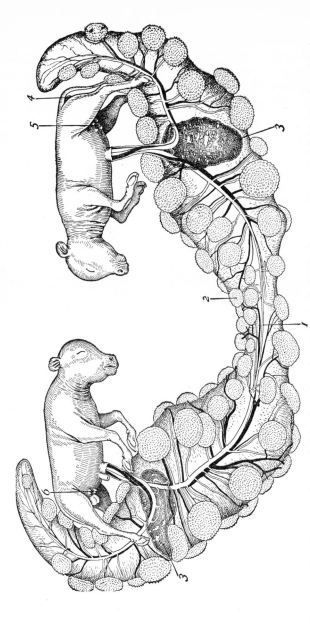

Fig. 158. A typical opposite-sexed pair of cattle twins, male on the left and freemartin on the right, showing: (1) the connecting artery between the two twins; (2) a single placental cotyledon entered by veins from both foetuses; (3) opening into the chorion through which the foetuses have been removed; (4) clitoris of the freemartins; (5) the well-separated anterior and posterior teats characteristic of the female; (6) the much closer teats characteristic of the male. (From Newman, after Lillie.)

female. As one might expect, there is no tendency for the female to be modified. In such cases the female developed as normally as did the twin male.

Many other striking situations similar to these have been brought to light in recent years, all illustrating the controlling effect of hormone mechanisms.

5. *Vitamins and Growth*

Within recent years biologists have become aware of certain important substances present in our common foods, substances whose chemical nature has not been ascertained, but which are essential to normal health and growth. In the strict sense these are not internal regulators, since they are taken in from the environment in foods; for that matter, so are all the materials in the living body. Hence this seems a reasonably appropriate place for the discussion of vitamins.

For want of better names these vitamins have been given such designations as "fat soluble A," "water soluble B," and "water soluble C." Vitamin A is essential to growth. Young animals fed on foods lacking vitamin A remain alive and apparently fairly healthy, but they do not grow. Fortunately this vitamin is present in a wide variety of common foods and is not likely to be lacking unless the diet has become extremely restricted. The lack of vitamin C causes scurvy, a disease long associated with a lack of fresh leafy vegetables, citrous fruits, tomatoes, and some other foods. Scurvy was most common among sailors on long sea voyages during which they could obtain no fresh vegetables or fruits. It is now known that a little lemon juice or canned tomatoes from time to time prevents the outbreak of scurvy, and will even cure fairly advanced cases. A new vitamine, discovered only a few years ago and called vitamin E, is necessary for the health and growth of the fœtuses of mammals during the last half of pregnancy. Fortunately again, this vitamin is widely distributed among common foods and is not very likely to be wanting. It is abundant, but none the less necessary.

The study of vitamins is in its infancy. There is much to be learned about their chemical character and other properties. The future has much in store for us in connection with research on these interesting regulators.

B. Nervous Regulating Mechanisms

Nervous regulatory and coördinating mechanisms range all the way from simple reflexes like some of those already described for the frog, through various types of conditioned reflexes, to the complex instincts of insects and other animals. Most nervous regulatory mechanisms are adaptive, but some are known to be harmful under special conditions, witness the attraction of moths and other insects to the flame. In this place we do not propose to cite many examples of nervous regulatory mechanisms, but merely to examine types of nervous mechanisms belonging to the different levels of complexity.

The REFLEX ACTION OF THE IRIS of the eye constitutes a fine example of a purely automatic and adaptive response based upon a simple reflex. When a beam of bright light strikes the eye, the pupil contracts; and when the light is shut off, the pupil expands. This result may be explained as follows: The rays of light striking the retina set up impulses that travel along the afferent nerves to the brain. These nerves form contacts with motor nerve cells in the brain, and the latter pass on the stimulus through efferent nerve fibers to the iris muscles. The stimulus causes these muscles to contract, and the diameter of the pupil is reduced. If the stimulus is removed, as when a light goes out and darkness ensues, the iris muscles relax because of lack of stimulation. All this happens without any voluntary act on the part of the individual and without his knowledge that anything has taken place. It occurs even under conditions of anæsthesia. For further examples of simple reflexes the student is referred to several cases described for the frog (p. 326).

Even the more complex forms of behavior in many animals are entirely involuntary and automatic, taking place normally even when the animal is entirely unconscious. Thus a frog with its cerebrum removed swims about if placed in water; while a decerebrated pigeon, if thrown into the air, flies for a time and then comes to rest in normal fashion. Without any exercise of the will and without being conscious of their movements, these animals carry on complex coördinated and adaptive activities that simulate purposeful action. Experiments on man under conditions of accidental or experimental anæsthesia show that he too carries on many of his activities in a purely automatic and mechanical fashion and without involving his higher nervous centers.

Many of the reflexes, both simple and complex, occur under given conditions with such mechanical precision that the result of any known stimulus is predictable. But this is not true of many of the conditioned reflexes of the most complex sort. The more nerve cells there are involved in a reflex, the less predictable becomes the result of a particular stimulus. Thus some reflexes do not depend so much upon the character of the immediate stimulus as upon previous experience. An animal that has always been fed when a bell rings behaves quite differently, when a bell rings, from an animal that has made no association between the sound of the bell and food. The bell stimulates a reflex in the first, but not in the second; in the first a conditioned reflex has been built up, but not in the second. Another way of saying the same thing is to assert that many of the more complex forms of reflex behavior are conditioned by, and depend upon, previous experience. This holds for human beings as well as for other animals.

The important question now arises as to just how much of human behavior is reflex in the sense that it is inevitably determined by previous experience; to what extent is any particular act that seems voluntary merely the inevitable and mechanical resultant of a complex of past experiences? Having raised this question, we do not propose to attempt to answer it, and this for various reasons. Chief of these is the fact that this is a textbook of Zoölogy and must not invade too far the fields of psychology and ethics.

C. Instinctive Regulating Mechanisms

Among many groups of animals, notably insects and birds, a large proportion of the so-called intelligent activities are so nearly machine-like in their regularity and so little dependent upon or modified by experience, that they stand in sharp contrast with the more plastic, or modifiable, types of intelligence exhibited by man and other mammals.

Investigation has shown that many, if not all, of these instinctive forms of behavior, no matter how complex and apparently purposeful they may be, are purely reflex in character. In many cases the instinctive acts take place without any previous training and show little or no improvement with practice. The web-building instinct of spiders and the nest-building and subsequent activities of birds may be cited as examples of complex chain reflexes. The first act involved in such behavior complexes seems to depend upon some immediate stimulus originating within the organism or coming from the environment. The first act furnishes the stimulus for the second, the second for the third, and so on to the end of the series. If the series be artificially interrupted at any point, it can not be resumed where it was broken off, but the whole series must be begun all over again. Thus, if a bird be seriously interrupted in nest building or while incubating eggs, it will usually start a new nest. This emphasizes the mechanical character of these types of behavior.

Various instinctive activities of insects have already been described for ants and other animals, and further examples of instincts are to be discussed in the chapter on adaptations. Therefore we shall refrain from the citation of further examples in this place. Suffice it to say that we are now confident that most, if not all, of these activities are the result of fixed and inherited nervous patterns. This being the case it is correct to speak of them as mechanisms that regulate the activities of the organism as a whole.

In the next three chapters we propose to discuss on a mechanistic basis the various means by which the organism adapts itself to its environment. In the chapter on *Sense Organs* we shall deal with those special mechanisms that put the organism in touch with the environment by giving him information about it. In the chapter on *Adaptations* we shall deal in a very general way with a wide range of structural and behavioral devices that help the organism to maintain itself in an environment that is partly friendly and partly inimical to its interests. In the chapter on the *Web of Life* we shall discuss primarily the important fact that in any animal and plant community there is an intricate interplay of life forces that necessitates an adjustment of each living type to others, resulting in an equilibrium of the whole ecological complex. This balance or adjustment of the various components of the complex is to be considered as a manifestation of a marvelously complex biological mechanism.

CHAPTER XXXIII

SENSE ORGANS

In previous chapters we have referred to many sorts of sense organs present in the various types of animals studied. Very little attention, however, has been given to the physiology of these organs or to the ways in which the organism employs them to keep in touch with the environment. These matters are now to receive our attention.

Even among some of the more highly specialized Protozoa there are recognized certain specialized parts that serve as receptors of particular types of stimulation. As a rule, however, the Protozoa lack specialized receptors, the entire surface being sensitive to stimuli of all sorts.

In some of the lowest Metazoa, moreover, there is little or no specialization of localized sense organs. In Hydra, for example, the whole surface may be considered as a generalized receptor for a great variety of stimuli. When we come to Planaria, however, the eyespots and the auricles constitute definite sense organs, the eyespots being specialized for the reception of light stimuli and the auricles for mechanical and chemical stimuli.

A. Sense Organs for Contact Perception and Distance Perception

Among the higher animals the organs of sense may be separated into two categories on the basis of whether they receive stimulation by direct contact with the object or whether they receive information about objects at a distance. Under the first type may be listed the tactile, temperature, olfactory, gustatory (taste), and equilibrium sense organs. Under the second type we may include only the auditory and the visual sense organs, although in a certain way the olfactory sense may also be thought of as a distance sense.

Among the contact senses we may characterize the TACTILE SENSE as that through which the organism becomes aware of the physical characteristics of surfaces. Closely allied with the tactile sense is the TEMPERATURE SENSE, for which there are special end organs distinct from tactile organs. The OLFACTORY and GUSTA-TORY sense organs are closely allied, the former receiving stimuli from chemicals in the gaseous condition, the latter from chemicals in the liquid state. The olfactory sense organs consist of specialized epithelial cells forming part of the lining of the nasal passages, while the organs of taste consist of little aggregations of specialized epithelial cells found in definite regions of the tongue and palate. In none of the types of sense units dealt with in the preceding paragraph is there any highly localized, compact grouping of the sensory elements into a well defined organ. Those sensory units are merely specialized epithelial cells scattered over considerable surfaces. The situation, however, is far different in the remaining organs of special sense, those of equilibrium, of hearing, and of vision. Each of these deserves separate and special treatment.

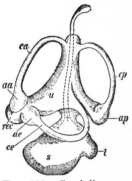

FIG. 159. Semi-diagrammatic view of the left membranous labyrinth of a lower vertebrate. *s, l,* sacculus; *u, rec,* utriculus. The three semicircular canals are lettered *aa, ca; ae, ce;* and *ap, cp.* Laguna, *l,* a derivative of the sacculus becomes the cochlea of higher vertebrates. (From Wiedersheim.)

B. ORGANS OF EQUILIBRIUM

In the vertebrates, which we shall call upon to furnish examples of all the remaining types of sense organs, the organ of equilibrium consists of the SEMICIRCU-LAR CANALS. These canals form part of the MEMBRANOUS LABYRINTH of the inner ear, a complicated system of fluid filled sacs and canals. The whole membranous labyrinth (Fig. 159) has two main parts, the SACCULUS and the UTRICULUS. From the utriculus come off the three semicircular canals, one in each plane of space. The sacculus is mainly devoted to the reception of vibrations and hence constitutes the organ of hearing, about which we shall have a good deal more to say in the next section. For the present, let us confine our attention to the semicircular canals.

Each canal terminates in an enlarged bulb, or AMPULLA, at the point of communication with the utriculus. The epithelium of the ampullæ is especially sensitive to movements of the fluid in the canals which take place when the body changes its orientation in space. The whole mechanism operates somewhat on the principle of a complex living spirit level that registers all changes in the orientation of the body. If the body tilts to the right, more fluid flows into the canal and ampulla inclined to that side. This produces an irritation in the nerve endings in that ampulla, an irritation that when conducted to the brain is interpreted as a definite tilt of the body in a given direction. Thus a bird flying, or a fish swimming in the dark, is able to keep right side up and trimmed both laterally and fore and aft.

Since the equilibrium sense necessitates immediate contact of moving fluid, it may be classed as a contact sense, but it differs from other contact senses in having a rather complex organ.

While in higher vertebrates the organ of equilibrium seems to be an accessory to the organ of hearing, this has not always been the case. On the contrary, there is good evidence that ancestrally the organ of equilibrium is older than the organ of hearing and that the membranous labyrinth was originally used mainly, if not exclusively, for equilibration. As evidence of this it may be said that in the lowest vertebrates now living, such as hagfishes and lampreys, the labyrinth seems to be almost entirely an organ of equilibrium, whereas the higher we go among the vertebrates the more important become the auditory specializations of this organ of dual functions.

C. Auditory Organs

The auditory organ of the higher vertebrates is a complicated piece of machinery. In addition to the sense organ proper, which resides in the sacculus of the membranous labyrinth, there are several sound collecting and sound transmitting accessories. Referring to the illustration (Fig. 160), we see that the human ear consists of an OUTER EAR, consisting of a PINNA and an external auditory passage; a MIDDLE EAR, provided with an eardrum (TYMPANIC MEMBRANE) separating the outer and middle ears, a set of small articulated bonelets (MALLEUS, INCUS, and STAPES), and the EUSTACHIAN TUBE; and an INNER EAR consisting of the spirally coiled COCHLEA, a derivative of the sacculus.

The external ear functions as an ear trumpet for gathering and modulating sound waves; the middle ear is a sort of resonating chamber equipped with a vibrating membrane to which is attached a transmitting apparatus that conducts vibrations to the sensory portion of the organ; and the inner ear contains the sound receptors. This whole mechanism is about as complex as a phonographic recording instrument and not unlike the latter mechanically.

The PINNA in man is quite degenerate as compared with those of some of the other mammals, notably the horse and other ungulates, in which we find a true sound-focusing trumpet. This instrument is provided with a set of muscles that turn it about in various positions in such a way that the direction of a sound can

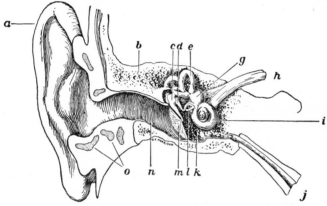

FIG. 160. Front view of the human organ of hearing, right side. *a*, pinna of outer ear; *b*, bone of skull; *c*, *d*, *l*, transmitting bones, malleus, incus, and stapes; *e*, one of the three semicircular canals; *g*, vestibule; *h*, auditory nerve; *i*, cochlea; *j*, Eustachian tube; *k*, tympanic chamber of middle ear; *m*, tympanic membrane; *n*, external auditory passage; *o*, cartilage. (From Woodruff.)

be determined. In man the same set of muscles is present in a paralyzed condition and the pinna is stiff and immovable, facts that indicate that the ancestors of man had movable ears.

The sensory portion of the auditory apparatus is located in the coiled COCHLEA. An examination of this structure shows the sensory epithelium in the form of elongated cells standing up more or less separately from the floor of the cavity. Each cell seems to terminate in minute bristlelike processes, that doubtless have to do with the reception of vibrations. In a sense, each sensory cell may be thought of as a living tuning fork capable of vibrating to sounds of a particular wave length. Each sense cell has a nerve fiber that runs to the auditory center of the brain, where vibrations are translated into terms of sound. Over the groups of sensory cells there lies a membrane, known as the membrane of Corti, that is believed to act as a dampener for vibrations, thus preventing any more than a momentary vibration from one stimulus. This whole apparatus is known as the ORGAN OF CORTI, and is a fine example of a complex living mechanism.

D. ORGANS OF VISION

Of all the sense organs the eyes of the higher vertebrates are most readily interpreted in mechanistic terms, for they are con-

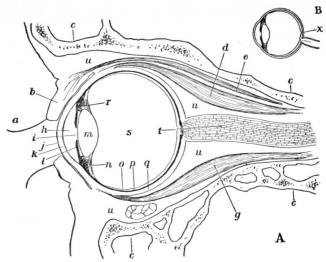

FIG. 161. **A,** vertical section of human eye *in situ.* **B,** horizontal section to show relation of optic nerve to fovea centralis (*x*), through which the optical axis passes. *a,* eyelash; *b,* lid; *c,* bony orbit; *d,* superior rectus muscle; *e,* muscle of upper lid; *g,* inferior rectus muscle; *h,* anterior chamber filled with aqueous humor; *i,* pupil; *j,* conjunctiva; *k,* cornea; *l,* iris; *m,* lens; *n,* suspensory ligament of lens; *o,* retina; *p,* choroid coat; *q,* schlerotic coat; *r,* muscles of suspensory ligament; *s,* vitreous chamber; *t,* point of entrance of optic nerve; *u,* fatty connective tissue. (From Woodruff.)

structed along lines analogous to those of man-made optical instruments, such as photographic cameras. The RETINA, though curved instead of lying flat like a film or plate, corresponds to the latter in being the light sensitive surface. The LENS of the eye plays the same rôle as the lens of the camera, at least up to a certain point. The IRIS of the eye operates in much the same way as the diaphragm of the camera. The eyelids are like the shutter, and the eye socket like the case of the camera. Beyond this the resemblances cease and marked differences are to be noted. Thus the focusing mechanisms of the two instruments are utterly different: The camera is focused by sliding the lens back and forth, increasing or decreasing its distance from the plate or film; while in the eye the lens changes its shape through the action of muscles attached to its rim, thus focusing without changing the position of the lens. The illustration (Fig. 161) gives a good idea of the cameralike construction of the human eye.

The nervous components of the visual organ consist of the retina, the OPTIC NERVE, and the VISUAL CENTER in the brain. Light rays of various wave lengths pass through the transparent chorion at the front of the eyeball, through the opening of the diaphragm-like iris (the pupil), and through the lens, by means of which they are focused on the retina in an inverted position. Each light sensitive cell (ROD or CONE) receives a stimulus from a ray of light of a particular wave length and transmits this stimulus along a nerve fibril to some cell in the visual center of the brain. There the various stimuli are correlated to form a mental

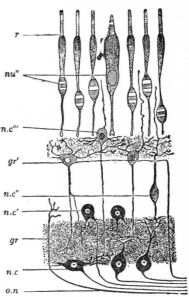

FIG. 162. Diagram of nervous elements of human retina. *gr, gr',* granular layers; *nc, nc', nc'', nc''',* nerve cells; *nu'',* nuclear layer of rods and cones; *o.n,* fibers of optic nerve; *r,* sensory cells (rods and cones). (From Wiedersheim, after Stöhr.)

picture of the object from which the light rays have emanated.

The RETINA consists of several layers, all of which are shown somewhat diagrammatically in Figure 162. The layer of nerve fibers lies next to the VITREOUS HUMOR of the eyeball. The layer of RODS AND CONES points toward the brain. The function of the other layers needs no special comment in a general discussion.

The eye as a whole is a very complex piece of machinery, which is to a very large extent self-operating and self-adjusting. Though imperfect in some respects, it is one of Nature's finest mechanisms.

CHAPTER XXXIV

ADAPTATIONS IN GENERAL

A. Fitness in the Living World

"Adaptability," says *Conklin,* "may be defined as the power of self-regulation, self-preservation, and race perpetuation, by means of which living things are enabled not only to remain alive but also to adjust themselves to varied environmental conditions and to leave offspring. From the standpoint of any species the best that can happen is to increase and multiply, the worst is to become extinct. Self-preservation and race perpetuation are the *summum bonum;* everything that prevents or hinders these is injurious or unfit. Adaptability is a fundamental property of living things without which life itself could not long persist, for, as *Herbert Spencer* has said, life is 'the continuous adjustment of internal relations to external relations.' The origin of this or of any other fundamental property of life, such as metabolism, reproduction, or irritability, is shrouded in the same mystery as the origin of life itself."

It has long been the fashion among biologists as well as among the laity to marvel at the perfection of everything in Nature. This is a backwash from the long prevalent doctrine of supernatural design, according to which everything was created perfect. Realization has gradually grown stronger and stronger that adaptiveness and fitness are purely relative terms. The most perfect adaptations we know leave much room for improvement. Even that wonderful adaptation, the human eye, falls far short of being a perfect mechanism. The well known physicist, *Helmholtz,* is reported to have said of the human eye that, were an optician to send him so imperfect an instrument, he would send it back to him with the request that he learn his business. Yet in many respects the human eye is as perfect an adaptation as there is in Nature. Thousands of kinds of eyes, some of them many times less efficient than that of man, exist in successful types of organisms. Evidently, then, adaptation is a relative matter and there is room for improvement all along the line.

For many years after the publication of Darwin's *Origin of Species* the chief pursuit of naturalists seems to have been to seek out and to describe marvelous adaptations. So popular did this search after the wonderful in Nature become that there arose a cult of "nature fakers," who, on the slenderest bases, built up extraordinary adaptive complexes that never existed and invented imaginary conditions to fit them. So uncritical as to adaptations was this period that it came to be assumed that everything about a surviving species must be adaptive, else it would have been eliminated in the course of natural selection. Thus, whenever apparently useless, negative, or even positively harmful characters were observed, these were explained as having at some former time been adaptive or as destined to have adaptive value in the future under changed conditions of life. Some even went so far as to assert that our failure to see the adaptive value of a character was due to our ignorance of its real function.

In spite of all this adaptation worship, it now has come to be generally admitted that many so-called adaptations have failed to meet a critical test of their values, and we are forced to conclude that every organism is a complex of both adaptive and nonadaptive characters. This being the case, it should be evident that nonadaptive characters have evolved and that causal theories of evolution based entirely upon adaptive values of individual characters are in need of modification.

B. Suggested Explanations of Certain Types of Adaptations

a. Ontogenetic Adjustments.—Many phases of the general adaptiveness of organisms may be attributed to the molding effect of the environment upon the growing individual; for in order to grow up in any given environment an organism must be in harmony with the environment at every stage of development. According to this view there is no escape from fitness; given a certain environment within which an organism must grow, the adaptiveness of an organism that succeeds in reaching maturity is inevitable. It is a common observation of experimental embryologists that any appreciable alteration of the environmental complex normal for a given species of embryo results in more or less profound modifications of the normal characters of the species. Such direct responses to changed environment are not truly adaptations, except in the sense that living protoplasm is plastic and has the capacity to change under changed external conditions. What we call normal, then, may not be any more truly adaptive than the abnormal, but merely the particular structural expression that results when a certain kind of protoplasmic complex develops under the usual or prevailing environmental conditions.

Many other adaptations are at least partially due to functioning during development. In a fish embryo, for example, the heart musculature develops poorly and atrophies if, for any reason, the embryonic blood supply is cut off or seriously diminished. Again, in certain types of one-egg human twins it is not uncommon for the placental blood vessels of the two individuals to anastomose in such a way that one twin gets more than its share of the common blood supply. The result is that the blood pressure of one twin becomes seriously reduced, the heart has too little work to do, and either atrophies or becomes greatly reduced in size and in strength; while the heart of the other twin, with more than the normal amount of blood and thus more fluid to keep in circulation, becomes abnormally large and muscular. These and many similar facts that might be cited tend to show that much of the fitness of certain organs for special functions is the result of practice during embryonic periods and afterwards. Some writers go so far as to claim that all structure is the result of function, that function is merely a special form of chemical activity that leaves its mark as structure. Thus, function has been compared to a stream that molds its banks and bottom, leaves a sand bar here or makes an island there as structural evidence of its activity. While there is doubtless much truth in this point of view, it should not be forgotten that there are many organs of the most definite functional importance whose structure is complete before they have any chance to exercise their special functions. Thus, the human eye, which develops up to almost the definitive condition in total darkness, if it may be said to have functioned at all, certainly cannot have functioned as an organ of vision. Similarly, the lungs are almost fully formed before the infant gets its first breath of air; the organs of taste develop before there is anything to taste; and the vocal cords are well developed before a single cry has been possible. It is obvious, of course, that all these organs have been functioning in a general way; they have had to carry on the ordinary processes of metabolism. But the point to be emphasized is this: that they have not functioned in the particular ways that we call adaptive until the adaptive features have already reached their definitive condition.

b. Habitat Selection.—The claim has commonly been made by ecologists that much of the alleged fitness of organisms to their environment is due to the fact that many animals try out a great variety of environments and select the one best suited to their individual needs. When they find an environment best suited to them, they tend to stay there because all less suitable environments cause them more or less unrest. It is to be expected therefore, if the above thesis be granted, that any species that has locomotor powers and a wide range of environments to choose from will appear well fitted to its environment. To what extent the theory of "habitat selection" solves the problem of the fitness of organisms to their special environments it is difficult to decide, but it is our conviction that only minor degrees of adaptiveness result from this factor.

Our purpose has been to present a fair and critical statement regarding fitness in the living world. While we are willing to grant that there has been a marked tendency to exaggerate the perfection of adaptations and to read into Nature a universal fitness, we cannot agree with those who have attempted to explain away adaptations altogether by showing that they are all ontogenetic, *i.e.*, repeated each successive generation under the molding influence of environment and function. This would be tantamount to a denial that any adaptations are hereditary. One extreme is as bad as the other.

C. Two Categories of Adaptations

There are, according to *Conklin,* two categories of adaptations: (*a*) racial or inherited adaptations, and (*b*) individual, acquired, or contingent adaptations. "Inherited adaptations are those which appear in the organism as if in anticipation of future needs and not as the result of present ones." In this category are the eyes, lungs, vocal organs, organs of taste, and many other organs of the human fœtus. This is the kind of adaptation that the physiologist cannot explain away as merely due to the molding effect of environment or function or to habitat selection. Such adaptations have obviously evolved in some way, but there is as yet no really adequate theory as to the causes responsible for their origin and fitness.

D. Some Remarkable Inherited Adaptations

1. *The Bird an Adaptation for Flight*

One of the most thoroughly adapted organisms in the world is a flying bird. Its various flight adaptations seem to be as definitely built for their varied purposes as are the parts of an airplane; of the two, the bird does the job of flying more expertly than does the man-made machine. Both the bird and the airplane are to be classed as heavier-than-air flying machines. Now, the requisites for a heavier-than-air flying machine are somewhat as follows: (*a*) broad planing surfaces capable of adjusting to varying wind pressures; (*b*) minimum weight with maximum rigidity of framework; (*c*) rapid and sustained production of power; (*d*) steering

Fig. 163. Heron flying: showing clearly the mechanism of flight. (From Jordan and Kellogg, after Marey.)

and balancing devices. The bird meets the first requirement by means of its highly perfected flight feathers (Fig. 163), that cooperate in such a way as to make up a pair of planes with just the right amount of rigidity combined with enough flexibility to admit of the necessary adjustment to sudden or unequal changes of air pressure. The wings are also propellers; in this they are distinctly different from the planes of an airplane. The second feature of importance is that of economy of weight without sacrifice of strength and rigidity. The bird meets this condition by the use of well known engineering principles, such as tubular instead of solid bones, the use of bony T beams, the use of diagonal braces and counterbraces of several kinds. Thus the bony framework of the bird has scarcely half the weight, as compared with the total body weight, of that in other vertebrates. Weight is further counterbalanced by the use of air sacs that fill all vacant spaces of the body, even the hollows of the bones, and by the use of feathers, whose lightness is proverbial for planes, rudder, and body covering.

Great and sustained power is secured partly through a most efficient engine—that great mass of pectoral muscles, whose work is nearly always so well within its capacity that tiring does not readily occur. Moreover, the lungs supply oxygen to the engine more effectively than do those of any other vertebrate; for the cold air goes directly to the air sacs, is heated before reaching the lung tissues proper, and then the exhausted air is passed out. There is thus a sort of through draft, and this prevents the admixture of pure with impure air. Even when at rest, the temperature of the bird's body is as high as 112 degrees Fahrenheit, and much higher when the bird is actively flying. At such temperatures metabolic activities go on more efficiently than at lower temperatures. For steering and balancing devices the bird has a tail capable of spreading fanwise so as to give a greater or less surface, and of lowering or elevating the path of flight. The planes, too, are jointed so as to enable them to adjust themselves to shifting wind pressures; while the head and the legs can be extended or drawn in to give the required balance. These and many other striking adaptations of the bird are examples of the kind of adaptations that are largely developed before they ever function in the particular ways for which they are adapted.

2. *Some Offensive and Defensive Devices*

Animals have anticipated man in the invention of nearly all of the standard methods of warfare. The use of armor has long been a favorite defense in such animals as the armadillos and the turtles. The use of spikes and spines of all sorts has been effective in such animals as sea urchins, hedgehogs, and porcupines. Attack-proof shelters have been made use of by mollusks, barnacles, trunkfishes.

The use of poisoned darts and spears has long been effective for both attack and defense in the cases of bees, wasps, scorpions; while many animals, such as serpents, lizards, spiders, and others, make equally effective use of poisonous fangs. As an expert in gas warfare let us recommend the skunk and his nonchalant tribe. The squid by shooting out his ink wad is said to becloud the water much as does a smoke screen in naval maneuvers. Killing by electric shock through charged wires is paralleled by several kinds of fishes (Fig. 164) in which masses of voluntary muscles have become modified in such a way that they function as storage batteries of such efficiency that they are able to give off an electric discharge strong enough to stun a large enemy.

The art of CAMOUFLAGE was learned by man after a serious study of the various schemes for protective coloration in common use among animals. The scheme of blending with the background is the commonest of all color adaptations. Green insects fade from view among the green leaves in the grass, and variously colored or mottled insects live among colored flowers or against the mottled background afforded by lichens. Kallima, the dead-leaf butterfly (Fig. 165), can scarcely be distinguished from a leaf. Transparent organisms live in the translucent waters of the sea. Many animals, such as chameleons and flounders, have the ability to change their colors in harmony with varied and changing backgrounds.

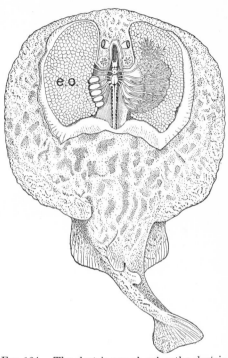

Fig. 164.   The electric ray, showing the electric organs, *e.o.* (Redrawn after Leuckart-Nitsche wall chart.)

Many well defended animals, such as wasps and venomous serpents, are commonly marked with contrasting bands or spots of different colors, a supposed adaptation said to function as a warning, like a sign reading "Dangerous. Keep off!" The idea involved is that birds or other enemies, once attacking these conspicuous animals and getting stung or bitten, will in the future associate an unpleasant experience with a particular color combination and avoid it.   This furnishes the basis for another alleged type of camouflage known as MIMICRY, the facts being these: Many otherwise defenseless animals resemble in very striking ways such animals as the bees and wasps, not only looking like them but humming like them and behaving like them. The interpretation usually offered for this situation is that these mimics assume the colors of well defended animals as a measure for self defense, thus flying a false flag. In this place it would hardly be feasible to enter into a detailed discussion as to the validity of the supposed phenomenon of mimicry, but it should be said that there are some potent reasons for refusing to accept at its face value the interpretation given.

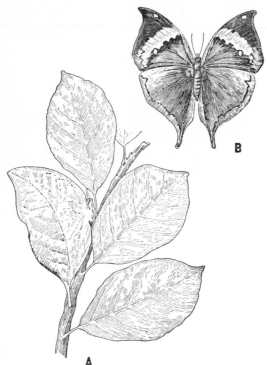

The art of disguise has been highly perfected among animals. They very frequently make use of the scheme of looking like something harmless or

Fig. 165.   *Kallima*, the "dead-leaf butterfly." **A,** butterfly resting among leaves; **B,** same seen from above with wings spread. (Redrawn after wall chart.)

attractive.   Thus a well known mantis, an insect of prey, looks almost exactly like a certain species of orchid blooms among which it awaits its prey.   Nectar-hunting insects fly into the waiting arms of this living trap.   In Java there lives a species of predacious spider closely resembling a bit of bird excrement upon which butterflies are wont to alight; and when they do so, they are caught and their blood sucked out by the disguised spider. The walking-stick insect (Fig. 166) exhibits as effective a disguise as any within our experience.   In shape, in color, in rigidity and immovability when in danger it perfectly simulates a twig.   The same scheme is employed by many species of caterpillars (Fig. 167).

After all, however, there is no passive defense that compares in effectiveness with a good vigorous offense. Thus, the majority of animals, even those of peaceful dispositions who would avoid a fight by the use of concealment, when hard pressed, make use of spurs, claws, teeth, fangs, horns, hoofs, spines, pincers, odoriferous

FIG. 166. A Walking-stick Insect, *Diapheromera femorata*, on a twig. (From Jordan and Kellogg.)

FIG. 167. Larva of a geometrid moth resting extended from a twig. (From Jordan and Kellogg.)

glands, nauseous exudations, slimy secretions, and many other defensive weapons, in a determined struggle for life and liberty. All of the adaptations described in this section are inherited and are not ontogenetically molded by functioning.

3. *Adaptive Behavior*

Instincts of every degree of adaptive value exist among animals. Many animals, without any preliminary training at all, perform marvelously expert tasks. The building of elaborate nests by birds, by spiders, by fishes, are examples of the inborn equipment of animals. It is claimed by some authorities that a bird's first nest is rarely so good as subsequent nests, but even the first nest indicates the inheritance of a highly adaptive type of nervous response, already practically perfected as though in anticipation of its use. Likewise, the salmon, after spending five years in the sea, is impelled by an uncontrollable instinct to swim up the parent river to the headwaters where it had itself been spawned, there to mate and produce its progeny. In doing this the adult salmon wear themselves out through their long and strenuous exertions. This instinct is highly adaptive, for it is essential that the eggs and young be laid in the cool, well oxygenated waters of the headwater streams.

The various instincts involving provision for and care of the young are among the most perfect of adaptations. The mother mud wasp builds clay galleries in which she stores fresh meat for the prospective young wasp grubs. The provender consists of living (sometimes dead) bodies of spiders or caterpillars, that have been stung in their nerve centers and thereby paralyzed. The instinct of the worker bees and ants to take care of and feed the young of the queen of the colony appears to be an instinct involving some evidences of altruism, but the authorities do not give it this interpretation. The workers are themselves females, but they are sterile and cannot have young of their own. Instead, they have an exaggerated obsession for taking care of the young of others, an instinct that is not infrequently imposed upon by parasitic dwellers in the homes of ants.

Instincts often appear precociously in larvæ in adaptation to an early need to shift for themselves. The most astonishing piece of instinctive behavior in very young animals was recently described by **Hartman** for fœtal opossums. Seven days after the egg was fertilized the tiny opossum fœtuses emerge from the maternal uterus as blind, naked, pink, grublike things less than a half inch in length. As they emerge one after the other, they quickly turn toward the anterior end of the mother and begin to plow with surprising vigor through the dense hair of the mother's abdomen, using the abnormally large, flipperlike fore limbs with a hand-over-hand motion like that of a swimmer. Each little fellow plows its way through the hairy forest straight to the marsupial pouch of the mother, enters the latter, and finds a slender teat, which it swallows deep into its throat and holds fast by means of a precociously developed larval holdfast mouth. If more young are born at one time than there are teats—and this is usually the case—a struggle for the right to live ensues, and sometimes an early occupant is ousted from his claim by a stronger though later claimant. Once thoroughly clamped to a teat, the larva remains attached for weeks on end, and can hardly be pulled away from it. Hence, unless removed before it is fully established, its success is assured. Thus the standard of strength and aggressiveness is maintained through the elimination of the weak.

4. *Reproductive and Developmental Adaptations*

As has already been pointed out, the mitotic mechanism is ideally adapted to be the machine for the maintenance of the integrity of hereditary materials and for their transmission to progeny. Similarly, the mechanisms of maturation and fertilization are wonderfully effective adaptations for inducing variety in organisms and thus helping to furnish the raw materials for evolution. It has been shown that sex is an adaptation to encourage reproduction, and that all of the secondary sexual characters, including mating instincts and behaviors, are adaptations to facilitate the most important of all ends, racially speaking, that of increasing the numbers and therefore the dominance of the species; for in numbers there is strength and perpetuity.

Special breeding habits afford interesting examples of fitness. One common adaptation is that of carrying the young in the oviduct or uterus of the mother until it is sufficiently advanced to take care of itself. This phenomenon is known as VIVIPARITY and is in contrast with OVIPARITY, or the laying of eggs containing undeveloped or only partially developed embryos. Examples of viviparity range all the way from quite lowly organisms up to man, and it is found in some representative of nearly every large group. Thus, it is found in snails, in many insects, in spiders, in many fishes, in sharks, in salamanders, in snakes and in nearly all mammals. In oviparous animals, where the young have to develop outside of the mother's body, many schemes for protecting the eggs are known, that of nest building being the most common. Some species make animated nests out of parts of their own bodies. Thus, the Surinam Toad (Fig. 168) lays her eggs, with the assist-

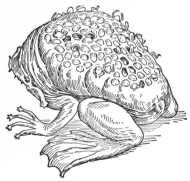

ance of the male, upon her back; these sink into pits in the soft, spongy skin, where they remain until hatched out as competent young toads. Again, the sea horse (Fig. 169), a very curiously modified teleost fish, exhibits a kind of paternal care that would shame many a higher type. The father fish takes the fertilized eggs into his bosom,

FIG. 168. The Surinam Toad, *Pipa americana*, showing method of rearing young on the back. (From Newman, after Lydekker.)

storing them in a brood pouch made by uniting his pelvic fins along their outer edges. He carries these about with him until they hatch, and even then does not abandon them but watches over them for some time.

Examples of the solicitude of the mother for her young are so numerous as hardly to need comment, but are none the less important from the adaptational point of view. A lower animal can have no premonition of offspring, nor can she realize the relationship existing between herself and her young; yet she will frequently give up her life for her young. The instincts associated with reproduction are among the strongest and most unreasoning of

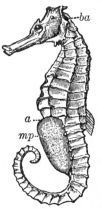

FIG. 169. *Hippocampus guttatulus*. Male, showing brood pouch (*mp*). *a*, anus; *ba*, branchial aperture. (From Boulenger.)

all instincts, and the hardest to break up or change; witness the " setting " hen or the clasping male frog.

5. *Adaptations of Deep-sea Animals*

One of the weirdest environments the world affords is the bottom of the sea at great depths. There it is dark and cold and almost lacking in oxygen, while the pressure is almost unbelievably great. Yet these vast and forbidding abysses are inhabited by all sorts

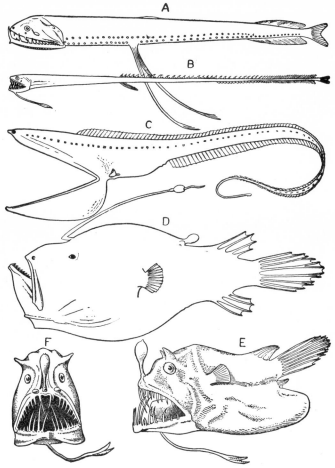

FIG. 170.   Deep-sea fishes. **A,** *Photostomias guernei,* length 1.5 inches taken at 3500 feet; **B,** *Idiacanthus ferox,* 8 inches, 16,500 feet; **C,** *Gastrostomus bairdii,* 18 inches, 2300–8800 feet; **D,** *Cryptopsarus couesii,* 2.25 inches, 10,000 feet; **E, F,** *Linophryne lucifer,* 2 inches. (From Lull, after Goode and Bean.)

of bizarre organisms.   Fishes of many sorts (Fig. 170), crabs, mollusks, worms, and many other forms thrive and multiply in this cheerless environment.   We do not at all understand the nature of the adaptive mechanism that enables these animals to withstand the steel-crushing pressures that prevail at such depths and that seem to bother them not at all. We do, however, know how some of the deficiencies of the environment are made good. Thus, many abysmal forms produce their own light by means of phosphorescent organs. Others have so-called telescopic eyes, which are highly effective in visioning lights of very low intensity. Could man view the sea bottom with the equipment possessed by these organisms he would doubtless add something very novel and weird to his scenic repertoire.

6. *Cave Animals*

Other creatures of darkness live curious lives in caves. Most cave dwellers are blind or nearly so, and usually have a pale ghost-like appearance because of the lack of body pigmentation (Fig.

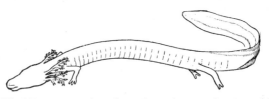

Fig. 171.   Blind *Proteus anguinus*, from the underground waters of Carinthia, Carniola, and Dalmatia. (After Gadow.)

171). It goes without saying that such animals are better adapted to cave life than they would be anywhere else. One crying question in biology is: How did the cave animals become blind? In a later chapter an attempt is made to answer this question.

7. *Parasitism and Its Consequences*

The world is full of parasites, human and otherwise. The easy, sheltered life of the parasite is usually associated with a softening of fiber, physical and mental, and a consequent degeneration of those organs which serve a useful function only in an active, independent life. Thus, we find that extreme parasites lose their sense organs, their locomotor organs, and their active food-catching organs, and tend to degenerate into mere passive food-absorbing and reproducing machines. Some animals start out, as larvæ, to lead a free and independent life, but sooner or later lose their activity and become reduced to a sluggish, dependent condition. So dependent upon a specific host do some parasites become that they cannot live anywhere else. Some parasites are dependent upon two or more hosts which they must inhabit successively during different phases of the life cycle; witness the flukes and the tapeworms already studied. The "nadir of parasitism" with the accompaniment of extreme degeneration is *Sacculina*, a description of which may be found on p. 423. (See Fig. 186.)

8. *Commensalism*

Many associations exist between different organisms in which the benefits are more nearly mutual than is the case in parasitism. When no harm is done to either animal concerned in the com-

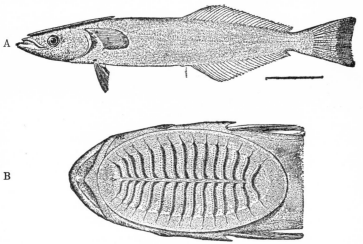

Fig. 172. **A,** the Shark Sucker, *Remora brachyptera*, Lowe; **B,** sucking disk of *Remora brachyptera*, Lowe, dorsal view. (From Jordan and Evermann.)

mensal arrangement, the condition is sometimes known as SYMBIOSIS. Some doubt exists, however, as to whether complete mutuality ever exists among commensals. A case in point is that of the shark sucker, Remora (Fig. 172), that attaches itself by means of a head sucker to the body of a shark and is carried about by the latter. Wherever the shark goes, the Remora gets free transportation and when he sees a convenient object of prey, he darts after it, devours it, and then returns to his accommodating conveyance. In this way the Remora, which is a good swimmer, conserves his strength for sudden, short forays after prey; but the relation lacks

FIG. 173. The Portuguese Man-of-War, Physalia, showing the various sorts of zoöids organized into an integrated colony. Certain elongated tentacle-like parts are used for paralyzing and capturing prey, but certain commensal fishes, as shown here, find shelter and protection from their enemies by swimming about among these tentacles, without themselves being in danger. Contrast this situation with that shown in the Frontispiece, where another species of Physalia is shown capturing a fish. (From Jordan and Kellogg.)

mutuality unless the shark enjoys a sense of companionship. Various species of cœlenterates, such as jelly-fishes and Siphonophora, harbor among their tentacles certain species of fishes. These tentacles are heavily armed with nematocysts or nettle cells which would readily be discharged by coming in contact with other species of fishes, but are neutral to the particular species that has been adopted as a commensal. The advantage of the well-armed shelter is obvious from the fishes' point of view, but wherein does the cœlenterate benefit? The frontispiece shows a species of Physalia capturing a fish, while Figure 173 shows another species of Physalia together with its commensal fishes apparently living harmoniously together.

Some of the most remarkable instances of commensalism are found in connection with ant communities. In some cases two species of ants live together in the relation of masters and slaves. The master species is unable to perform even the simplest household duties, such as securing food, taking care of young, digging new galleries. In some instances they cannot even feed themselves unassisted and have to be fed by the slaves. The masters are specialists, doing only one thing well: they are fighters and marauders, with an instinct to raid the strongholds of the slave species and capture their young, which they take home for the adult slaves of their own household to rear. Here again mutuality is lacking, for the

slave species is quite capable of conducting its own life independently, while the master species is completely dependent upon the
slaves.

9. *Communal Life*

Some of the most successful species of animals owe their success
largely to their social organizations.   Chief among social animals
are man and the ants.   In man, societies are largely artificial and
are loosely organized, but none the less adaptive in the highest
degree.   In the ants, a community is simply an enlarged family
in which all members have been derived from a common parentage.
The typical ant community consists of the queen (the only fertile
female in the colony), several males (mates of the queen), ordinary
workers (sterile females of the first type), soldiers (sterile females of

Worker-bee.   Queen-bee.   Drone.

Fig. 174.   The Honey-bee, *Apis mellifica*, showing the three castes.   (From
Shipley and MacBride.)

the second type), and sometimes officers (especially powerful sterile
females).   All of these castes are produced from eggs laid by one
female, or queen, and the various kinds of female castes are determined by variations in diet furnished during the larval period by
the workers, who seem to have an almost infallible instinct as to
the need of the colony for additional new individuals of the various
types.

Among the bees also there is one queen, the mother of the colony,
and there are several drones, or males, and many sterile female
workers (Fig. 174).   Each individual does uncomplainingly some
special task that its structural make-up renders it adapted for,
and there is no ambition on the part of one caste to invade the
domain of another.   Thus communal life, as found in these social
insects, must be looked upon as an adaptation for the good of the
race, though individuals may be denied the fullness of life, and the
good of the individual thus subserviated to the good of the race.

But this is the essence of all specialization: some faculties must be lost or reduced in effectiveness whenever others attain some special aptitude. Specialization entails a loss of versatility, and this is as true of human life as it is anywhere else. Nevertheless, specialization is one of the most effective means of acquiring greater fitness: it is the *modus operandi* of adaptation.

E. Individual, Acquired, or Contingent Adaptations

In contrast with inherited, or racial, adaptations, acquired adaptations arise in the individual during its lifetime under the stimulus of special environmental conditions, which may cause a marked structural or functional change or response in the somatic tissues. Examples of such individual adaptive responses are: the increased pigmentation of the skin in response to exposure to intense sunlight, the deposit of pigment acting as a light screen in preventing further injury to the cells of the skin; the increased thickness of the skin (callousing) as the result of friction which serves also to prevent injury; changed responses to higher or lower temperatures, which we call acclimation; the formation of antibodies in the blood when foreign toxic agents enter the body; regeneration of lost parts or healing of wounds; the increased strength or efficiency of organs resulting from increased use.

a. Sunburn.—It is well known that strong sunlight, especially those rays known as actinic, is injurious to living tissues, and that when a person exposes himself to the sun he gets sunburned. An incidental product of skin injury is the formation of brown pigment, which, if abundant enough, serves as a protection against further injury to the skin. So sunburn is an adaptive response, but is not inherited.

Many organisms respond to high temperatures and the accompanying drought by becoming more or less completely desiccated. Nevertheless when proper life conditions return, they take up water and resume their normal structure and activities. Other organisms can be gradually inured to high temperatures which, if applied suddenly, would kill or even cook them.

b. Tolerance to Poisons.—Tolerance to all sorts of poisons can be acquired if the initial dosage is small and the amount increased gradually enough. Thus is the drug habit built up, for the body adapts itself to the drug so that it requires larger and larger doses to produce the desired response.

c. Immunity to Disease.—Such immunity is but one of the adaptive responses of organisms to invasions of foreign substances harmful to the body. Certain diseases once recovered from cannot be reacquired, for the body has built up against the invading organism certain specific antibodies whose effect is to kill the invaders or weaken them to such an extent that the leucocytes can easily handle them. Thus, one who has had diphtheria cannot have it again because the body has elaborated in self defense certain permanent blood materials, antibodies, that inhibit the growth of diphtheria bacilli.

d. Hormones.—Considerable interest has been taken of late years in the regulatory functions of the various glands of internal secretion. Hormones are believed to be excreted into the blood by each of these glands at times when they are needed as stimuli for important bodily activities. Thus the suprarenal glands are said to become active and to excrete adrenalin into the blood whenever one under great pressure nerves himself to an unusual effort in self defense. Some believe that a successful fighter or football player is one who has large and active suprarenals, glands that secrete the "do or die stuff."

Other internal secretions produce adaptive responses of structural, functional, and psychological character. Thus the testes secrete hormones that are responsible for all of the male secondary sexual characters, including masculine behavior and instincts; while ovaries secrete hormones that are responsible for female secondary sexual characters and instincts. There is an intricate interplay of hormones during pregnancy that stimulates lactation and inhibits ovulation.

e. Regeneration.—The powers of organisms to regulate or regenerate lost parts or to produce whole individuals out of pieces is one of the most peculiar of the properties of living organisms, and, withal, one of the most strikingly adaptive of vital phenomena. In last analysis regeneration is merely a phase of reproduction, and we have already shown that reproduction is far and away the most important adaptation possessed by living things.

f. Autotomy.—Certain examples of the uses made of the ability of animals to regenerate lost parts are especially noteworthy in this connection. Taking advantage of their ability to regenerate lost organs, some animals have adopted the habit of self mutilation as an easy way of escaping an enemy. Thus a sea cucumber, when in danger of being eaten, eviscerates itself, shooting out its soft internal organs as a sop to the enemy, while the body wall escapes and is able to regenerate a new set of viscera.   Similarly, a lizard, when seized by the tail by a pursuing enemy, gives up his tail by an apparently voluntary act, and easily regenerates another; while a crab, when seized by its claw by a more powerful adversary, breaks off its own claw and thus escapes a worse fate, the claw being only a temporary loss.   These and similar instances of self mutilation throughout the animal kingdom illustrate the phenomenon of autotomy.

Conclusion.—While the above account of adaptations does not in any real sense cover the entire field of adaptive phenomena, it at least serves to indicate the nature of adaptations and how widespread is adaptiveness in organisms.   Adaptations, in fact, are essentially part and parcel of life, and as such must be taken into account in any considerations dealing with the origin and development of organisms as we find them today.   In this discussion of adaptations it has not been possible to deal exclusively with adaptations for self preservation, for quite often these are curiously blended with adaptations for race preservation.   We have reserved for special treatment, however, all those special mechanisms involved in reproduction proper as distinguished from those that are associated with the care of offspring.

The next chapter is to be considered as an extension of the present discussion of the relation of the organism to the environment, emphasizing a particular aspect of it.

CHAPTER XXXV

THE WEB OF LIFE

ONE of the most skillful of modern biological writers, **Professor J. Arthur Thomson,** has written a chapter entitled *The Web of Life* in which he makes the following statement:—

"We may use the metaphor 'web of life' in two ways. On the one hand, Nature has woven a pattern which science seeks to read, each science following the threads of a particular color. There is a warp and woof in this web, which to the zoölogist usually appears as 'hunger' and 'love.' There is a changing pattern in the web, becoming more complex as ages pass; and *this is evolution.* But the essential idea of a web is that of interlinking and ramifying. We can never tell where a thread will lead to. If one be pulled out, many are loosened. This is true of Nature through and through.

"The phrase 'web of life' suggests another picture—the web of a spider—often an intricate system, with part delicately bound to part so that the whole system is made one. The quivering fly entangled in a corner betrays itself throughout the web; often it is felt rather than seen by the lurking spinner. So in the substantial fabric of the world part is bound to part. In wind and weather, or in the business of our life, we are daily made aware of results whose first conditions are very remote, and the chains of influence, not difficult to demonstrate, link man to beast and flower to insect. The more we know of our surroundings the more we realize that nature is a vast system of linkages, that isolation is impossible."

We must realize the interdependencies that exist within the organic world. Nothing can live unto itself alone. All species have numerous linkages with others. The following gem from THOMSON will serve to illustrate the point:—

"Nexus between Mud and Clear Thinking.—To keep a famous inland fish pond from giving out, some boxes of mud and manure were placed at its sides. Bacteria—the minions of all putrefaction—worked in the mud and manure, making food for minute Infusorians which multiply so rapidly that there may be a million from one in a week's time. A cataract of Infusorians overflowed

391

from box to pond, and the waterfleas and other small fry gathered at the foot of the fall and multiplied exceedingly. Thus the fishes were fed, and, as fish-flesh is said to be good for the brain, we can trace a nexus between mud and clear thinking. What was the mud became part of the Infusorian, which became part of the Crustacean, which became part of the fish, which became part of the man. And it is thus that the world goes round."

Nutritive chains of this sort, reminding the author of *The House That Jack Built*, are very common in the world of life; in fact, there is probably no organism that does not form a link in one of these chains. **Charles Darwin** has given an account of one of these chains that is now famous:—

The Connection between Cats and Clover.—"Plants and animals, remote in the scale of nature, are bound together by a web of complex relations. . . . I have found, from experiments, that humble-bees are almost indispensable to the heart's-ease (*Viola tricolor*), for other bees do not visit this flower. I have also found that the visits of bees are necessary for the fertilization of some kinds of clover—thus 100 heads of red clover (*Trifolium pratense*) produced 27,000 seeds, but the same number of protected heads produced not a single seed. Humble-bees alone visit red clover, as other bees cannot reach the nectar. . . . Hence we may infer as highly probable that, if the whole genus of humble-bees became extinct or very rare in England, the heart's-ease and red clover would become very rare, or wholly disappear. . . . The number of humble-bees in any district depends in a great measure on the number of field-mice, which destroy their combs and nests; and **Colonel Newman,** who has long attended to the habits of humble-bees, believes that more than two-thirds of them are thus destroyed all over England." The relationship between cats and field mice is not far to seek, and is well stated by Colonel Newman: "Near villages and small towns I have found the nests of humble-bees more numerous than elsewhere, which I attribute to the number of cats that destroy the mice." Thus we see that the abundance of the clover crop in certain districts depends on the abundance of cats.

The Relation between Fishes and the Pearl-Button Industry.—Some years ago the prosperous industry in pearl-button manufacturing along the Mississippi River was threatened with collapse on account of the pronounced falling off of the catches of clams.

Alarmed at this situation, the Missouri state authorities commissioned **Professors Lefever** and **Curtis** of the State University to investigate the matter. It was found that the larvæ (glochidia) of the clam, after developing up to that stage in the gill chambers of the mother, sally out and gain attachment to the gills of certain fishes, a necessary step in their life cycle. After they have been freed from the gill cavity of the mother clam they float or swim about in the water until drawn into the gill chambers of certain species of fish. Contact with these tissues causes the bivalve glochidia to snap shut upon gill filaments, there to hold fast until the host tissue, under the stimulus of the adhering parasite, grows around the latter like a cyst or gall. Surrounded thus by highly vascular tissues, the young clams develop parasitically until they are ready to lead an independent life on the muddy bottom. The key discovery then was that the clams depend directly upon certain common river fishes, such as suckers, and that the depletion in the fishes had caused a corresponding depletion in the clams. The thing to do then was to build up the fish population by artificial propagation. This was done, and now, we understand, the button industry is thriving once more.

The Equilibrium of Nature. — One can scarcely realize how many elements enter into the nice balance of life in any complex community. Each organism in an ecological complex is definitely related to one or more other organisms, and the whole makes up an elastic web which cannot be broken in one place without raveling badly for some distance from the break and thus disturbing the balance of the whole. A typical example of a community in equilibrium is that in a fresh-water pond. The food relations in the pond are, according to **Shelford,** those shown in Figure 175. "Any marked fluctuation of conditions is sufficient to disturb the balance of an animal community. Let us assume that because of some unfavorable conditions in a pond during their breeding period the black bass decreased markedly. The pickerel, which devour young bass, must feed more exclusively upon insects. The decreased number of black bass would relieve the drain upon the crayfishes, which are eaten by the bass; crayfishes would accordingly increase and prey more heavily upon the aquatic insects. The combined attack of pickerel and crayfishes would cause insects to decrease and the number of pickerel would fall away because of decreased food supply. Meanwhile the bullheads, which are

general feeders and which devour aquatic insects, might feed more
extensively upon mollusks because of the decrease of the former,
but would probably decrease also because of the falling off of their
main article of diet. We may thus reasonably assume that the
black bass would recover its numbers because of the decreased
pickerel and bullheads, the enemies of its young." Shelford
further points out that if, instead of merely diminishing in numbers,
the black bass had been exterminated, an entirely new equilibrium

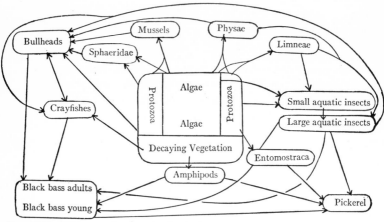

Fig. 175. Diagram showing food relations of a pond community. Arrows
point from the organisms eaten to those doing the eating. (From Shelford.)

would have to be established—an equilibrium that would probably
involve the complete or nearly complete elimination of other elements in the complex.

Professor Forbes, a veteran student of animal life in the fresh
waters, has pointed out the most important lesson that we must
learn from a contemplation of the nice balance of Nature: "There
is a general consent that primeval nature, as in the uninhabited
forest or the untilled plain, presents a settled harmony of interaction among organic groups which is in strong contrast with the
many serious maladjustments of plants and animals found in
countries occupied by man. To man, as to nature at large, the
question of adjustment is of vast importance, since the eminently
destructive species are the widely oscillating ones. The insects
which are well adjusted to their environments, organic and inor-

ganic, are either harmless or inflict but moderate injury (our ordinary crickets and grasshoppers are examples); while those that are imperfectly adjusted, whose numbers are, therefore, subject to wide fluctuations, like the Colorado grasshopper, the chinch bug, and the army worm, are enemies which we have reason to dread. Man should then especially address his efforts first, to prevent any unnecessary disturbance of the settled life of his region which will convert relatively stationary species into widely oscillating ones; second, to destroy or render stationary, all the oscillating species injurious to him; or, failing in this, to restrict their oscillations within the narrowest limits possible. For example, remembering that every species oscillates to some extent and is held to relatively constant numbers by the joint action of several restraining forces, we see that the removal or weakening of any check or barrier is sufficient to widen and intensify this dangerous oscillation, and may even convert a perfectly harmless species into a frightful pest."

The lesson here pointed out is obvious. Man should beware of senseless slaughter even of animals that appear to him to be useless or even a nuisance, lest a worse thing befall him. The killing of snakes is to be decried: they occupy a position in the web of nature where many strands cross and thus play a useful rôle in maintaining a stationary balance. The deforestation of large areas has had a very bad effect not only in altering the rainfall but in removing animals that prey upon agricultural pests. The question arises as to whether any animal is valueless. It is easy to assume that the extermination of some forms of animal life could be only a boon to mankind; but it is difficult to be sure that the results would all be so beneficial as we might assume. What, for example, would become of the parasites that now pass part of their life cycles in these despised animals? It is not inconceivable that these parasites might be forced to invade and adapt themselves to the bodies of man's domesticated animals or even to the bodies of men themselves. Parasites that are fairly benign in the bodies of lower animals sometimes cause the most virulent diseases in man and his stock animals. This then is a question worth pondering over.

Charles Darwin was the first man to make clear the fact of Nature's intricate interconnections. It was the realization of what we have been calling the *Web of Life* that led him to value even small changes in species and to believe that no change that might take place in a balanced system could be considered as unimportant. Adaptations, he thought, must be considered not as isolated phenomena, but each one in relation to the whole intricate system of interdependent species.

CHAPTER XXXVI

REPRODUCTIVE MECHANISMS

In this chapter we propose to classify and discuss all of the principal modes of reproduction in the animal kingdom. These various methods of maintaining the continuity and perpetuity of races and species are to be thought of as only one part of the adaptive mechanism of race preservation. In the chapter on *Adaptations* various structural and behavioral mechanisms for the care of eggs and young have already been dealt with. In this chapter we shall confine ourselves to a discussion of the various methods by means of which the bodies of parents give rise to offspring.

A. Two Main Kinds of Reproduction

Several schemes for classifying the various modes of reproduction have been offered. For a long time the standard categories of reproduction have been spoken of as sexual and asexual, but this has certain unsatisfactory features. In the recently revised edition of his book, *The Cell*, Wilson suggests the two categories SOMATO-GENIC and CYTOGENIC, "the former including asexual multiplication by fission or budding in which the body itself divides to produce offspring that are essentially multicellular fragments of itself. Cytogenic reproduction (cytogony) on the other hand, is effected by means of unicellular GERM CELLS which by growth and division may build up a new multicellular body. In the Protista this distinction does not properly exist, since the whole body is in itself unicellular; here also, nevertheless, it is convenient to speak of reproduction as cytogenic."

According to this view somatogenic reproduction must be always asexual, for no sex act is involved; but cytogenic reproduction may be either sexual or asexual. Thus reproduction by spores may be classed as cytogenic, for a whole new individual arises from a single cell. In the majority of animals cytogenic reproduction involves the union of two germ cells, GAMETES, to form a ZYGOTE, but there are very many in which the egg, female gamete, is able to develop without union with the male gamete, a process known as PARTHE-

NOGENESIS. This process is not to be thought of as a type of spore reproduction but as a secondary modification of SYNGAMY, or reproduction by the union of gametes.

The various modes of reproduction will now be discussed without attempting to separate completely the cytogenic and somatogenic modes.

B. Modes of Reproduction Described and Discussed

1. *Transverse Fission*

We have already encountered, in dealing with the various types of animals presented in Part II of this text, several specific instances of transverse fission—namely, in Paramecium (Fig. 44), in Planaria (Fig. 72), in the tapeworm (Fig. 78). In all these cases it is thought that, either because of the elongation of the principal axis or a slowing down of the metabolic rate of the apical or controlling region—probably for both of these reasons—the basal or posterior part of the organism gets out of control and ceases to be an integral part of the parent organism. At first it becomes independent physiologically without showing any visible morphological evidences of isolation; but later, actual physical separation takes place and a new apical region appears, a definite indication that a new individual has been produced.

2. *Lateral Budding*

An excellent example of lateral budding is that described for Hydra (Fig. 58) and for the colonial cœlenterates, such as Bougainvillea (Fig. 66). This type of budding is more plantlike than animal-like, and is characteristic of forms that are fastened to the substratum by the basal end so that they are not free to cut off the posterior part without casting adrift the anterior part. When a new individual arises, it does so at a point far distant from the apical end, where the dominance of the apical end has become weak. A lateral outgrowth occurs with a new axis of its own approximately at right angles to the parent axis. The rapidly growing tip of the bud becomes the new apical region, and this proceeds to organize the outgrowth into a new individual that may or may not break loose from the parental body. In Hydra the buds always break off and become free; while in the colonial hydroids only certain highly specialized buds, medusa buds, break loose, and these become independent sexually mature individuals.

Among the higher phyla of animals lateral budding is found only in association with degenerate bodily conditions and sessile life. Among the chordates, for example, lateral budding is common in the colonial TUNICATES, or sea squirts. By this method of reproduction elaborate colonies are formed, as in Pyrosoma (Fig. 176), where the individuals are so arranged as to give the colony

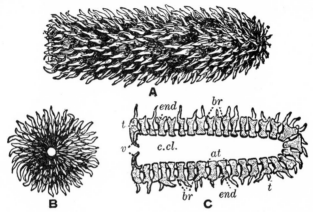

FIG. 176. The free-swimming colonial ascidian, *Pyrosoma*. **A,** lateral view (nat. size); **B,** view of the open end; **C,** diagram of longitudinal section; *at,* atrial pores opening into the central cavity or cloaca, *c.cl,* of the colony; *br,* branchial or oral apertures opening to the outside; *end,* endostyle; *t,* test or tunic; *v,* velum or diaphragm at terminal opening. (From Herdman.)

the appearance and the action of a single individual of a higher order; for the numerous zoöids behave as though under one centralized control.

3. *Longitudinal Fission*

We have shown that, in transverse fission, the original anterior or apical end remains the same while a new basal individual, at first subordinate to the apical individual, is cut off. Thus the products of transverse fission are characteristically unequal at the time when the division occurs. The same is true of lateral budding. In longitudinal fission, however, two equivalent individuals are produced from two equal halves of the parent individual. The daughter individuals are true twins and are essentially alike in all respects except that one is the mirror image of the other. Moreover, neither individual is subordinate to the other.

This kind of reproduction is common in the Protozoa, especially in the CLASS MASTIGOPHORA. The fission of Euglena (Fig. 177) is typical. Here the nucleus divides after elongating transversely, and the cytoplasm follows suit, splitting first at the anterior and

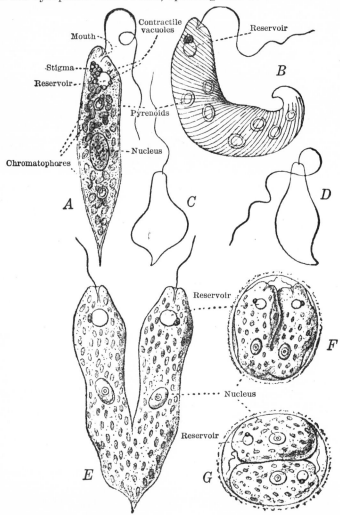

FIG. 177. *Euglena viridis.* A, view of free-swimming specimen showing details of structure; B, another animal showing change of shape and striations; C and D, outlines showing stages of contraction; E, reproduction by longitudinal fission; F and G, division within a cyst. (A–D, from Bourne; E–G, from Bourne, after Stein.)

last at the posterior end. The two individuals, as they lie before separation, are seen to be mirror-image duplicates of each other, a characteristic feature of true twins. Among the higher organisms TWINNING is of quite frequent occurrence. Even in man we have DUPLICATE TWINS which often show mirror-image asymmetry between the two individuals; and there is strong evidence that such twins are the products of the longitudinal fission of the early embryo. In the nine-banded armadillo (Fig. 178) twinning of this sort is a specific characteristic. In practically every litter there are four young, all of a litter being of the same sex. It is now definitely known that in this species the early embryo divides by fission to form twin embryos, and that almost at once each twin divides again by longitudinal fission, thus giving rise to two pairs of duplicate twins—QUADRUPLETS, as they are commonly called. Such quadruplets are much more nearly identical than are brothers or sisters derived from different germ cells of the same parents. The four individuals derived from one fertilized egg inherit but one assortment of hereditary genes, while ordinary brothers or sisters inherit each a different assortment. Partial twinning gives rise to Siamese twins and a long array of two-headed monsters, or forms with one head and two bodies. Twinning is common in earthworms, in echinoderm larvæ, in Amphioxus, in fishes, in frogs, and in many other animals. The conditions that favor twinning are to a certain extent known. It appears that any agency that lowers the rate of development at a critical period, when the axis of symmetry is being established, may induce the partial or complete isolation of the primordia of the right and left halves of the axis, and cause each lateral half to behave like an independent individual. Here again the basis of reproduction is PHYSIOLOGICAL ISOLATION, followed by physical separation of parts of an individual and the regeneration of a whole individual from a part.

4. *Internal Budding*

We have not yet encountered a case of internal budding. It occurs chiefly among Porifera (sponges) and Bryozoa (moss animalcules), two relatively low phyla. The characteristic feature of this type of reproduction is that minute representative aggregations of cells are cut off from various internal parts of the parent, without any direct reference to the axes of the parent. These little sample packages of cells are known as GEMMULES (Fig. 179) in the

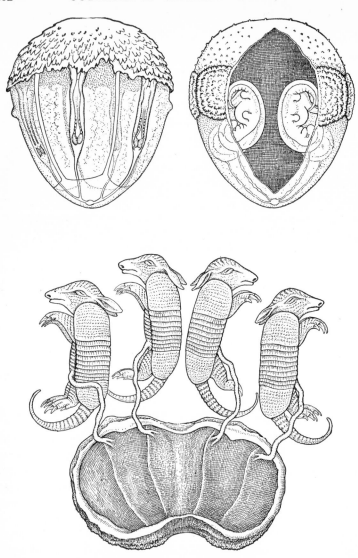

Fig. 178. Three stages in the development of armadillo quadruplets. In each case the four individuals have been obtained by the fission of a single embryonic primordium. In the lower figure the egg has been cut open and the foetuses removed, but left attached to the egg membranes by means of their umbilical cords. (Original.)

sponges, and STATOBLASTS in the Bryozoa. In gemmule formation, a small mass of representative cells, consisting of samples of
each of the kinds of cells in the parent body, proliferate in the loose
MESOGLŒA, the gelatinous middle layer of the sponge. The cell
mass rounds up and becomes inclosed in a dense coat of spicules.
In this state the young gemmule is capable of surviving the death
of the parent and of developing a new sponge the following spring.
Gemmules float about far and wide in the
sea currents, and the species is thus distributed over large areas. In most of the
points mentioned statoblasts are essentially
similar to gemmules.

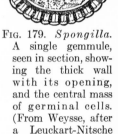

5. *Sporulation*

A great many species of Protozoa, not
only within the Class Sporozoa but in other
groups as well, reproduce by spores. The
process of sporulation is one involving repeated nuclear divisions, at first not accompanied by divisions of the cytoplasm but
sooner or later resulting in the formation of
a large number of excessively minute nu-
cleated masses of protoplasm, sometimes naked and sometimes
in elaborate capsules. These minute cells are spores and the
process is called sporulation. Each spore is of course a sort of
minute "germ cell"; for each is capable of reproducing a new
individual of the species. A good example of sporulation is that
of the protozoan parasite, *Coccidium schubergi*, which is found
in the intestine of the centipede, *Lithobius forficatus*. The life cycle
of this form is shown in the accompanying illustration (Fig. 180),
where the events in the history are numbered from I to XX. Part
of the life cycle takes place in the body of the centipede and part
of it outside. The centipede, in feeding, picks up cysts of the parasite such as that shown in XX; from these cysts minute sporozoites
(I) emerge and enter the cells of the intestinal wall (II), where they
multiply (III, IV) and form numerous small cells (V, VI, VII) that
in turn become motile individuals (VIII, IX, X). These free
motile individuals, merozoites, which are really spores, then proceed to differentiate into sex cells, some growing large and becoming
female gametes (XI *a, b, c*), others multiplying more rapidly and

Fig. 179. *Spongilla.*
A single gemmule,
seen in section, show-
ing the thick wall
with its opening,
and the central mass
of germinal cells.
(From Weysse, after
a Leuckart-Nitsche
wall chart.)

remaining small male gametes (XII *a, b, c, d, e*). Male gametes unite with female gametes to form the equivalent of zygotes (XIII, XIV, XV) and something like cleavage takes place (XVI–XX), resulting finally in the production of numerous asexual sporozoites like those we started out with. This history seems so much

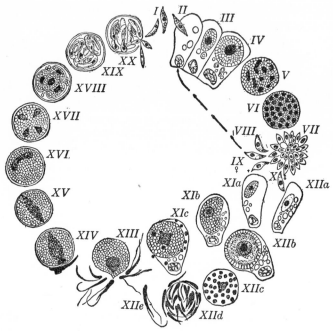

Fig. 180. Reproduction in the protozoan parasite, *Coccidium schubergi*. Stages represented by stages *II–VII* and *XIa–XIIc* are intracellular; *IV–VIII*, represent sporulation; *IX–XIII*, developing gametes; *XIV–XX*, development of spores. (From Shull et al., courtesy of McGraw Hill Book Co.)

like the life cycle of the Metazoa that one might be permitted to compare spores to germ cells, some being parthenogenetic and some syngamic. If this view of spores be permissible, there would appear to be no sufficient reason for excluding some phases of sporulation from the category of gametic reproduction.

6. *Gametic Reproduction*

Typical gametic reproduction involves, as the name implies, the union of two gametes to form a combination cell or zygote. In the metazoa there are two kinds of gametes, ova and spermatozoa (Fig. 181), which unite to form the zygote or fertilized egg. In the higher forms the gametes are the only cells that have retained the capacity to produce new individuals. A highly characteristic

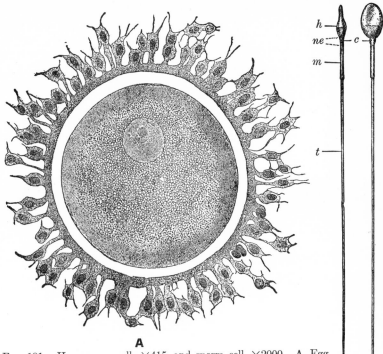

A

B

Fig. 181.   Human egg cell, ×415, and sperm cell, ×2000.   **A,** Egg just removed from the ovary, surrounded by follicle cells of the ovary and a clear membrane. The central part of the egg contains metaplasmic bodies and the large nucleus. Superficially there is a clear ectoplasmic region. (After Waldeyer.) **B,** two views of the human sperm. *c,* centrosome; *h,* 'head' consisting of the nucleus surrounded by a cytoplasmic envelope; *m, ne,* middle piece; *t,* tail or flatellum. (From Woodruff, after Retzius.)

feature of gametes is that they undergo maturation divisions. If, as sometimes happens, an individual arises from a single cell of an early embryo, as, for example, a blastomere of a cleavage stage, this is not a case of gametic reproduction, for such a cell does not undergo maturation. Another point that should not be forgotten is that gametes are specialized cells. The ovum is a gorged cell in which metabolic activity comes almost to a standstill—a cell that must be activated in some way in order to produce a new individual. As a rule, activation is accomplished by another specialized cell, the spermatozoön, a tiny starved cell that uses up its store of energy producing material in active locomotion and is doomed to die unless it finds the appropriate food supply furnished by the egg. Each kind of gamete thus furnishes what the other lacks, the egg supplying a large amount of inert energy producing material and the sperm furnishing the additional energy necessary to make this material available for growth and cell division.

Each gamete is also the bearer of heredity materials. It has already been shown that the diploid chromosome complement of the unmaturated germ cells is reduced during maturation to the haploid chromosome complement, and that the union of two gametes to form a zygote reinstates the specific diploid chromosome complement. Thus we see that the process of fertilization, or union of gametes, has two distinct values: it serves to initiate development in the inert ovum and it furnishes a means of uniting the hereditary characters of two different genetic stocks.

Sexual or Gametic Reproduction in the Protozoa.—The process of gametic reproduction in the Protozoa is believed to be essentially the same process and to have the same significance as it has in the Metazoa. It differs, however, from the latter in that the whole unicellular body is at once somatic and germinal, for there are no separate germ cells. This means that, for a series of generations during which binary fission is going on, the somatic phase of the life cycle is in the ascendancy; but when the period of conjugation intervenes and cells fuse with each other wholly or in part, the germinal phase is in the ascendancy and the cells are essentially gametes. In a sense, then, we may say that, in these Protozoa, many generations of somatic individuals are followed by one generation of gametes and that there is an alternation of generations. In many species of Protozoa, especially among the Mastigophora, the gametes are alike in size and appearance. If any difference exists, it must be of a subtle physiological, rather than of a grosser morphological sort. Between this condition of ISOGAMY, where gametes are visibly alike, and the condition of HETEROGAMY, where the gametes are typical eggs and sperms, there is a long series of intermediate conditions showing stages in the differentiation of gametes of the two sexes. In all these types of gametic reproduction in the Protozoa so far cited there occurs complete fusion of both nucleus and cytoplasm of one gamete with those of another—a union of entire cells.

Gametic Reproduction in Paramecium.—In Paramecium, however, and in a large number of other infusorians, gametic reproduction takes on a more specialized aspect. Let us recall for a moment the events of conjugation where there is only a temporary association of two individuals accompanied by an exchange of nuclei. After two preliminary divisions of the micronucleus, which simulate the maturation divisions of the metazoan germ cells, the remaining nucleus divides unequally into a larger stationary nucleus, resembling the egg nucleus, and a smaller migrating nucleus, resembling the sperm nucleus. The smaller nucleus of each individual migrates across the protoplasmic bridge into the other individual and fuses with the larger nucleus of the other individual. This closely resembles the behavior of male and female nuclei in metazoan fertilization. We may now ask ourselves whether the conjugating Paramecia are gametes or whether only their nuclei play the rôle of gametes. This difficult question cannot be satisfactorily answered, but the results of the process appear to be the same as in the Metazoa, for there is a renewal of growth and division energy and a new combination of hereditary materials is produced.

7. *Parthenogenesis*

This mode of reproduction may be defined as the development of ova without union with spermatozoa. Leading authorities consider parthenogenesis as a phase of gametic reproduction, for the ovum undergoes one or two maturation divisions, sometimes reducing the number of chromosomes and sometimes not. That parthenogenetic ova really are potential gametes is seen in cases such as those of the bees and wasps, in which all eggs are capable of development whether fertilized or not. If any egg happens to be fertilized, it produces a female (a sterile worker or a queen), while all unfertilized eggs produce males, or drones. Furthermore, many types of eggs that normally require fertilization may readily be induced to develop without fertilization by the use of simple chemical or merely mechanical stimulation, a process known as ARTIFICIAL PARTHENOGENESIS. We may then conclude that parthenogenesis is not just an archaic asexual mode of reproduction, but a modern specialization of the gametic type.

8. *Pædogenesis*

While not strictly a mode of reproduction comparable with or contrasting with those already described, pædogenesis is a widespread and interesting reproductive phenomenon. Typically, reproduction is a phenomenon of old age, or more accurately, of SENESCENCE. So long as an individual is physiologically young, is carrying on all of its activities at a high metabolic level, and has no blocks in its system of communications between controlling centers and outlying parts, it cannot reproduce, for reproduction means that some part of the body has lost its relations with the parent organism. When the organism grows physiologically old, some of its outlying regions fail to receive the integrational stimuli necessary for holding them in subordination to the central government of the parent body, and they become physiologically isolated. If they are to live at all, they must become new individuals. This is true whether reproduction is by fission, budding, twinning, sporulation, or gamete formation. Reproduction ordinarily does not occur until maturity or even old age, but there are many cases of precocious reproduction, young being produced during larval or embryonic stages of the parents. We can account for such cases only by assuming that these apparently young parents are physiologically old—senescent. When reproduction, especially that involving gametes, takes place in embryonic or larval stages, the phenomenon is termed pædogenesis (meaning literally reproduction by young). We recognize both parthenogenetic and bisexual (syngamic) pædogenesis.

The best known instance of pædogenesis among the vertebrates is that of the AXOLOTL LARVA of the tiger salamander, *Amblystoma tigrinum* (Fig. 182). In the mountain lakes of Mexico and New Mexico these larvæ, while still in possession of their external gills and other larval characters, become sexually mature and produce young. This, it will be noted, is a case of pædogenesis associated with bisexual or syngamic reproduction. Pædogenesis is also found to occur in parthenogenetic forms. A good example of this combination is that of MIASTOR, a species of fly belonging to the family Cecidomyidæ. This fly, while still in the larval condition and before oviducts for the escape of eggs have been differentiated, produces young in the body cavity. This generation of grublike larvæ escapes from the body of the infant mother by boring through the body wall. Several generations are produced in this fashion, but finally a generation is produced that goes through the larval and pupal stages without reproducing, emerging as full-fledged males and females that reproduce in the usual way.

Another striking instance of pædogenesis associated with parthenogenesis is that of the liver fluke (*Fasciola hepatica*), the life history of which has already been described in another connection

FIG. 182. Axolotls or larvæ of *Amblystoma tigrinum*. ✕½. (From the Cambridge Natural History.)

(Fig. 77). It may be recalled that the very young larva of this species, the miracidium, forms a sporocyst, within which a number of ova are produced. These ova undergo maturation and develop parthenogenetically into redia larvæ. These in turn produce more redias in the same fashion, and several successive generations of redias are produced one from another. Finally a generation of redias produces parthenogenetically a generation of cercarias, that grow directly into adult liver flukes if they are lucky enough to be eaten by a sheep.

9. *Hermaphroditism*

This phenomenon is to be thought of not strictly as a separate mode of reproduction, but as a complication arising out of gametic reproduction. It is also, we believe, not a relic of an archaic condition, as some authors suppose, but a relatively modern or cenogenetic condition commonly developed in connection with racial senescence in forms that have sedentary and parasitic habits.

When the sexes are separate, we speak of the condition as diœcious; when both sexes are represented in one individual, whether simultaneously or in succession, the condition is monœcious and the result is hermaphroditism (a compound word made up of Hermes and Aphrodite).

No better examples of this phenomenon could be given than those already described for Hydra, Planaria, the liver fluke, and the earthworm. In some cases hermaphroditism is associated with self-fertilization; in other cases, with cross fertilization. In forms that live an absolutely fixed parasitic life, self-fertilization seems to be the most feasible method; but when hermaphroditic forms are either somewhat mobile or live in colonies, cross fertilization is possible and is usually adopted; for the advantages of continually bringing together different genetic lines outweigh the advantages of somewhat more ready fertilization.

Many interesting combinations of the various modes of reproduction exist, but we have noted enough examples to gain some realization of Nature's mechanisms for preserving the continuity of life.

CHAPTER XXXVII

ORGANIC EVOLUTION (INTRODUCTORY STATEMENT)

A. Importance of the Concept of Evolution

THE principle of evolution is so all-pervasive that it touches in some respect practically every aspect of biology. Hence, at least by implication, evolution has been a matter of central interest throughout this whole book. It must be obvious to any student that the mere classification of animals into phyla, classes, orders, families, genera, and species implies evolution, for the resemblances that make it possible to group organisms into any of these assemblages are explained as inheritances from a common ancestor. Classification is quite meaningless on any other grounds. In this connection it should be recalled that the order of treatment of the various animal phyla is largely determined by the Diphyletic Tree Theory, a new scheme for expressing the main lines of evolutionary change in the animal kingdom. Thus the evolution concept runs like a complex pattern throughout the whole fabric of biological science.

Although, as has been said, evolution has been a guiding principle throughout this book, there has been as yet no adequate discussion of those special facts and theories that are specifically evolutionary. It is our purpose in the remaining chapters of the book to present in an orderly and logical way the main facts and theories that constitute the subject of evolutionary biology.

The plan to be pursued is as follows:—First, we intend to present the evidences of evolution, upon which the validity of the theory largely rests; and second, we shall describe the various causal mechanisms involved in the process. It is now definitely known that the primary mechanisms of evolution are cell mechanisms, especially those having to do with the chromosomes of germ cells. Hence it is important to consider in detail the mode of origin of germ cells, the peculiar mechanisms involved in the production of gametes, the process of union of gametes to form zygotes, sex as a factor in evolution, how sex is determined, the rôle of chromosomes in heredity and variation, and the laws of heredity that are the result of the known regularities in the operation of chromo-

411

somal mechanisms. In a final chapter the causal factors of evolution are discussed in relation to one another, and an attempt is made to show how they are all essential and all work together as parts of a single complex mechanism.

B. THE NATURE OF THE PROOF OF ORGANIC EVOLUTION

Although it is still customary to speak of the Theory of Evolution, one must not assume that the word "theory" implies uncertainty. We still speak of the Cell Theory, though the implications of this great generalization are quite unquestioned. The Theory of Evolution rests on the same kinds of evidence as do other great scientific generalizations. It is supported by as extensive and as strong evidence as are the Law of Gravitation, the Law of Conservation of Energy, the Law of Uniformitarianism, the Atomic Theory, and others. All of these are no more than explanations of how nature works. The proof of their validity depends upon how satisfactorily these explanations continue to account for the facts within their range of application.

Now the nature of the proof of evolution is this: that using the idea of evolution as a working hypothesis, it has been possible to rationalize and explain a vast array of observed phenomena, the real facts upon which evolution rests. Thus classification, comparative anatomy, embryology, blood tests, palæontology, geographic distribution, and genetics, become consistent and orderly branches of science when based on evolutionary foundations, but when viewed in any other way they are thrown into the utmost confusion. There is no other explanation of organic phenomena that is of the least service in giving these bodies of facts any sort of scientific coherence or unity. In other words, the working hypothesis of Organic Evolution does all that can be asked of it and is therefore worthy of credence, at least until a better hypothesis appears to take its place. No rival hypothesis of a scientific nature is in sight, and none is likely to appear, for confidence in the validity of the Theory of Evolution is increasing year by year. The theory not only serves admirably as a working hypothesis that never fails to work, but with the steady accumulation of more and more facts, the weight of evidence is now so great as to overcome all open-minded opposition by its sheer mass. In the next chapter a limited sample of the evidences supporting evolution will be presented.

CHAPTER XXXVIII

EVIDENCES OF EVOLUTION

THE main bodies of biological data that are rationalized by and therefore support the Principle of Evolution are the following:—

1. Comparative anatomy.
2. Classification.
3. Blood tests.
4. Embryology.
5. Palæontology.
6. Geographic distribution.
7. Genetics.   (See Chapter XLI.)

A. EVIDENCES FROM COMPARATIVE ANATOMY

a. The Principle of Homology.—A general survey of the animal kingdom brings to light the fact that there are several distinct main types of architecture, each of which characterizes one of the grand divisions of the animal kingdom. Within any one of these grand divisions there are all kinds of structural diversities, but in spite of this the fundamental plan is obvious. The situation reminds one of the variations upon a theme in music: no matter how elaborate the variations may be, the skilled musician can recognize the common theme running through it all. This fundamental unity of architecture underlies the principle of homology and is the basis of comparative anatomy as well as of other branches of morphology.

Homologous structures are those that arise from similar embryonic rudiments and have equivalent relations to other structures. Homology has nothing to do with the function of the organ nor with the superficial adaptive features of it. If we examine the arm of man, the flipper of a whale, the wing of a bird or that of a bat, the foreleg of a horse or that of an ox, we may not see at first any similarity, but a detailed study of their anatomical make-up reveals a surprising amount of resemblance (Fig. 183). We find the

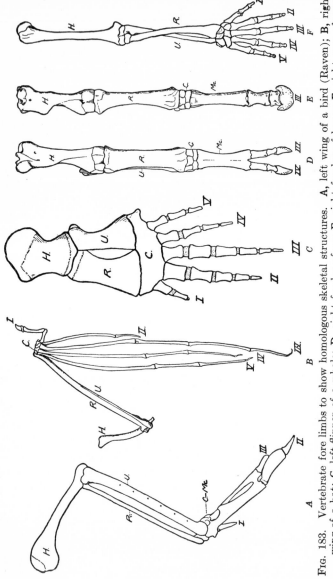

FIG. 183. Vertebrate fore limbs to show homologous skeletal structures. **A**, left wing of a bird (Raven); **B**, right wing of a bat; **C**, left flipper of a whale; **D**, right foreleg of ox; **E**, right foreleg of horse; **F**, right arm of man. *C*, carpals; *H*, humerus; *Mc*, metacarpals; *R*, radius; *U*, ulna; *I–V*, digits. (From Scott.)

same bones, muscles, nerves, but differing in size, proportions, and degree of development.   Although the plan of structure is the same in all, the variations upon the plan are very different and are of such a character as to render the organs especially useful for various purposes: flying, swimming, or general versatility.   The Principle of Evolution rationalizes this situation.   The reason why all these organs, so diversified in appearance and in uses, have a common ground plan is that they have all inherited their main structural features from a common ancestral group, but each has undergone a different sort of adaptive modification.   This is merely a paraphrase of the Principle of Evolution.

b. Vestigial Structures.—Even more in need of an evolutionary explanation than ordinary homologies are those homologies termed

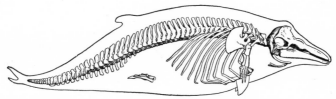

Fɪɢ. 184.   Skeleton of porpoise (a small whale).   The vestigial pelvic bones are shown embedded in the flesh.   (From Lull, after Pander and D'Alton.)

vestigial structures.   In the foreleg of the horse, for example, there are two little bones, shaped like toothpicks, lying closely applied to the two sides of the metacarpal bone.   These have no known function and would be meaningless were it not for the principle of homology.   These tiny vestiges are now recognized as the last remnants of the second and fourth toes, the homologues of which were well developed in many extinct species of horses.

Whales furnish another classic instance of vestigial structures. Deeply imbedded under the blubber in the pelvic region of the body is a little handful of bones (Fig. 184) that are totally immovable and cannot possibly function as bones at all.   Yet there is no question but that they represent all that remains of the pelvic girdle and the hind legs.   This being the case, the only possible inference is that the whale has been derived by descent from an ancestor that had functional hind legs.

There are, according to Wiedersheim, no less than 180 vestigial structures in man—enough to make the human body a veritable walking museum of antiquities.   Among these are: the vermiform appendix, the abbreviated tail, a whole set of useless caudal muscles, muscles for moving the ears, miniature third eyelids, a complete coat of hair (lanugo) on the embryo, and a long list of others. All of these are represented among lower types of animals by functional homologous organs. The only reasonable interpretation of these vestiges is that man has descended from ancestors in which these structures were functional. Man has, as a matter of fact, never completely lost these inherited structures though they may no longer be of any value. They exist in man's body because of the stubbornness of heredity, which seems to cling persistently to some expression of all that the race has once possessed, even though chiefly concerned in the elaboration of its more recent adaptive acquisitions.

The fundamental assumption underlying the principle of homology is that homologies are due to heredity; that unity of type implies common ancestry. We have ample proof that structural resemblances are due to heredity. Studies of identical twins and of armadillo quadruplets strongly support this contention, for in both of these cases the closest known resemblance is associated with the fact that, being products of a single egg, they have the most nearly identical heredity possible. *Real homologies are inherited similarities.*

c. **Homology versus Analogy.**—It is not uncommon to find structures that look alike and function alike but are not homologous. Thus, the eye of the squid, a cephalopod mollusk, has a chorion, a lens, a retina, an optic nerve, and a general aspect very like the eye of a fish. It also functions in the same way as a vertebrate eye. A study of its embryonic development, however, shows that not in a single particular is the eye of a cephalopod homologous with that of a vertebrate. The two eyes are ANALOGOUS, not homologous. They are the result of the convergent adaptation of quite different materials to subserve a common function—that of vision. HOMOLOGOUS structures, on the other hand, are frequently, though not always, adapted for quite different functions, and in accord with this they may exhibit vast differences in form and in superficial appearance. Yet, in spite of the greatest divergence in form and function, structures are homologous if they arise from equivalent embryonic rudiments and have equivalent morphological relations.

Both analogy and homology imply change in structure and in

function in relation to environment, and in that way they plainly suggest adaptive change in organisms. This, in turn, implies evolution.

Comparative anatomy then rests upon an evolutionary foundation, and is a science only in so far as it makes use of the principle of homology, a corollary of evolution.

B. Evidences from Classification

The object of classification is to arrange all animals and plants in groups of various degrees of inclusiveness, which shall express as closely as possible the actual degrees of relationship existing between them. Accordingly, we put into one group all animals that are alike or are essentially of the same kind; and we call such an assemblage a species. Thus, the European wolf is a species and has been designated *lupus* (the Latin word for wolf). There are also several other species of wolf, each with its Latin name, and all of these are grouped with dogs—believed to be domesticated wolves—into a group, or genus, called *Canis* (the Latin word for dog). Several other genera (the plural of genus), made up of assemblages of such doglike animals as the foxes and the jackals, are placed with the genus Canis in a larger group called the Family Canidæ—meaning the Dog Family. The assumption underlying this grouping is that all animals within the Family have been derived from some common doglike ancestor. Other families, such as the Felidæ (Cat Family), Ursidæ (Bear Family), and several other families of terrestrial beasts of prey, are gathered into the Suborder Fissipedia. These, in turn, are grouped with the marine beasts of prey—seals, sea lions, and walruses—into the Order Carnivora. Several other orders of beasts, such as Insectivora, Rodentia, Primates, Ungulates, Cetacea, and others, constitute the Class Mammalia. The latter (together with several other classes such as Pisces, Amphibia, Reptilia, Aves) make up the Subphylum Craniata (Vertebrates), which (together with several assemblages of vertebrate-like forms) comprise the Phylum Chordata.

The underlying assumption of classification is the same as that which underlies comparative anatomy: that degrees of blood relationship run strictly parallel with degrees of true resemblance; that the most nearly identical individuals are the most closely related and that those bearing the least fundamental resemblance to each other are either unrelated or, at the most, descendants of an extremely remote common ancestral type. The assumption is merely an affirmation of the fact of heredity: that like tends to produce like. The validity of the principle of heredity has been demonstrated in so many ways that it needs no justification here. Recall, if you will, the data concerning armadillo quadruplets, where the closest possible blood relationship is associated with a close approach to identity, and you will realize how strong is the force of heredity.

Let us examine somewhat critically the content of the unit of classification—the SPECIES. When we look over a large number of individuals of the same species, we find that no two of them are exactly alike in any one or more respects. As a rule, there is a wide range of diversity within a species, and extreme variants are often very different from one another. The several species of a prosperous genus are often so variable that it becomes a matter of great difficulty to determine just where one species stops and another one begins. Moreover, it sometimes happens that some of the individuals occupying extreme parts of the range of the species are so different from the central type that they would doubtless be diagnosed as belonging to a different species were it not for the fact that all intergrades between the extremes are known to exist. A species is, therefore, rarely a fixed and definite assemblage, such as it should be if species were specially created and had not evolved. In fact, any intensive study of a species gives the impression of a vast network of interrelated individuals changing in all sorts of ways.

When we have finished classifying a group of animals such as the vertebrates, we find that we have a sort of treelike arrangement. The phylum, one of the major branches of the tree of life, divides into several somewhat smaller branches, the classes. The classes divide into orders, the orders into families, the families into genera, the genera into species, the species into subspecies, varieties, or races, which may be looked upon as the terminal twigs. This treelike arrangement is just what we would expect to find in a group descended from a common ancestry and modified along many different lines. If all this is the result of special creation, it is indeed unfortunate that it speaks so plainly of descent with modification, which is none other than evolution.

C. Evidences from Blood Tests

There is another way of classifying animals: on the basis of chemical similarities in their blood. It is known that the blood of an animal contains certain materials that are even more sharply specific than are its structural peculiarities. These blood elements form the basis for an extremely delicate means for testing organic relationships. Thus, if we wish to find out which animals have a blood resemblance to man, we proceed in the following fashion: Human blood is drawn and allowed to clot, thus separating the solid from the fluid constituents. The watery fluid—the serum—contains the specific human blood elements and is the material used in all of these experiments. Small doses of human serum are injected intravenously into a rabbit—any other mammal would probably do as well—and the injections are repeated at intervals of about two days until the rabbit is considered thoroughly sensitized. At first the injected animal is more or less sickened by the foreign material in its blood, but before long it shows no ill effects. What has happened is that the rabbit's blood has reacted to the presence of human serum in such a way that the latter is neutralized. The specific neutralizing substance is termed an ANTIBODY. Serum of the experimental rabbit contains much of this substance and is therefore called antihuman serum. Now, if a quantity of this antihuman serum be mixed with human serum, a heavy white precipitate is formed. When antihuman serum was mixed with serum of any of the anthropoid apes, the precipitate was somewhat less abundant and took longer to form, but was very positive in character. The tests, however, revealed a less prompt and abundant reaction with the sera of other Primates. The strength of the reaction ran strictly parallel with the supposed relationships based upon homologies. "It is a remarkable fact," says **Nuttall,** "that a common property has persisted in the bloods of certain groups of animals throughout the ages which have elapsed during their evolution from a common ancestor, and this in spite of differences of food and habits of life. The persistence of the chemical blood-relationship between the various groups of animals serves to carry us back into geological times, and I believe we have but begun the work along these lines, and that it will lead to valuable results in the study of various problems of evolution."

The tests carried out with other groups of animals showed a

remarkable, though not mathematically exact, parallelism between the relationships revealed by this new technique and those that had been previously worked out by the older methods. Many relationships that were obscure to the morphologists seem obvious to the serologist, for blood tests of relationships are more sensitive than are those based on homologies. Had blood tests and homologies failed to agree, our faith in the validity of both would have been severely shaken; but they are in essential agreement—a fact that greatly strengthens our confidence that they both speak truthfully about the descent of different animal groups from common ancestors.

D. Evidences from Embryology

There should really be no sharp distinction between evidences from comparative anatomy and those from embryology. The two branches are inseparable: one must be interpreted in the light of the other. Comparative anatomy ostensibly deals with the structures of adult organisms; but whenever there is any question as to obscure homologies, recourse is had to an embryological investigation of the relations of the structures in question. If it is found that the further back the two structures are traced the more closely do they approximate each other and that ultimately they are traced back to homologous embryonic primordia, the relationship of the structures in question is believed to have been established. We cannot be certain of homologies until confirmed by embryological study.

It should always be remembered that an individual is not merely the last stage of its development, but that it includes also the whole ontogeny from the egg stage till the end of life. Very closely related individuals will keep step all the way through their developmental stages, diverging only slightly at the end; distantly related types diverge comparatively early in their developmental paths; while unrelated types may be different from the beginning. The most advanced groups of organisms travel a much longer journey before reaching their destination than do the simpler organisms. In many instances certain early stages in the development of an advanced type resemble in unmistakable ways late stages of less advanced types. This apparent repetition in the development of the higher organisms of conditions characteristic of some of the lower organisms has so impressed certain biologists that they have come to the conclusion that *the development of the individual may be regarded as an abbreviated repetition of the ancestral history of the species.* This conception has taken shape as the BIOGENETIC LAW, or the LAW OF RECAPITULATION.

Attractive as it sounds, there is reason for serious doubt as to the validity of this generalization. In the first place, we know that no embryonic stage, as a whole, is equivalent to any adult organism of a lower order. While it may have some characters strongly reminiscent of those of adult structures of lower groups, the *tout ensemble* is not at all like the latter. Again, developmental stages must be adapted to the environment at all times, and therefore acquire many embryonic or larval organs that are of the utmost importance for the maintenance of individual life but have no ancestral significance at all. Furthermore, different systems of organs develop at entirely different rates according to the immediate necessities of the particular case. In some forms, for example, the nervous system may be far along its course of differentiation before the circulatory system has even begun to differentiate. No adult ancestor is likely to have had so discordant an organization.

In spite of its shortcomings, however, the idea that *ontogeny recapitulates phylogeny* is a very useful tool in the hands of the skilled embryologist, who realizes the chances of error and applies the principle in critical fashion. As an example of the legitimate use of the principle of recapitulation let us consider for a moment the following case: The circulatory system of man passes through a condition closely paralleling, first, that of a fish, then that of an amphibian, then that of a reptile, and finally reaches the typical mammalian condition. Again, we find that the human embryo closely resembles the fish in having gill slits (Fig. 185) which never function as such, but become either obliterated or else remodeled so as to be scarcely recognizable for what they are. Thus one pair of gill slits in man has been transformed into the Eustachian tube which connects the pharynx with the middle ear and aids materially in hearing.

The relationships of many obscure forms that in their adult stages seem almost without affinities to any known species have been cleared up by studies of their developmental histories. Thus, the BARNACLES, curious sessile animals, fastened on rocks or timbers, had been variously classified as mollusks, as vertebrates, and as members of a distinct phylum; and it was only when *J. V.*

Thompson studied their embryonic and larval life that they were found to be crustaceans. They are now classified as members of the Subclass Entomostraca, and the Order Cirripedia has been created for them and their relatives. This order is peculiar in having as a first larva a NAUPLIUS, similar to that of other Entomostraca. The Nauplius, however, metamorphoses to form a

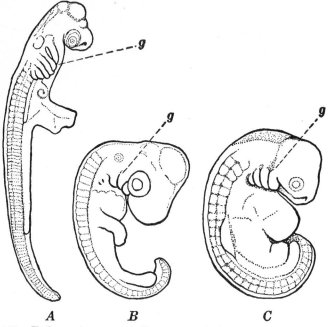

A	*B*	*C*

FIG. 185. Embryos in corresponding stage of development of shark (**A**), fowl (**B**), and man (**C**). *g*, gill-slits. (From Scott.)

second type of larva, known as CYPRIS, which is found only in the Cirripedia. The Cypris larva, after a short free-swimming life, settles down and becomes sessile, using its antennæ as anchors. It then undergoes a second metamorphosis, during which it takes on the peculiar characters of the adult barnacle with its mantle and shell and reduced head.

Years after the true relationships of the barnacles had been discovered there was found a strange parasitic growth, called SACCULINA, resembling a tumor, attached to the body of a certain kind of crab (Fig. 186, C). It consisted of a sort of soft sac with numerous rootlike processes invading the crab's body. It bore no resemblance to anything else in nature and was therefore a complete mystery until its eggs were discovered and its embryonic history worked out.   It then proved to be a relative of the bar-

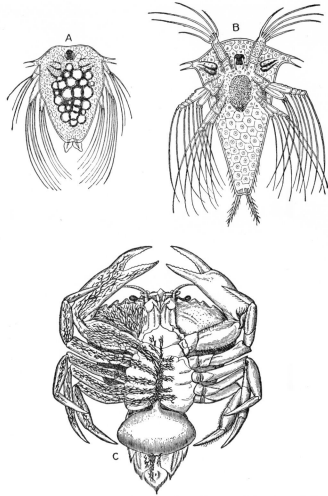

FIG. 186. The nadir of parasitism, *Sacculina carcini*.   **A** and **B,** larval (nauplius) stages; **C,** crab, *Carcinus mænas*, with a mature *Sacculina* in situ, showing ramifying "roots" (omitted from right side) which extract nourishment from the crab.   (From Lull, after Delage, from Leuckart.)

nacles; for it had both the Nauplius (Fig. 186, A, B) and the Cypris larva as well as the habit of settling down upon its antennæ.   But, instead of settling down and becoming merely sessile, as do the barnacles, it becomes profoundly parasitic. When the Cypris settles down, it thrusts its antennæ into a hair follicle of a crab; then its body tissues become disorganized into a fluid condition resembling a cellular emulsion. This flows through the hollowed-out antennæ into the blood spaces of the crab. There the loose cells round up into a ball-like mass that floats about in the blood of the crab until it reaches the intestine of the host, where it fastens itself by rootlike processes and lives parasitically upon the body fluids surrounding it. This almost formless parasite then reveals itself through its embryology to be a still more profoundly degenerate relative of the degenerate barnacles and, through the latter, a descendant from the free-living crustaceans.

These are only isolated examples of the ways in which the principle of recapitulation, when properly used, aids in the work of classification. They also serve to emphasize the fact that, in the hands of the trained expert, the evidences of evolution as derived from embryology are perhaps the most convincing evidences we have; whereas, in the hands of overenthusiastic or uncritical amateurs, they become decidedly treacherous and dangerous playthings. The literature of evolution is full of false inferences based upon inadequate embryological data, and this has done much to destroy confidence in the whole body of embryological evidence.

E. Evidences from Palæontology

1. *The Incompleteness of the Record*

Palæontology is the science of ancient or extinct life. Its materials are the fossil remains of animals and plants that once were living. Fossils are real: they cannot be explained away. If evolution has taken place and sample specimens of all of the animals and plants that ever lived were available for study, we should be able not only to prove the fact of evolution, but to show exactly the courses it has followed. Even if every specimen were labeled with the geographic locality where it was found and with the geological period when it lived, it would still be a staggering task to unravel all of the interwoven lines of descent. If, even with a complete fossil record, the task of reconstructing the history of the evolution of organisms would be a difficult one, how much more difficult must we expect to find this task when we realize how very incomplete the record really is!

The best of reasons exist why the palæontological record must forever be, at best, interrupted and fragmentary. In the first place, a very large proportion of the lower strata of the earth—strata that must have once contained the fossils of the oldest forms of life—have been so modified by heat and pressure that all traces of fossils have inevitably been obliterated. In the second place, enormous masses of fossil-bearing rocks have been destroyed by the eroding effects of rainfall and rivers, waves and glaciers. In the third place, only a small fraction of the fossil-bearing rocks are as yet, or are likely ever to be, available for study. Finally, the chances of an animal dying under such circumstances that its body would be preserved as a fossil are so small that only representatives of numerous and widely distributed species are likely to have been preserved at all.

2. *Different Kinds of Fossils*

Several different sorts of fossils are distinguished:—

a. Dead and Preserved Bodies.—The actual dead and preserved bodies, or parts of bodies, of animals or plants, with the original tissues intact, and inclosed either in ice or in amber (Fig. 187), or else mummified in various ways, form one class of fossils. Thus there have been recovered from the arctic ice or from the permanently frozen soil the still fresh bodies of mammoths, dead probably thousands of years. Again, many extinct species of insects have been preserved with the utmost faithfulness in amber, a transparent, petrified, resinous gum.

b. Petrified Fossils.—This type is important and numerous. In these fossils, organic matter has been replaced, particle for particle, by mineral matter in such a way that the finer structure of the tissues has been faithfully duplicated and rendered permanent.

c. Casts.—Perhaps the most numerous of all fossils are casts of animals. An animal or plant has lain in mud or clay long enough to have left its impress; the mud hardens about the body and forms a mold; the organic matter disintegrates and the mold is filled with hard mineral matter; and the matrix may then be removed so as to leave the perfect cast.

d. Prints.—Prints and traceries constitute the last of the kinds of fossils to be dealt with. An animal walking in partially hardened mud may leave a footprint that becomes preserved when the mud hardens into rock. Traceries have been left in the lithographic stone quarries, representing the forms of jellyfishes or the

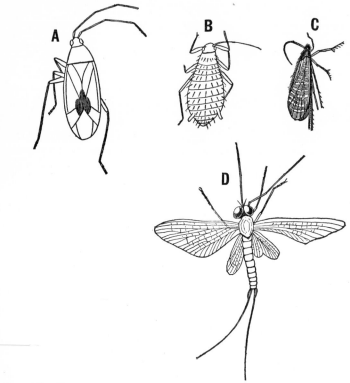

Fig. 187.   Insects preserved in amber.   A, bug; B, aphid; C, caddice-fly; D, may-fly.   (From Lull, after Neumayr.)

delicate lacy wings of insects.   These are as real as any other kind of fossil.

3. How Fossils Are Formed

The usual conditions of fossilization involve the death of the animal under such conditions that the body lies in water where it may rapidly be covered with sediment.   The mouth of a river during a flood would furnish such a situation.   Animals drowned in the flood might readily be preserved in considerable numbers in this fashion.   Marine organisms, at least those living along the coast or in shallow bays, meeting death in the water and falling to the bottom as they do, have naturally been preserved more abundantly than have terrestrial forms. Other animals have been preserved by sinking in quicksand, by falling into asphalt lakes, or by being covered up by sand drifts on the open plains or deserts.

4. *The Causes Underlying the Stratification of the Earth's Crust*

Geologists inform us that in early times the earth's crust was all hard and rocky, composed chiefly of granites, basalt, and other crystalline materials. This hard mass was gradually softened and disintegrated through the action of rain, sun, wind, and atmospheric gases. The loosened fragments were washed away by the rains and streams and deposited in depressions of various sorts, forming horizontal or stratified layers. Had the earth's surface been entirely rigid all irregularities would long ago have been leveled down and we would have a smooth surface; but the earth's crust has undergone a slow process of wrinkling, accompanied by uprisings in some parts and depressions in others. When a region becomes considerably elevated, as in a mountain chain or a high plateau, the tendency is for it to be worn down by erosion and for its materials to be deposited in the valleys or else to be carried by rivers to the lakes or seas. A further wrinkling may elevate the low places and depress the high places, resulting in another shift of materials. In this way the earth's crust has been shifted back and forth. One stratum is sharply marked off from the next because of the fact that while an area is elevated, much of its thickness is washed away, bringing its deeper parts to the surface; and when this same area once more becomes depressed and begins to receive another layer of sediment, the type of sediment has changed in character and the organisms that die and become fossilized are many thousands of years more recent than those embedded in the worn-down layer just below. This is one of the reasons why the fossils of contiguous strata so often appear to be so sharply different in character.

5. *The Age of the Earth*

According to the most recent estimates, based on the rate of radium emanation, 1,000,000,000 years have elapsed since the earth attained its present diameter. Various other estimates range from about one tenth of this figure to one considerably

greater than that given. Calculations as to when life first appeared
on the earth's surface give results varying from 50,000,000 years to
twenty times that figure. The latter estimate is believed to be
accurate within no more than 30 per cent error.

6. *The Geological Time Scale*

Geologists have subdivided the strata of the earth's crust into
Eras, Periods, and Epochs. The accompanying table (Fig. 188)
gives in concise form the data as to the ages of the various rock
levels together with the characteristic fossils. It will be noted that
only the upper half of the strata, beginning with the Cambrian,
are fossil-bearing. The layers below that level are composed of
igneous or metamorphosed rock. Only indirect evidences of the
former existence of fossils below the Cambrian level are at hand,
but there is every reason to believe that from one half to two thirds
of the evolution of life had been completed prior to the beginning
of the Palæozoic Era. About these earlier chapters in evolutionary
history we shall probably never have any further information.

7. *The Main Facts Revealed by the Fossil Record*

(*a*) None of the animals or plants of the past are identical with
those of the present. The nearest relationship is between a few
species of the recent past and some living species, which are sufficiently alike to be placed in the same genus.

(*b*) The animals and plants of each geologic stratum are at least
specifically different from those of any other stratum, though in
some cases they belong to the same genera.

(*c*) The animals and plants of the lowest geologic strata represent all of the existing phyla except the Chordata (vertebrates),
but the representatives of the various phyla are relatively generalized, rather simple forms, as compared with modern representatives
of the same phyla.

(*d*) The animals and plants of the uppermost strata are most like
those of the present and serve as links between the present and the
more remote past.

(*e*) There is to be seen a gradual progression from simpler and
more generalized types toward more complex and specialized types
as one proceeds from the lower toward the upper strata.

(*f*) Many groups of animals and plants have long ago reached
the climax of their paths of specialization and have become extinct.

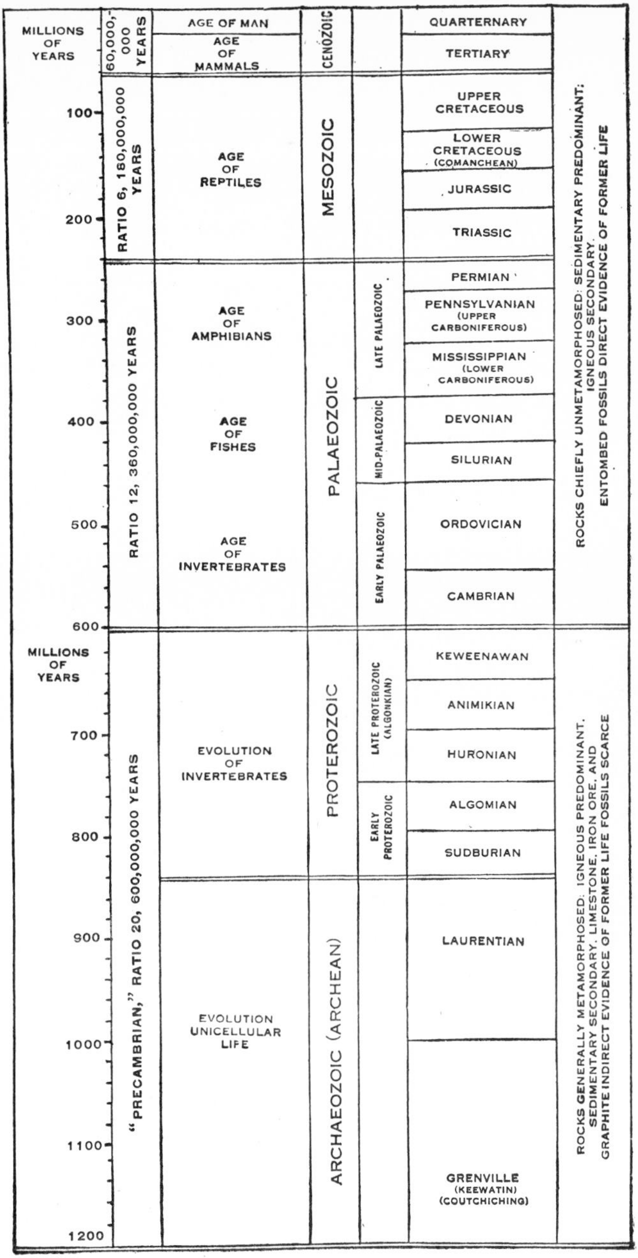

Fig. 188. Total Geologic Time Scale, estimated at 1,200,000,000 years. (From Newman, after Osborn, modified to agree with the more recent estimates.)

429

(*g*) Only the more generalized representatives of groups that, as a whole, have become specialized have succeeded in weathering the vicissitudes of changing world conditions and have survived up to the present.

(*h*) It is common to find a new group arising near the close of a geologic period during which great climatic changes were taking place. Such an incipient group almost invariably becomes the dominant and characteristic group of the next period, the probable reason for this being that the group in question arose in response to the conditions that were ushering in the new period and were therefore adapted to the new situation.

(*i*) The evolution of the vertebrate classes is more satisfactorily shown than that of any other group because they arose within the period of which we have a fossil record. Of the vertebrates, the history of the mammals is most complete, partly because they belong to relatively modern times and partly because the mammalian skeleton has been readily preserved in fossil form.

(*j*) Although many of the invertebrate phyla had already reached an advanced stage of evolution when we get our first glimpse of them in the Cambrian, many beautiful ancestral series have been found that enable the palæontologist to describe in detail the courses of branching descent leading to the surviving types of today.

(*k*) Many complete fossil pedigrees, connecting specialized modern animals with much more generalized ancestors, have been worked out. Such pedigrees as those of the horse, of the elephant, of the camel, are classic instances. These essentially complete series afford perhaps the most convincing evidence at our disposal that evolution has taken place. A single example of this type of evidence will be given—that of the horse. Any one of several others would serve equally well.

8. *The Pedigree of the Horse*

As recorded by **Dendy,** the course of evolution of the horse family (Equidæ) "has evidently been determined by the development of extensive, dry, grass-covered, open plains on the American continent. In adaptation to life on such areas structural modification has proceeded chiefly in two directions. The limbs have become greatly elongated and the foot uplifted from the ground, and thus adapted for rapid flight from pursuing enemies, while the middle digit has become more and more important and the others, together with the ulna and fibula, have gradually disappeared or been reduced to mere vestiges. At the same time the grazing mechanism has been gradually perfected. The neck and head have become elongated so that the animal is able to reach the ground without bending its legs, and the cheek teeth have acquired complex grinding surfaces and have greatly increased in length to compensate for increased rate of wear. As in so many other groups, the evolution of these special characters has been accompanied by gradual increase in size. The EOHIPPUS, of Lower Eocene times, appears to have been not more than eleven inches high at the shoulder, while existing horses measure about sixty-four inches, and the numerous intermediate genera for the most part show regular progress in this respect.

"All these changes have taken place gradually, and a beautiful series of intermediate forms indicating the different stages from Eohippus to the modern horse have been discovered. The sequence of these stages in geological time exactly fits in with the theory that each one has been derived from the one next below it by more perfect adaptation to the conditions of life. Numerous genera have been described, but it is not necessary to mention more than a few."

The first indisputably horselike animal appears to have been HYRACOTHERIUM, of the Lower Eocene of Europe. Another Lower Eocene form is Eohippus, which lived in North America, probably having migrated across from Asia by the Alaskan land connection that then existed. In Eohippus the forefoot had four well developed hoofed digits and a "thumb" reduced to a rudiment. In the hind foot the great toe had entirely disappeared and the little toe is represented by a splint-bone vestige. Then came OROHIPPUS of the Upper Eocene, MESOHIPPUS of the Lower Miocene, PROTOHIPPUS of the Lower Pliocene, PLIOHIPPUS of the Upper Pliocene, and finally EQUUS of the Quaternary and Recent. This history, in so far as it concerns changes in the feet and in the teeth, is well shown in the accompanying illustration (Fig. 189). Palæontological evidence of this sort is difficult to controvert. We are not only convinced that the modern horse has descended from a tiny five-toed ancestor, but we can actually read the story of evolutionary progress step by step. And, what is even more important,

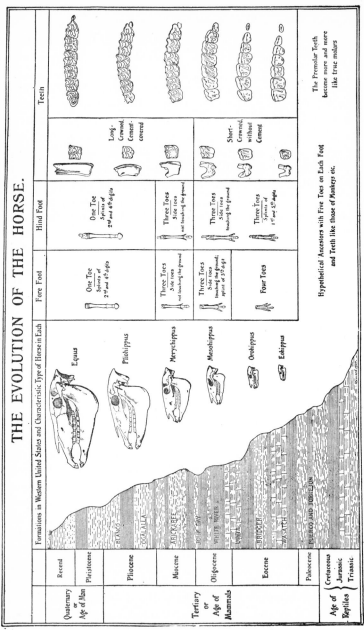

FIG. 189.   Graphic presentation of the evolution of the Horse.   (From Matthew, 1926.)

the horse pedigree is essentially duplicated by that of many others, some of them adjudged by experts to be even more complete.

F. Evidences from Geographic Distribution
1. *General Discussion*

Just as Palæontology may be spoken of as the vertical distribution or distribution in time of organisms, so Geographic Distribution may be referred to as a study of the horizontal distribution of organisms upon the earth's surface at various periods of time. Geographic distribution represents a sort of cross section of vertical distribution, giving a "still" picture of the complex evolution of organisms at one moment of geologic time. The student of geographic distribution is chiefly, but not solely, concerned with the present situation. The study is carried on by explorers and collectors, whose materials are worked over and classified by specialists in the various groups concerned. A map showing the irregular and overlapping ranges of all the species in any one area would be the most complicated picture-puzzle imaginable, and it would be a task of gigantic proportions to make sense out of it. At first thought it might be supposed that organisms are distributed according to climatic conditions or habitat complexes, each species occupying that region of the world best suited to it. A moment's reflection teaches us that this is not at all the case. Precisely similar climatic complexes in different parts of the world have totally different inhabitants; whereas quite similar species commonly occupy very different habitats.

That animals are not always, or even very frequently, found in the best possible habitats is evidenced by the fact that in many instances animals carried far from their native abodes into quite different territory have thriven much better than in the old habitat. The European rabbits, for example, when transported to Australia, throve and multiplied beyond all expectation until they overran the country and became a pest. Again, the English sparrow has found in North America a much more favorable environment than it left behind.

If animals are not distributed according to the plan of having each in the best habitat, how then can we account for their distribution? It is hardly likely that they have always occupied the same ranges they now occupy; for all living things migrate from place to place. The present distribution would be almost totally without meaning were we to confine our attention to it alone: we must study the distributions of the past and thus learn whence the various groups have come. It is only when we study distribution historically that we obtain a clue as to its meaning. Certain facts about the present distribution of species have in themselves a peculiar significance. It seems to be frequently true, for example, that two very closely similar species occupy adjacent ranges and are separated from each other by some natural barrier, such as a body of water or a mountain range. This suggests that one species has been derived from the other and that isolation has kept the derived species from mixing back with the parent species and thus being swamped out by interbreeding. Again, it not infrequently is the case that in a group of species belonging to a single genus the most generalized species occupies the center of generic range and that of the most specialized species are found in the more or less isolated outskirts of the range. Taking these and hosts of other facts into consideration, we seem to have no alternative but to believe that any given species originates in a well defined locality, that it multiplies there and migrates in all available directions, modifying as it goes in accord with various new conditions encountered, and becoming thus split up first into local varieties and, in the course of time, into species. What we have said is a mere paraphrase of the process of evolution, and it thus becomes obvious that the working hypothesis underlying the science of Geographic Distribution is the general principle of descent with modification. The proof that this hypothesis is valid inheres in the fact that, by its use, the whole intricate picture puzzle presented by the distribution of animals takes on a new significance and becomes intelligible, whereas on any other basis it remains absolutely confusing and meaningless. In other words, the working hypothesis works. It may then be considered valid until proven inadequate to account for the facts, or until a better hypothesis is forthcoming.

If any one phase of geographic distribution may be said to furnish more conclusive evidence of evolution than another, that phase has to do with the peculiar faunas and floras of oceanic islands.

2. The Inhabitants of Oceanic Islands

Oceanic islands are small, isolated bodies of land of volcanic origin and located far from continents. They are really no more than the tops of oceanic mountains that appear above the surface of the sea. All such islands have their inhabitants, and a study of these should furnish a crucial test of the rival theories, evolution and special creation. Both evolutionists and creationists agree that these islands have obtained their populations from the continental bodies; for no one has the hardihood to suppose that each tiny island has been the theater of a special creation. If then island species turn out to be exactly like those of the nearest continent, we would be justified in concluding that there has been no evolution of species; but if, on the contrary, the island species turn out to be practically all different from continental species, we would be equally justified in claiming that new species have arisen on the islands. Now the facts are these: Practically all the species inhabiting oceanic islands belong to the faunistic groups of the nearest continent; they consist of types that have the capacity for enduring prolonged transportation through the air during storms or upon floating débris; and the great majority of the species are characterized as "peculiar," *i.e.*, different from species anywhere else in the world. They sometimes belong to the same genera as those on the continent, but they are at least specifically distinct. The extreme case is that of the island of St. Helena, a very isolated oceanic island 1100 miles from Africa. On this island there live 129 species of beetles, all but one of which are peculiar. These species belong to 39 genera, of which 25 are peculiar. There are also 20 species of land snails, of which 17 are peculiar. Of 26 species of ferns, 17 are members of peculiar genera. St. Helena presents almost a separate small world of species, allied among themselves as though descended from common ancestors, but diverging so far from other known forms as to constitute, for the most part, quite distinct genera.

The Azores, the Bermudas, the Galapagos Islands, the Sandwich Islands, and many others, tell much the same story, but their populations are not quite so peculiar, being for the most part peculiar in species but not in genera—an indication that they are somewhat more recent in origin than St. Helena.

The facts of geographic distribution in general speak very plainly in favor of the idea that, when any branch of an old species is isolated from the parent stock, especially if the invaded region presents a distinctly different environment, new species arise. *Isolation appears to be a potent aid in establishing new species.*

G. Summary of Evidences of Evolution

All the lines of evidence that have been examined, and several others, such as domestication and experimental breeding, point strongly to organic evolution; and none of them are contrary to evolution. Moreover, most of the facts are utterly incompatible with any other theory. Not only do these evidences strongly favor the principle of evolution, but each line of evidence is consistent with all the others, each one helping to make the others more intelligible. Thus, embryology greatly illuminates comparative anatomy; geographic distribution is often greatly aided by palæontology; blood tests aid and are aided by taxonomy. The evolution idea is thus a great unifying and integrating conception that renders the various branches of biology parts of one coherent science. Any conception that is so far-reaching, so consistent, and that has led to so much advance in our understanding of nature, is at least an extremely valuable idea, and one not to be lightly cast aside in case it fails to agree with anyone's preconceived convictions.

CHAPTER XXXIX

GERM PLASM AND SOMATOPLASM

SINCE in all higher animals germ cells constitute the only bridge between two successive generations, it is natural to suspect that much of the mechanism of organic evolution is intimately tied up with the various regular changes involved in the germ cell cycle. It is proposed to study in some detail the nature of germ cells and the changes that go on in them.

A number of problems arise in this connection, the most important of which are as follows:— What is the relation between the germ plasm and the rest of the organism? At what period in the development of the individual are primordial germ cells first distinguishable? How do gametes arise? What happens to the chromosomes during gamete formation, and what is its evolutionary significance? How are zygotes formed and what is the significance of the process?

A. THE CONTINUITY OF THE GERM PLASM

One of the most extensively discussed theories of

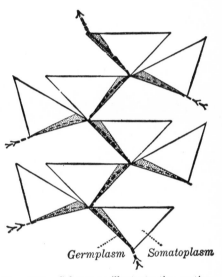

Germplasm   Somatoplasm

FIG. 190. Scheme to illustrate the continuity of the germ plasm. Each triangle represents an individual composed of *germ plasm* (dotted) and *somatoplasm* (clear). The beginning of the life cycle of each individual is at the apex of the triangle where both germ plasm and somatoplasm are present. In biparental (sexual) reproduction the germ plasms of two individuals become associated in a common stream which is the germ plasm and gives rise to the somatoplasm of the new generation. This continuity is indicated by the heavy broken line and the collateral contributions at each succeeding generation by light broken lines. (From Walter.)

437

modern times is Weismann's theory of the Continuity of the Germ Plasm. According to this theory, a germ cell (zygote) divides by mitosis to form daughter cells that have the same hereditary components as the parent cell. Sometimes very early, sometimes later, some of the cells derived by repeated division of the original zygote become differentiated for various bodily functions and lose their germinal potentialities. Once having become specialized for any bodily function these cells can never form germ cells. There are always left undifferentiated some cells, and these are able to produce new organisms if isolated from the parent body. Thus germ cells produce body cells, but body cells do not produce germ cells; and continuity of type is maintained through an unbroken lineage of germ cells from generation to generation (Fig. 190). Various implications of this theory have given rise to important controversies, especially as to whether the germ cells are entirely insulated from the body so that changes in the body, due to functioning or responses to environmental changes, could have no effect on them. Without attempting at present to discuss this problem, let us examine the facts upon which the Germ Plasm Theory rests.

If there be an unbroken descent of germ cell from germ cell *ad infinitum*, we should be able to keep track of germ cells from the beginning of one generation to that of the next. This history is known as the germ cell cycle.

B. PERIODS IN THE GERM CELL CYCLE

The following periods may be more or less arbitrarily marked off in this essentially continuous process:—

1. The fertilized egg or zygote—the beginning of a new individual.

2. The definite segregation or differentiation of one or more PRIMORDIAL GERM CELLS.

3. The early multiplication of primordial germ cells.

4. The rest period, during which there is no mitosis in the primordial germ cells. They merely gather into one or two groups to form the primordia of the gonads (ovaries or testes).

5. The period of multiplication. During this period mitosis is resumed, usually resulting in the production of large numbers of OÖGONIA or SPERMATOGONIA.

6. Some oögonia differentiate into nurse cells and others remain germinal; some spermatogonia differentiate into nutritive or SERTOLI CELLS and others remain spermatogonia.

7. The growth period. During this period there is no further mitosis, but oögonia and spermatogonia grow to form, respectively, primary OÖCYTES and SPERMATOCYTES.

8. The period of maturation, during which the number of chromosomes is reduced to one half that characteristic of the soma of the species.

9. Fertilization, resulting in the production of a zygote with the full number of chromosomes. This is the beginning of another generation.

Some of these periods will now be discussed in further detail.

1. *The Segregation of Primordial Germ Cells*

The exact mode of setting apart of the germ cells is crucial for the Germ Plasm Theory. There is the widest difference as to the stage of development at which cells may be said to be definitely distinguishable as germ cells. In some cases we can identify germ cells as different from body cells as early as the four-cell stage of cleavage, while in other cases no germ cells can be distinguished as such until a later embryonic or a larval period. The time at which visible segregation of germ cells occurs seems to depend upon how early in embryonic history cellular differentiation of any kind occurs. In many animals the egg, even before cleavage, is definitely organized into regions, and the cytoplasm contains many "organ-forming substances" that are destined to appear only in certain definite blastomeres. These blastomeres, in turn, are set aside for certain definite organs or tissues. The type of cleavage that seems to entail a mere partitioning off of egg regions already differentiated and destined for special organs is known as DETERMINATE CLEAVAGE. There are many other animals, however, in which there is little regional differentiation at the time of fertilization and in which cell multiplication goes a long way before there is any obvious differentiation of cells. We speak of this kind of cleavage as INDETERMINATE.

In general, it may be said, that in species or groups characterized by determinate cleavage an early segregation of the germ cells may be expected; while in those with indeterminate cleavage a

late segregation is the usual thing. An entirely different way of
looking at this problem is to consider all early embryonic cells as
germinal and to watch for the first evidences, not of the differentiation of germ cells, but of the differentiation of somatic cells for
particular functions. This point of view implies that all cells that
have not lost their generalized germinal character by specializing
for some particular function or by losing some of the heredity

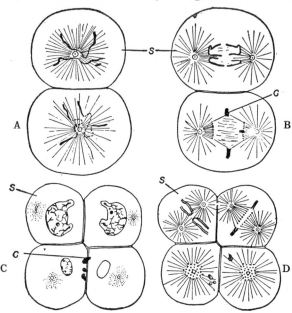

Fig. 191. *Ascaris.* Stages in early cleavage showing the chromatin diminution (*c*) process in all cells except the stem cell (*s*). **A,** two-cell stage; **B,**
beginning of the four-cell stage; **C,** four-cell stage; **D,** beginning to form
8 cells. (From Boveri, 1892.)

material, chromatin, are germ cells. If this view be adopted, it
becomes easy to maintain the validity of the continuity-of-the-
germ-plasm doctrine, for there could be no break in the lineage of
germ cells. Some classic cases that show early segregation of
somatic and germinal cells are those of Ascaris and of Miastor.

a. The Case of Ascaris.—*Ascaris megalocephala,* the parasitic
mawworm of the horse, has long been a classic object for cytological study. Boveri, in 1887, studied and described the early cleavage, especially the early setting aside of the germ cells (Fig. 191).
The first cleavage gives rise to two daughter cells, each with two

horseshoe-shaped chromosomes. During the second cleavage one cell divides normally; the other divides in a different way, for each of the two chromosomes breaks up, giving rise to two solid end pieces (c) and numerous small granular bits of chromatin derived from the middle of the chromosome. The four massive end pieces of chromatin (heredity material) take no active part in the mitotic division and are later resorbed by the cytoplasm; this is known as

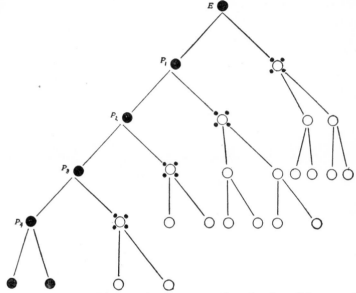

Fig. 192. *Ascaris.* Diagram showing segregation of primordial germ cell. E=egg; P_1, P_2, P_3,=stem (germinal) cells; P_4=primordial germ cell. Circles represent somatic cells, while the four black dots outside of the circles represent the masses of chromatin that are eliminated. (From Boveri, 1910.)

CHROMATIN DIMINUTION, and the implication is that these cells that have lost some of their heredity material cannot retain the full capacity for producing a new individual, but can give rise only to certain specialized types of organs. As a matter of fact, these first cells to have lost chromatin produce only somatic tissues, while the other two cells that have retained the full complement of chromatin may be looked upon as still germinal. Now, in the next division, passing from the four- to the eight-cell stage, one of the two "germinal" cells divides normally and the other divides with the accompaniment of chromatin diminution, as before, and the division products of this latter cell are set aside to form somatic tissues. The remaining cell retains all of its chromatin and is therefore still germinal. It, however, divides into two cells, one of which undergoes chromatin diminution and gives rise to somatic tissues; the other remains germinal. This last cell contributes once more to the formation of the soma; after that it divides several times more, giving rise only to germ cells. This history is shown in the accompanying diagram (Fig. 192). It is clear then that in Ascaris there is no break in the continuity of the germ plasm.

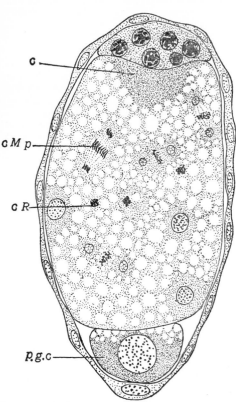

FIG. 193. *Miastor americana.* Longitudinal section of egg with one germ cell (*p.g.c*) and nuclei undergoing chromatin-diminution process. *c*=cytoplasm; *cMp*=chromosome middle plate; *cR*=chromatin remains. (From Hegner.)

b. **The Case of Miastor** (Fig. 193).— This case is not so very different from that of Ascaris. The egg is rather definitely organized before cleavage begins. At the vegetal pole of the egg there is a mass of material known as POLE PLASM. When the first division of the egg occurs, one daughter nucleus goes into the pole plasm and becomes the first germinal nucleus, destined to give rise by further divisions to all the germ cells of the individual. The other daughter nucleus divides several times, undergoing chromatin diminution each time and thereby sealing its fate as a possible mother of germ cells. Many similar cases of early germ cell segregation—perhaps it

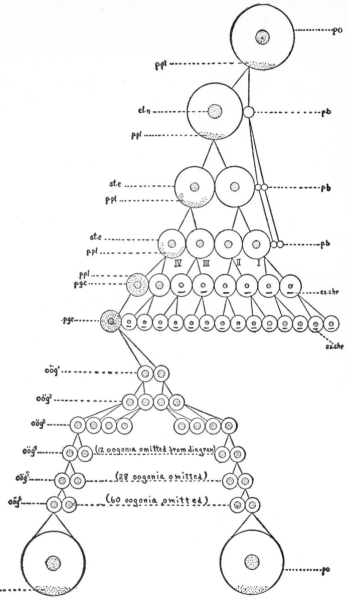

Fig. 194. *Miastor americana.* Diagram illustrating origin and history of germ cells from one generation to the next. *cl.n* = cleavage nucleus; *ex.chr* = extruded chromatin; *oög* = oögonia; *p.b* = polar body; *p.g.c* = primordial germ cell; *p.o.* = primary oöcyte; *p.pl* = pole-plasm. *st.c* = stem cell. (From Hegner.)

would be more correct to say early somatic differentiation—have been described in species belonging to most of the large groups of animals.

In the vertebrates the germ cells and body cells cannot be distinguished until relatively late, but the vertebrates are slow to specialize tissues of any sort, and perhaps it would not be incorrect to say that for a long time vertebrate embryonic cells are all essentially germinal. In concluding this phase of the discussion, it may be said that there is probably an absolute distinction between germ cells and somatic cells in some groups of animals, but that in other groups the distinction is not a rigid one, and that in such animals there is always the possibility that certain unspecialized somatic cells may take on a germinal function when the conditions demand.

2. *The Period of Multiplication*

Soon after the primordial germ cells aggregate to form the early gonads a period of multiplication ensues, which results in the dividing cells becoming smaller and smaller as they become more numerous, because very little growth takes place between mitotic divisions. In Miastor (Fig. 194) this period results in the formation of sixty-four oögonia. In several other species the number is equally limited and exactly known.

3. *The Period of Growth*

Growth of the oögonia and spermatogonia takes place more or less at the expense of some of the potential germ cells that give up their germinal function and become nurses and feeders to the cells destined to be mature germ cells. Thus a few cells are enabled to grow large and well fed at the expense of a good many others. One very important event occurs during the growth period: homologous chromosomes come together in pairs—the phenomenon known as SYNAPSIS. This event seems to look forward to reduction in the number of chromosomes to one half the somatic number, thus making it feasible for the male and female gametes to unite without increasing the specific number of chromosomes.

4. *The Period of Maturation*

The process of maturation (Fig. 195) involves two divisions of the germ cells that differ entirely from any others in that in one of

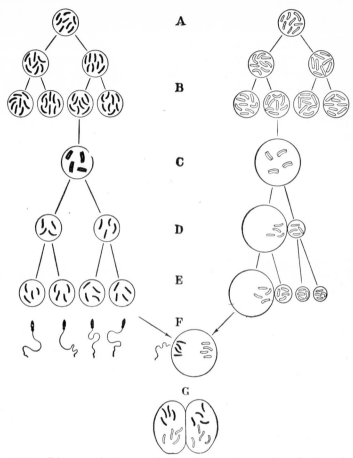

FIG. 195. Diagram of the general plan of spermatogenesis and oögenesis in
animals. The somatic, or diploid, number of chromosomes (duplex group)
is assumed to be eight. Male, to the left; female, to the right. **A,** primordial germ cells; **B,** spermatogonia and oögonia, many of which arise
during the period of multiplication; **C,** primary spermatocyte and oöcyte,
after the growth period with chromosomes in synapsis; **D,** secondary
spermatocytes and oöcytes, with haploid number (simplex group) of
chromosomes, which have arisen by the first maturation (reduction)
division; **E,** spermatids (which become transformed into sperm) and egg
and three polar bodies which have arisen by the second maturation (equa-
tion) division; **F,** union of sperm and egg (fertilization) to form zygote
with diploid number (duplex group) of chromosomes; **G,** chromosome
complex of cells after first division of the zygote, and of all subsequent
somatic cells, and germ cells until maturation. (From Woodruff.)

these divisions whole chromosomes, instead of half chromosomes, go to the two daughter cells. More specifically, the paired homologous chromosomes that had united during synapsis separate and go to different daughter cells. This means that homologous maternal and paternal chromosomes contributed by the parents always go to different gametes. Now since the distribution of the maternal and paternal components of one pair of chromosomes is quite independent of that of all other pairs of chromosomes, there is possible a very wide range of diversity in the shuffling and dealing of the hereditary characters of the germ cells. The second maturation division is somewhat of a puzzle. It does not affect the distribution of the hereditary units, but it does allow chromosomes, already split lengthwise during the first maturation division, to become properly distributed to daughter cells. This is necessary if the number of chromosomes in the gametes is to be reduced to one half in preparation for the union of gametes into zygotes. The maturation mechanism is believed to be one of the most important factors involved in evolution, for it gives rise to a tremendous variety of combinations of maternal and paternal characters.

5. *The Formation of Zygotes (Fertilization)*

From the evolutionary standpoint the chief effect of the union of gametes to form zygotes (Fig. 195 F, G) is the production of a great variety of combinations of different assortments of hereditary units of two different stocks. This makes it possible for the most favorable characters of different stocks to become united in a single individual. The evolutionary significance of this can scarcely be overemphasized.

C. The Germ Plasm Theory Criticized

There are at the present time many zoölogists, especially those who have a physiological bent, who abhor the idea of the separateness or apartness of the germ plasm. They look upon the organism as a unit, each part of which is integrated with all others. In view of all of the coördinating systems with which the higher organisms are endowed, it seems to them inconceivable that one part of an organism could be physiologically isolated from all the rest. Objection is also raised to the doctrine that germ cells are always derived from previously existing germ cells in an unbroken line of germinal antecedents; for the claim is made that in many animals, and especially in some vertebrates, the primordial germ cells disintegrate during larval life and new germ cells are differentiated out of epithelial cells—cells that have always been classed as somatic. Even if functional germ cells in certain cases are derived from epithelium and not from primordial germ cells, there is involved no genuine break in germinal continuity, for even epithelial cells are linear descendants of the original zygote. The only question at issue is whether epithelial tissues are to be considered as having become specialized for a particular function; whether, in other words, we are justified in calling them somatic tissues rather than reserve germinal tissues. The second alternative seems more reasonable.

CHAPTER XL

SEX AS AN EVOLUTIONARY MECHANISM

A. The Phenomena of Sex Outlined

a. Sex Defined.—It is not easy to give an adequate definition of sex. Dictionaries define it as "the distinguishing peculiarity of male and female"; as "either of the two divisions of organic beings distinguished as male and female." These definitions really evade the issue, but it is very difficult to offer a suitable substitute. We can get at a definition in a somewhat roundabout way by saying that sex comprises that whole set of phenomena that center about gametic reproduction. Any individual, then, is sexual if it produces gametes—ova or spermatozoa, or their equivalents. Thus we would be justified in calling any individual that produces ova a female, and one that produces spermatozoa a male. One that produces both kinds of gametes is a male-female or, more technically, a HERMAPHRODITE. Thus we may say that the PRIMARY SEXUAL CHARACTERS of individuals are the ova or the spermatozoa, and that maleness or femaleness is determined by the possession of one or other of these two types of gametes.

b. Secondary Sexual Characters.—There are usually, especially in higher animals, many differences between males and females in addition to the possession of eggs or sperms. The two sexes may differ in size, in form, in coloration, in the accessory organs of reproduction, in instincts and behavior, in adaptations for feeding and taking care of young. While some of the lower animals differ visibly only in their primary sex characters, the general rule is a more or less pronounced SEX DIMORPHISM. An extreme case of this phenomenon is that of one of the scale insects, *Aulocaspis rosæ* (Fig. 196), in which the adult male is a fairly typical insect with wings, antennæ, and legs, but has no mouth; while the adult female has no legs, wings, or antennæ, but has a mouth.

c. Sex as an Adaptation.—In discussing any biological phenomenon, one question inevitably comes to be asked: What is the advantage of it or in what way is it of value to the species possess-

ing it? In previous chapters we have had occasion to point out
some of the ways in which sex appears to be of value. It is obvious
that sex is an important agency in promoting reproduction; but
it should not be forgotten that in very many instances reproduction
is carried on successfully without the intervention of mating or

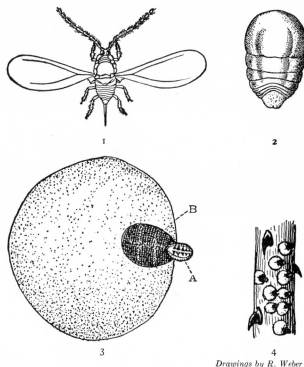

Drawings by R. Weber

FIG. 196.   The rose scale (*Aulocaspis rosæ*), an extreme case of sexual dimorphism.   1, Adult male, with 2 wings, 2 antennæ, 6 legs, but no mouth.
2, Adult female; legs antennæ, and wings not developed, but mouth (on
under side) well developed.   This female never leaves the scale (3).
The scale shows the cast skin of the larva at *A*, the second cast skin at
B, and the white adult scale covering the female.   4 shows the scales on
a rose branch, twice natural size.   (From Cockerel's "Zoölogy"[World
Book Co.])

true sexual congress. Among the higher organisms, however, sexual dimorphism accompanied by sexual congress is practically
universal. The more highly specialized organisms are in other
respects, the more pronounced sexual dimorphism they are likely to
display. Thus sexual dimorphism is merely one phase of speciali-

zation. Just as it is a better scheme to have certain cells or tissues performing but one function apiece and doing the job expertly, so it is in the interests of increased efficiency to have the two sexes as highly specialized and differentiated from each other as possible, so long as the characters in which they differ are of value.

We can readily understand that sex in its more advanced and highly perfected states is a reproductive adaptation of great consequence, but what can be said of the value of the simplest expressions of the sexual phenomenon that consist of nothing more than a union of apparently similar gametes? A ready answer to this question might be that whenever gametes unite they bring together germ plasms that differ in certain respects and that such combinations may be more favorable than either of the uncombined conditions. In the higher animals it is clear that, during the maturation divisions, a sort of shuffling and dealing of maternal and paternal genes—the determiners of adult characters—takes place, and this results in a great variety of different combinations of the parental genes, a different combination being distributed to each gamete. This being true, whenever any two gametes unite to form a zygote, a unique individual is likely to be produced; for it is very unlikely that, with so many different combinations possible in different gametes, the same kind of sperm and egg would ever chance to come together more than once. Thus it seems certain that sex is an agency capable of producing almost infinite diversity among the individuals of a species, and out of a very wide range of individuals differing in a great many ways there will obviously be some that are better adapted to the conditions of life than others. This forms the basis for Natural Selection, or the survival of the fittest, believed to be an important factor in progressive evolution. Sexual reproduction then may be looked upon as a mechanism that is continually grinding out new forms that have to run the gauntlet of selection.

B. The Determination of Sex

a. Early Theories.—What is it that settles whether a given zygote, or fertilized egg, shall give rise to a male or a female? This is an old problem, and many theories have been advanced to explain it. *Hippocrates* long ago guessed that the sex of any offspring depended upon the relative vigor of the two parents, the stronger of the parents impressing his or her sex upon the child. This theory fails to account for the fact that in many animals that give birth to several young at a time there are both males and females in the litter. Several authors have claimed that sex depends on the relative ripeness or staleness of the gametes at the time of fertilization. Another theory, widely accepted for some time, was that the condition of nutrition of the mother during pregnancy, or during the growth period of the eggs, determined the sex: that a well-nourished mother tended to produce females and a poorly-nourished mother, males. Some color was lent to this hypothesis by the fact—if it is a fact—that there is an increased ratio of male to female births in the human species during and immediately after periods of war and of famine, when conditions of nutrition are bad.

b. Sex Determined at the Time of Fertilization.—Evidence has been steadily accumulating within the past twenty years or more that sex is determined definitely, and in some cases irrevocably, when the egg is fertilized by the sperm; that the particular combination of chromosomes that is brought together when the gametes unite settles the sex. Perhaps the most positive proof of this, apart from cytological examination of the germ cells themselves, comes from a study of the reproduction of the nine-banded armadillo. This interesting mammal has the specific peculiarity of always— the exceptions are almost negligible—producing four offspring at a litter (Fig. 178). Invariably all the members of a set of quadruplets are of the same sex and are nearly identical in their other bodily characters. The explanation of this is that in every case a set of quadruplets is derived from one zygote that divides at an early embryonic period into four separate embryos. The sex must have been decided before the four embryos separated, and it never changes afterwards. Moreover, the separation of embryonic rudiments occurs so early that the presumption is that the sex was already determined at the time of fertilization. Other cases of the same sort are those seen in some of the parasitic hymenoptera and in human identical twins. In some parasitic hymenoptera the eggs are laid in the eggs of butterflies by the wasplike mother, and at an early embryonic stage the embryo parasite divides into hundreds of separate embryonic parts, each of which produces a complete grublike larva parasitic in the body of the larva of the butterfly. Each grub produces an adult, and all individuals derived from one egg are of the same sex. Human identical twins are also either both males or both females, and there is every reason to believe that they are the product of the division of a single egg in each case; yet this has never been absolutely demonstrated as it has in the case of the armadillo.

C. The Chromosomal Mechanism of Sex Determination

a. Chromosomal Mechanism as Exemplified by Drosophila.— When geneticists first came to realize the importance of the chromosomal mechanism of heredity, it was natural enough for them to look for sex differences in the chromosomes. Investigation showed that the cells of the males and of the females in many species of animals differ in the number, size, or shapes of chromosomes. Moreover, there were usually some of the chromosomes that showed sex differences while all of the others were alike in both sexes. This difference in chromosomes according to sex is well illustrated by the germ cells of the classic fruit fly, *Drosophila melanogaster* (Fig. 197), which has furnished so much valuable data to genetics. The cells of the female possess eight chromosomes, two of each of four kinds. There are two pairs of rather large bent chromosomes, one pair of minute spherical chromosomes, and one pair of straight rodlike chromosomes—the latter shown in black in the figure. The first three pairs mentioned are known as AUTOSOMES and are the same in both sexes. The pair of straight chromosomes, shown in black, are known as the X-CHROMOSOMES and are believed to play an important rôle in sex determination. When we examine the male germ cells, we find that the only difference to be noted is in connection with the X-chromosomes, for, instead of two straight X-chromosomes, as in the female, the male cells possess one X-chromosome and one hook-shaped chromosome of about the same size, known as the Y-CHROMOSOME. A female Drosophila has the chromosomal combination XX, while the male has the combination XY. All of the body cells have the same chromosomal condition as have the germ cells of the same individual. So far, we have only succeeded in describing another type of sex dimorphism, but we fortunately have been able to discover the mechanism by means of which this dimorphism and its consequences have been brought about. The accompanying diagram (Fig. 197) shows the maturation divisions leading to the formation of both eggs and spermatozoa. Note that, in the case of the egg, when the numerical reduction of chromosomes has taken place, each gamete has an X-chromosome. In the case of the sperm, however, the gametes are of two kinds, one having an X-chromosome and the other a Y-chromosome. Thus two kinds of sperms

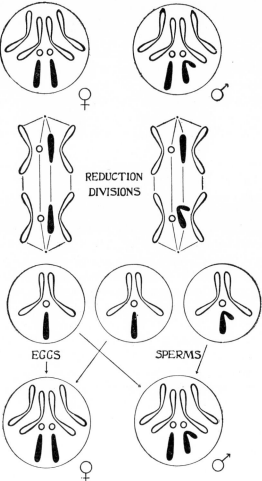

REDUCTION DIVISIONS

EGGS   SPERMS

Fig. 197.   Diagram to show chromosome relations in the inheritance of sex in *Drosophila melanogaster*. (From Babcock and Clausen.)

are produced in equal numbers and each kind has an equal chance to fertilize eggs. The result is that half of the eggs are fertilized by X-sperms and half by Y-sperms. When an X-sperm fertilizes an egg, the result will always be an XX-zygote, which is a female;

but when a Y-sperm fertilizes an egg, the result will always be an XY-zygote, a male. Thus we have in the process of maturation and fertilization a mechanism not only for producing males and females, but one for maintaining a 50: 50 ratio between the sexes.

Until quite recently it has been supposed that the X- and Y-chromosomes carried special determiners for sex, but *Bridges* has demonstrated that it is not so simple a matter. According to this keen investigator, the important factor is the balance, more or less quantitative in character, between the X- or the Y-chromosomes and the rest of the chromosomes (AUTOSOMES). Two X-chromosomes, which are female in their tendencies, are sufficient to over-balance the six autosomes in the female direction; but if only one X-chromosome is present, it is insufficient to overbalance the autosomes, and the male condition prevails, for the combined tendency of the autosomes is toward maleness. In certain exceptional cases Bridges found that, as the result of a slip in the maturation mechanism, some female gametes were produced with extra autosomes. When such eggs were fertilized by sperms carrying the X-chromosome, zygotes were produced with two X-chromosomes and seven or eight autosomes, instead of the usual six. Individuals developing from such zygotes were not females, even though they had the XX combination, but were INTERSEXES, showing all sorts of conditions intermediate between those of regular males and females. Thus an equilibrium between the sex tendencies was produced. In some cases an additional X-chromosome was shown to swing the balance entirely to the female side once more. At first it appeared that the Y-chromosome had no part in the physiology of sex, but Bridges has shown that in certain rare cases where zygotes had been formed without a Y-chromosome, male individuals, apparently normal in other respects, were produced, but they were always quite sterile. Certain other revelations as to the chromosomal mechanism of sex determination have come to light, but the above analysis has proceeded far enough for our purposes.

The question now arises as to whether the mechanism which seems to have been definitely demonstrated in Drosophila is paralleled in other animals. With various modifications as to details, it seems to be true that some such mechanism as that described is responsible for sex determination in at least the vast majority of animals and in not a few plants. It may be a universal vital phenomenon. Man, for example, has 48 chromosomes, with two X-chromosomes in the female and an X- and a Y-chromosome in the male.

b. Sex Determination in Moths.—In moths the mechanism just described for Drosophila is just reversed, in that the males have the XX condition and the females the XY condition. Thus two kinds of eggs are produced and only one kind of sperm. Apart from this shifting of the chromosome condition between the two sexes everything else works out essentially as in Drosophila.

c. Sex Determination in Parthenogenetic Species.—Even in those well-known cases where development takes place without fertilization, the facts are consistent with the above analysis of the mechanism of sex determination. In the bees, for example, all fertilized eggs produce females—either fertile queens or infertile workers—and all unfertilized eggs produce males, known as drones. Cytological examination shows that all eggs undergo maturation and that each egg possesses one X-chromosome. All functional spermatozoa, for reasons that will presently be explained, also possess one X-chromosome. The result is that all eggs that are fertilized receive an X-chromosome from each gamete, giving the XX combination, and therefore produce females; while all eggs that pass out of the oviduct without fertilization have the reduced number of chromosomes, including but one X-chromosome, and therefore produce males. Two points need further elucidation. One is this: If sex determination depends on the balance between the X-chromosomes and the autosomes, why is it that in the bees two X-chromosomes and the diploid number of autosomes give the female condition, while one X-chromosome and the haploid number of autosomes give the male condition? Obviously the balance between autosomes and X-chromosomes is exactly the same in both sexes. From this it would appear more logical to assume, as has usually been done, that in this group of animals the autosomes have little to do with sex determination and the one X-chromosome by itself determines maleness and the two X-chromosomes, femaleness. The other point still unexplained is this: Why is it that, in the bees and wasps, all functional spermatozoa have the same chromosome complex—that with one X-chromosome? Let us remember that males have the reduced number of chromosomes from the start, and that, therefore, they cannot very well undergo further chromosomal reduction. So strong is the force of heredity, however, that the male spermatocytes go through the motions of undergoing maturation, but omit the essential feature of this process, the reduction division. When the first maturation mitosis takes place, all the chromosomes go to one pole and a very unequal cell division takes place, resulting in one large spermatocyte of the second order possessing the normal haploid number of chromosomes and a small abortive spermatocyte without any nucleus, which of course is incapable of life. Hence each functional spermatozoön possesses the normal haploid number of chromosomes with one X-chromosome.

In other parthenogenetic groups, such as the aphids, parthenogenetic eggs for several generations produce only females. Later in season, however, a generation of males and females is produced parthenogenetically. The problem is to account for the origin of the males. It has been found that at a definite point of the germ cell cycle some of the germ cells have extruded an X-chromosome, thus giving rise to the male condition. The males and females of this generation mate and produce winter zygotes capable of living through the winter and developing the following spring. When they develop they form exclusively females, stem mothers, that start off the series of parthenogenetic generations. The reason why only females are produced as the result of the mating of males and females is that only one kind of spermatozoön is viable, the one lacking an X-chromosome never living long enough to be functional.

D. CONCLUDING REMARKS

It now seems clear that not only are the mechanisms of gamete formation and of the union of gametes to form zygotes important factors in evolution, but equally important are the mechanisms by means of which male and female individuals are produced. In some of the higher animals, especially the vertebrates, it has been shown that the chromosome mechanism alone is inadequate to complete the job of producing full-fledged males and females. In our discussion of various physiological processes controlled by hormones we have already brought out the fact that in vertebrates the complete differentiation of secondary sexual characters depends upon sex hormones. Since this aspect of sex biology has already been dealt with we shall pass it by without further comment.

It may be stated in concluding this account of sex as an evolutionary mechanism, that we have shown that the chromosomes have a very definite rôle in the determination of sex. It will soon become equally obvious that chromosomes are equally important in variation and heredity in general. In the next chapter the Chromosome Theory will be expounded in detail.

CHAPTER XLI

VARIATION AND HEREDITY

OF the various factors involved in the process of organic evolution it is generally agreed that variation and heredity are of primary importance. So firmly established is this idea that most modern experimental study of evolution confines itself to these two fields. To all intents and purposes the science of genetics is essentially no more than the science of variation and heredity. The present chapter, then, might equally well be entitled Genetics.

A. The Methods of Genetics

Three principal methods have been employed in the attack upon the difficult problems of genetics:—

a. Experimental Breeding.—This method was first employed in a systematic and analytical manner by *Gregor Mendel*. The usual procedure is that of breeding together two individuals possessing certain contrasting characters and then determining the ratios in which these characters reappear in the successive generations of offspring and descendants. Experimental breeding has been extremely fruitful in throwing light not only on the laws of heredity but upon the origin of new characters and the mechanism of their transmission.

b. Cytology.—This second method involves the microscopic examination of the germ cells during the critical periods of their cycle. As the result of this study it now seems possible that we may view under the microscope the actual operations of the heredity machine. In the preceding two chapters the main facts of cytology have already been presented.

c. The Statistical Method.—*Sir Francis Galton* may be credited with having originated this method of studying genetics. By means of correlation tables and mathematical formulæ he was able to arrive at an accurate basis of comparison between large groups of parents and their offspring. The method deals not with individual cases but with populations, and the results are summations or averages of large numbers of individual likenesses and differences. Of the three methods of genetics the third has been somewhat less fruitful than either of the others.

B. Variation

Variation as a genetical concept is difficult to define, for the term has long been used loosely and in a variety of senses. It is sometimes used as a term to express the idea of organic diversity, and in that sense deals primarily with the fact that no two individuals are alike in the finer details of their structure. This almost infinite diversity among individuals of a species is said to be at once the hope and the despair of the breeder; for without variation there would be no possibility of producing improvements, while with variation ever present the task of maintaining standard types is extremely difficult.

Besides this somewhat abstract use of the term variation, it is sometimes used more concretely to mean the process of change from one organic condition to another; again, the changed character itself is frequently spoken of as a variation, in which sense it is practically synonymous with the word "mutation."

1. *Variations Classified*

Individual differences (variations) may be viewed from several different angles, depending upon what particular aspect of variability happens to be uppermost in our interest. We may be primarily interested in their heritability, in their nature, in their gradations, or in their definiteness or indefiniteness of direction from age to age.

a. Heritability.—Variations may be merely particular changes in parts of an individual organism in response to changes in the environment. These structural or functional adjustments of the bodies of individuals are not thought to be heritable and are classed as SOMATIC MODIFICATIONS.

A second type of variation is the result of a combination of the hereditary characters of two differing strains or races. Nothing distinctly new is thought to be produced in such cases, but it is possible to bring together the favorable characters of two races in one individual and thus to produce a new and better type. This category of variations may be designated as COMBINATIONS.

A third type of variations consists of those that have come to be known as MUTATIONS; they are to be accounted for neither as the result of the action of the environment or functioning on the part of the soma, nor as the result of the recombination of already existing hereditary units, but as the result of some hereditary change in the germ plasm itself, due to some local chemical change in the chromatin that seems to take place more or less spontaneously, *i.e.*, without the intervention of any external agency. It need hardly be said that this type of variation is the only one that is inherently hereditary, although combinations may sometimes be repeated in successive generations, and there is a little evidence that somatic modifications may possibly be sometimes heritable.

b. Nature.—According to their nature we may classify variations as morphological, physiological, psychological, ecological. Instances of morphological variations are, for example, differences in the numbers of spines, scales, feathers; differences in size, proportions, colors, shapes. Examples of physiological variations are, among others, differences in state of nutrition, in vitality, in productivity, in susceptibility to various adverse conditions. Instances of psychological variation are differences in mental traits, in disposition, in responsiveness. Examples of ecological variations are those that result from a fixed relation to the environment, such as differences between members of the same species of plant some of which have grown in swampy soil and some under desert conditions.

c. Gradations.—Variations may be of that very common sort that occur even between individuals with identical heredity, such as variations among the leaves of the same plant, or those found in the offspring derived from a single zygote; such variations usually grade one into another so as to form an unbroken series from one extreme to the other. Variations, such as the heights of human beings or the lengths of leaves or even the numbers of veins in leaves of one plant, form graded series, and are known as CONTINUOUS VARIATIONS. If, however, certain individuals occur in a species that possess characters that are distinctly out of series with the main body of the species and are therefore separated more or less abruptly from the others, such variations are known as DISCONTINUOUS. Mutations constitute one type of discontinuous variations.

d. Direction.—Variations may be either ORTHOGENETIC or FORTUITOUS. ORTHOGENESIS means literally straight development, and may be paraphrased to mean evolution along definite lines or paths. Thus the evolution of the horse has been orthogenetic because the changes or variations have proceeded along definite and logical paths from the little five-toed ancestor, through the four-toed, the three-toed, and finally one-toed types. These changes have been definite in direction; they are therefore orthogenetic. Fortuitous variations seem to be mere fluctuations back and forth about a mean and are largely due to fluctuations in the environment or to the miscellany of recombinations of minor hereditary factors, several of which may be involved in the determination of a single character. There is much palæontological evidence that evolution has been the result of orthogenetic changes, but we do not know the factors responsible for the definiteness observed.

2. *The Influence of Environment and of Function in the Production of Individual Differences*

Differences in the environment and change of function undoubtedly exert a modifying influence upon the development of hereditary characters. No organism can develop at all without certain environmental conditions and without functioning of embryonic tissues in proper fashion at every stage of development. What the particular individual comes to be as an adult is the resultant of the interaction of the two factors: heredity on the one hand, and environment and functioning on the other. Changing the temperature, oxygen, food, moisture, light, or other environmental factors of a developing organism may readily alter the whole aspect of the individual so that it would hardly be recognized as the same sort of animal that it would have become under a normal environment. The degree of modification from the typical condition depends on the degree of change, the length of exposure, the time at which the change was applied. Thus, all sorts of monsters, one-eyed, two-headed, headless, dwarfed, colorless, or with changed color, may be produced in a single lot of fish reared from a batch of eggs allowed to develop under unfavorable environmental conditions.

So far as we know, however, these changes are entirely somatic and are not hereditary; and as such they have very little significance for the theory of evolution.

3. *The Causes of Hereditary Variations (Mutations)*

At the present time it must be admitted that very little is known about the actual causes of mutations. In some few cases mutations are the result of aberrations in the chromosome complex, due to irregularities in the maturation machinery, but we have not been able to determine the causes of these disturbances in the germinal machine. Thus, it may be said that most of the mutations of *Œnothera lamarckiana*, the classic evening primrose made famous by **Hugo de Vries,** are associated with chromosomal aberrations. Some mutants have twice the specific number of chromosomes, others one and a half times the normal number, and still others one or two more chromosomes than the normal. These new numbers may be accounted for by a failure of either an egg or a sperm to undergo reduction, a failure to reduce on the part of both gametes that go to form a given zygote, or finally, a failure on the part of one or more pairs of homologous chromosomes to separate during maturation, so that both of a pair goes to one gamete; this is known as NON-DISJUNCTION.

While there is evidence that some, perhaps many, other plant mutations may have a causal basis similar to that just described, there is very little evidence that tends to indicate that animal mutations are caused in this manner. Hundreds of mutations of the fruit fly, *Drosophila melanogaster*, for example, are accompanied by no visible chromosomal changes, and can only be explained as the result of invisible local chemical changes in the chromosomes. The problem of the causes of mutations is, therefore, almost entirely unsolved. Its solution constitutes one of the greatest tasks for future generations of biologists. The recent work of **Muller** and others in vastly increasing the rate of mutation by X-rays is a step in the right direction.

4. *The Reality and the Significance of Mutations*

To say that we do not as yet understand the causes of mutations is no more damaging an admission than are admissions we have already had to make in connection with other difficult biological problems. We have to admit that we do not know exactly what life is, that we do not understand just why an egg is able to develop into an adult, that we comprehend only very vaguely what are the forces at work in mitotic cell division. These are ultimate problems and are in all probability so interdependent that the solution of one may open the way for a solution of the others. Who knows what day or year may see the discovery of a crucial clue that will lead to the understanding of all these knotty problems?

Our failure to understand the causes of mutations has no more bearing upon the reality of mutations than has our lack of under-

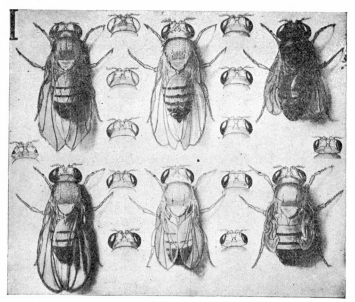

Fig. 198. Mutants of *Drosophila melanogaster*, showing changes in wings, body, eyes, legs. (From Morgan.)

standing of developmental mechanics upon the plain fact that such development actually takes place. Mutations are realities. Scores, probably hundreds, of species of animals and plants have been observed to mutate, *i.e.*, to produce new types that cannot be accounted for as the result of recombinations of previously existing heredity units.

A classic case, typical in every way, may be described to show just how mutations occur and are discovered. Some years ago, in a stock of fruit flies (*Drosophila melanogaster*) that had bred true for red eyes for a considerable number of generations, there appeared a single white-eyed male fly, one among thousands with the normal red-eye color. This conspicuous new character was soon shown to be hereditary and it was perpetuated in hundreds of descendants. Some four hundred other mutations, involving changes in all parts of the body, have now been observed in the same species. Similar, and in some cases identical, mutations have been reported in several other species of Drosophila. The same story could be repeated about mice, about guinea pigs, about maize, about jimson weed, and about all sorts of other animals, including man.

Now these mutations are doubtless occurring with greater or less frequency in all living organisms, and there is no reason to

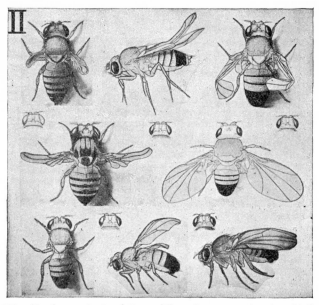

Fig. 199. Further mutants of *Drosophila melanogaster*, showing chiefly wing mutations. (From Morgan.)

suppose that mutations are anything new in the world of life. This type of change has almost certainly been going on since life began. The observed mutations (Figs. 198, 199) are multifarious in character; they concern all organs of the body—eyes, body color, wing size and shape, legs, feet, chemical constitution, vigor or the lack of it, sex characters, and what not. Some mutations seem to be confined to one small part, others to involve more or less extensively many if not all parts of the body. The great majority of mutations are changes for the worse, but this is only to be expected, for the normal characters of any species are a picked lot that have survived the vicissitudes of long ages of testing and have passed muster as the most satisfactory under the prevailing conditions of life. **William Bateson** has gone so far as to claim that all observed mutations are retrogressive, backward steps due to the loss of some positive factor. This, I believe, is an overstatement. Certainly some mutants are at least as valuable as are types from which they have been derived, and have shown their ability to survive in actual competition with the latter. Moreover, even if only one mutation in a thousand involved an actual improvement, the summation of such over the millions of years of racial descent would be amply sufficient to bring about changes of vast consequence; for what is once gained is not readily lost.

Mutations have been defined as hereditary variations. Our next task is that of understanding their modes of inheritance and the laws that govern their distribution among the successive generations of offspring and descendants.

C. HEREDITY

Definitions.—"Heredity is commonly defined as the tendency of offspring to develop characters like those of the parents."— *Babcock and Clausen.*

"Heredity may be defined as organic resemblance based on descent."—*W. E. Castle.*

In our discussion of certain aspects of the principle of homology we have already had occasion to assume the principle of heredity (p. 416). Thus, the idea of community of type based upon descent from a common ancestor is founded upon the principle of heredity as defined by Castle. This constitutes the basic assumption underlying the science of Taxonomy. The reason why a whale's flipper, a bird's wing, a horse's leg, and a man's arm are homologous—why they all have the same general architectural plan—is because they have all inherited from some remote common ancestor the characters that they have in common. In our present consideration of heredity we shall not concern ourselves with homologies—the major inherited resemblances between the larger groups of animals—but with the minor resemblances and differences existing within a species.

1. *Genes, or Factors*

Many years ago it was discovered by **Mendel** and by **Galton** that an individual is made up of a collection of more or less independently inherited characters. Such characters as stature, eye color, hair texture, shape of nose, were called unit characters. Each UNIT CHARACTER of the adult organism was thought to have in the germ cell a minute representative which constitutes the differential for that character. The germinal representative of a bodily character has received a variety of names, some of which are: DETERMINER, FACTOR, GENE. A zygote, or fertilized egg, is believed to contain two genes for each hereditary character, such as eye color or shape of nose. The reason for this belief is that, as we have already pointed out, there is a double or duplicate set of chromosomes in the zygote, one of each kind having been contributed by each parent. On this account all of the body cells, as well as the germ cells, that arise from the division of the zygote possess the double set of chromosomes and with them two genes for each hereditary difference.

Up to the time of maturation the germ cells retain the double set of chromosomes and genes. During maturation, however, homologous chromosomes—those carrying equivalent genes—unite temporarily in pairs, and in the reduction division one of each kind of chromosome, and consequently of each kind of gene, goes into a different daughter cell. Thus each gamete comes to have only a single set of chromosomes and a single set of genes. If the two parents of the individual we are dealing with differed with regard to their homologous genes, the eye-color genes for example, one having a brown eye-color gene and the other a blue eye-color gene, the zygote would possess two opposed eye-color genes, the stronger of which will prevail over the other in the determination of the color of the eye. Before maturation both of the eye-color genes are present in the hybrid germ cells; but when maturation has been completed, each gamete contains only one eye-color gene, either brown or blue, and there are equal numbers of gametes of the two kinds. The gametes are pure for one or other of the alternative genes. This is a very fundamental fact in heredity and has been dignified by the somewhat imposing title of the PRINCIPLE OF THE PURITY OF THE GAMETES.

In ideally pure races the zygote contains identical homologous genes throughout, and gametes would be all alike in their hereditary potentialities. Such a race is spoken of as a PURE LINE or a completely HOMOZYGOUS RACE. It is a question whether any absolutely pure line ever existed, for minor mutations are constantly occurring in the various chromosomes, involving one homologous gene without the other. When two genes of a pair are different the individual is said to be HETEROZYGOUS

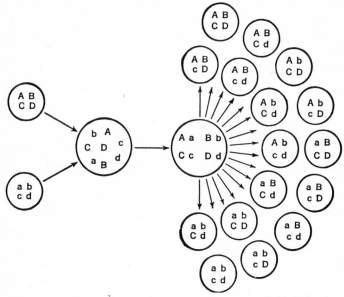

FIG. 200. Diagram to show the union of simplex groups of either the chromosomes or of the genes of the gametes to form the duplex condition of the zygote and animal body; and then their pairing at synapsis, and segregation in the gametes. With four pairs of chromosomes or of genes (Aa, Bb, Cc, Dd) there are sixteen possible types of gametes. (From Woodruff, after Wilson.)

with regard to that character. An animal is practically certain to be homozygous in some characters and heterozygous in others.

When maturation occurs, the mechanism employed for chromosome reduction is the familiar mechanism of mitotic cell division, diverted from its usual function of maintaining the exact continuity of hereditary materials. When the first maturation spindle is organized, the various pairs of homologous chromosomes move to the equator of the spindle as independent bodies, apparently uninfluenced by the movements of one another. The result is that, more or less by mere chance, some paternal elements of homologous chromosomes turn toward one end of the spindle and others toward the other end. Thus all sorts of shuffling and redealing of maternal and paternal genes takes place, and scarcely any two gametes, in a species with large numbers of chromosomes, receive exactly the same assortment of genes. The accompanying diagram shows a simple case of the results of shuffling and dealing in a form with eight chromosomes (Fig. 200). This scheme makes for an almost infinite variety of combinations of the varying parental characters represented in the germ cells.

The mechanism for producing gametic diversity that has just been described might appropriately be called the VARIATION MACHINE, for it is at least one of the most important factors in the production of organic diversity. The product that this machine turns out in the way of various ratios of offspring, inheriting one, two, three, or more contrasting characters, is what has been called MENDEL'S LAWS, because Mendel was the first to discover the regularity and lawfulness of these ratios. Although Mendel worked entirely with plants, it seems more appropriate in a zoölogical textbook to make use of animal materials, for these show modes of Mendelian heredity just as well as do plants. A typical case of Mendelian heredity among animals is that described for guinea pigs by *Castle.*

2. *The Inheritance of Coat Characters in Guinea Pigs*

Guinea pigs have long been among the favorite animals for experimental work in various branches of biology; hence it was but natural that they should be chosen for experimental breeding. Many fancy breeds have been produced and these possess many differentiating characters suitable for Mendelian analysis. Some of the varieties have been long bred from pedigreed stock, so that their genetic composition is known. Thus to start with we have certain homozygous races that breed true to certain characters. For example, there are pure breeding black races and pure breeding white, or albino, races; there are pure long-haired, or angora, races and pure short-haired races; there are pure smooth-haired races and pure rough-coated, or rosetted, races.

If we wish to see the workings of the heredity machine at its simplest, we should breed together two of these pure races differing in only one respect, say hair color. A pure black guinea pig—it makes no difference whether the black parent is the male or the female—is mated with a pure white individual. Somewhat to our surprise, if we were to perform this experiment for the first time, we would find invariably that all of the offspring would be black and none white. When these crossbred black individuals are interbred, brother to sister as is commonly done in animal breeding, we may be surprised to find that in addition to blacks there will be a definite proportion of pure whites. If large numbers of such experiments as the above are carried out, it will be found that there are three blacks to one white in the third generation.

The results of this experiment may be stated in tabular form as follows:—

P	(parents)	Black	$\times$	White
F_1	(first offspring generation)		All Black	
F_2	(second offspring generation)	3 Blacks		1 White.

In this diagram we have used the conventional terms most commonly used in describing Mendelian experiments. P stands for the parent generation; F_1 stands for the first hybrid generation or first filial generation; and F_2 stands for the offspring generation derived by interbreeding individuals of F_1.

In our experiment the white character disappears in the F_1 generation and only the black appears. We speak of the black character as DOMINANT and the white as RECESSIVE. The dominant character does not in any way destroy or affect the gene for white, but merely excludes it more or less completely from expressing itself in the body cells when both black and white genes are present in the same zygote. This is clearly brought out when, in the F_2 generation, the white character reappears pure in one fourth of the offspring. A recessive character is therefore one that can express itself fully only in the absence of the alternative or homologous dominant character. Recessives are therefore homozygous or pure breeding.

Before we can proceed very far with our analysis of Mendelian heredity we must, for the sake of clearness and brevity, adopt some of the stock conventions that are now recognized as standard. Thus it is customary to represent the dominant character gene by a capital letter, usually the initial letter of the name of the character of which the gene is the differential, while the recessive is represented by the corresponding small letter. We may then restate the above experiment in terms of the genes involved:—

P (zygotes)   BB   ×   bb
P (gametes)   B   b
F_1 (zygotes)   Bb
F_1 (gametes)   B   and   b (for both eggs and sperms)
F_2 (zygotes)   1 BB;   2 Bb;   1 bb (the F_2 genotypic ratio).

Several important principles are illustrated by this formulation: (*a*) both of the parents are shown to contain two coat-color genes of the same kind and are therefore homozygous for that character; (*b*) the reduction division results in gametes with only one gene of the kind possessed by the parent; (*c*) the F_1 zygotes are all heterozygous, containing both B and b; (*d*) the gametes of F_1 are pure with respect to either B or b, never having both in any one gamete; (*e*) just half of the gametes of F_1 possess B and half possess b; (*f*) if the male and female gametes unite by chance, the following combinations will occur with equal frequency—BB, Bb, bB, bb; (*g*) but Bb and bB are the same, and therefore this combination occurs twice as frequently as either of the other two, BB or bb; (*h*) there is little if any difference in appearance between the individuals having the zygotic combinations BB and Bb, and we have to lump together all individuals of both kinds as blacks, thus accounting for the PHENOTYPIC RATIO of 3 blacks to 1 white.

The only sure way of assorting the blacks of the F_2 generation into the two groups, homozygous and heterozygous, is to breed each of them with a white. If the black individuals are homozygous, all offspring will be black; but if the black individual is heterozygous, half of the offspring will be heterozygous black and half white, for the chances of a white gamete meeting with a black or with a white gamete are equal.

It is easy to carry out Mendelian experiments to the F_3 and the F_4 generations, but nothing new in principle is revealed; for the homozygous individuals, BB and bb, always breed true, while the heterozygous individuals, Bb, always split up into the three groups —1 BB, 2 Bb, 1 bb.

The same analysis as the above can readily be made for all other pairs of homologous hereditary units. Thus, in the case of the character HAIR LENGTH, where short hair is found to be dominant over long hair, we would arrive at the following formula:—

P (zygotes)	SS	$\times$	ss	
P (gametes)	S		s	
F_1 (zygotes)		Ss		
F_1 (gametes)	S	and	s	(in both eggs and sperms)
F_2 (zygotes)	1 SS;	2 Ss;	1 ss	(the F_2 genotypic ratio).

It is also found by experiment that rough, or rosetted, hair (R) is dominant over smooth hair (r). A formula for this cross would be practically the same as those given above for hair color and hair length.

MONOHYBRID CROSSES are those like the three just described, where only one pair of differentiating characters exists (or is to be considered) in the analysis. While each pair of characters, when considered by itself, behaves just like those already considered, much new light has been thrown upon the nature of the heredity machine by following the simultaneous inheritance of two or more pairs of characters. We speak of a cross involving two pairs of differentiating characters as a DIHYBRID CROSS and of one involving three pairs of different genes as a TRIHYBRID CROSS.

3. Dihybrid Crosses

Let us consider the simultaneous inheritance of two of the pairs of different characters that have been dealt with separately; namely, those of hair color and hair form. For the parents we might select one (either male or female) guinea pig with, say, white rough hair, and another guinea pig with black smooth hair (Fig. 201). Since black is dominant over white and rough dominant over smooth, we would have the following formulation:—

P (zygotes)	BBrr	$\times$	bbRR		
P (gametes)	Br		bR		
F_1 (zygotes)		BbRr			
F_1 (gametes)	BR,	Br,	bR,	br	(in equal numbers in both eggs and sperms)
F_2 (zygotes)		9 black roughs; 3 black smooths; 3 white roughs; 1 white smooth (the dihybrid phenotypic ratio for F_2 generation).			

The genotypic ratio for the F_2 zygotes is best represented by the so-called PUNNET SQUARE, as follows:—

SPERMS OF F_1

	BR	Br	bR	br
BR	BR BR	BR Br	BR bR	BR br
EGGS Br OF F_1	BR Br	Br Br	Br bR	Br br
bR	BR bR	Br bR	bR bR	bR br
br	BR br	Br br	bR br	br br

There are two ways of interpreting this formulation: phenotypically and genotypically. If we are concerned merely with appearances or with the characters of the single generation, we can obtain the phenotypic dihybrid ratio rather easily as follows: All of the zygotes, represented one to a square, that contain both dominant characters, B and R, irrespective of the presence of the recessive characters, will appear to be black and rough. Of the sixteen squares—each of these constitutes one out of every sixteen possibilities of the union of the four kinds of gametes concerned—nine will be found to contain both B and R; three contain B but no R; three contain R but no B; and one contains neither R nor B. This would account for the phenotypic ratio of: 9 black roughs; 3 black smooths; 3 white roughs; and 1 white smooth, which is a typical example of an F_2 dihybrid, phenotypic ratio and is illustrated graphically in Figure 201.

Now it is clear that, on the basis of the genes present, there are at least three kinds of black roughs: those homozygous for both B and R, those homozygous for B but heterozygous for R, and those homozygous for R but heterozygous for B. Similarly, there are two genotypes for the phenotype black smooth: those in which B is homozygous and those in which B is heterozygous. Again, there are two genotypes of the phenotype white rough: one in which R is homozygous and one in which R is heterozygous. Finally, there is but one genotype of the phenotype white smooth, for both white and smooth are homozygous, else they would not be able to appear.

4. *Trihybrid Crosses*

It is not difficult to go one step further in the process of following paired characters simultaneously and to work out the ratios for

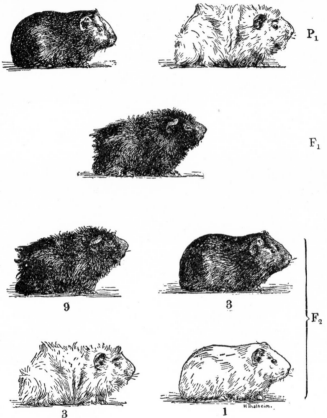

FIG. 201. Pictorial diagram of a dihybrid cross, showing the results of crossing black smooth and white rough guinea-pigs. F_1 is black rough. F_2 is in the ratio 9 black rough: 3 white rough: 3 black smooth: 1 white smooth. (From Babcock and Clausen, after Baur.)

the inheritance of three pair of independently segregating characters. We can most readily do this by simply adding one more pair of contrasting characters to the two pairs already dealt with, using as the additional character that of hair length, involving the dominant gene for short fur (S) and the recessive gene for long fur, which may be thought of as the lack of S, and designated s. In this case we shall have to be satisfied to go no further than a phenotypic analysis, for though the genotypic analysis as based on a Punnet square is not difficult, it is rather cumbersome for present purposes. Diagramming the experiment, we obtain the following formula:—

P (zygotes)   BBSSrr   +   bbssRR
P (gametes)   BSr   bsR
F_1 (zygotes)   BbSsRr
F_1 (gametes)   BSR, BSr, BsR, bSR, Bsr, bSr, bsR, bsr (equal
                        numbers of each kind in both eggs and sperms)
   F_2 (zygotes) 27 black short rough; 9 black short smooth; 9 black long rough; 9 white short rough; 3 black long smooth; 3 white short smooth; 3 white long rough; and 1 white long smooth. This is the typical F_2 trihybrid phenotypic ratio. By the use of the Punnet square the student can readily work out the genotypes concerned in each of the phenotypes.

5. Linkage

In the dihybrid and trihybrid experiments given above, the pairs of contrasting characters behave as though their genes were carried by three different chromosomes, each quite independent of the others. There are many reasons for believing that this is the true condition, but in order to make the point clear we shall have to transfer our attention from the slow breeding guinea pig to the rapid breeding fruit fly, *Drosophila melanogaster*, whose chromosome complex we have already examined. It will be recalled that there are only eight chromosomes: two of each kind, or four kinds in all. (See Fig. 197.)

Over two hundred different hereditary units have been identified in this species, and, with only four kinds of chromosomes present in the germ cells, it is obvious that there cannot be a chromosome for each gene. This only alternative conclusion is that each chromosome must contain many genes. Now, if a large number of genes are located in a single chromosome, all of them should be inherited in a group, for chromosomes are supposed to maintain their identity from generation to generation and not to break up. The facts of the case are these: Certain characters are inherited as though they are quite independent in their distribution—in other words, as though their genes were in different chromosomes; but equally numerous instances are noted in which characters tend to hold their relations to one another in heredity—in other words, they behave as though their genes were in the same chromosome. The latter type of association is known as LINKAGE and the former as INDEPENDENT ASSORTMENT. Linkage is rarely complete, but any degree of association of separate genes greater than that expected of independently assorting genes is interpreted as linkage.

Now it is very significant that in Drosophila, with its four kinds of chromosomes, there have been discovered just four and no more linkage groups of genes, each group showing quite independent assortment with genes of other groups. One large group of about a hundred genes is sex-linked, and is therefore assigned to the X-chromosomes. Two other even larger groups are not sex-linked and have been assigned to the large autosomes II and III. Lastly, a very small group of linked genes has been assigned to the microchromosome, IV. If any other linkage groups were to be discovered, there would be no chromosome to which they might be assigned. It seems hardly likely, however, that any further linkage groups will be discovered, for such a discovery would almost entirely invalidate the present theories as to the mechanism of Mendelian heredity.

For the present we may assume that the real cause of linkage is the one assigned: that genes in the same chromosome tend to be linked in heredity. But if that assumption be warranted, why is it that different genes are rarely completely linked and some are only slightly more linked than are independently assorting genes? If chromosomes actually do retain their complete identity during the germ cell cycle, complete linkage should always result between genes in the same chromosome. The very fact that every degree of incomplete linkage occurs is almost conclusive proof in itself that chromosomes do not retain their integrity from generation to generation, but that they commonly break up into sections and reunite with parts of other chromosomes. But there is equally strong evidence that the reunion of segments occurs only between homologous chromosomes, for the alterations in linkage relations occur only among the genes of the same linkage group. The question now arises as to the mechanism responsible for segmentation and reunion of equivalent segments of homologous chromosomes.

6. *Crossing-over*

One theory that is supported by a great mass of evidence is the so-called CROSSING-OVER HYPOTHESIS, the essence of which is as follows: When homologous chromosomes unite in pairs during synapsis, they twist about each other in such a fashion that equivalent blocks of genes pass from one chromosome to the

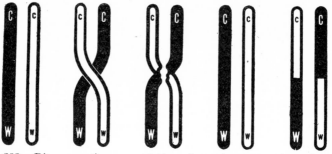

FIG. 202.   Diagrammatic representation of crossing-over and results.   At the left, the two original chromosomes.   In the middle, the twisted condition of the chromosomes in synapsis and their subsequent separation. At the right, the four types of chromosomes that result and their proportions.   (From Babcock and Clausen.)

other (Fig. 202).   A good many cytological observations indicate that chromosomes actually do twist about each other in this fashion, but there is no definite cytological evidence that they separate in such a way as to exchange blocks of chromatin.   The genetic evidence, however, as derived from the intensive study of crossing over, goes far toward a demonstration that this mechanism actually does exist, for such a mechanism is exactly what is needed to account for the genetic results.

It is obvious, on this hypothesis, that genes situated close together on the chromosome would be less likely to be severed by chromosome breaks and thus crossed-over than would genes situated far apart. On the basis of this assumption an ingenious scheme has been devised for locating the positions of all linked genes on any given chromosome. Thus, genes with the highest cross-over values are located at opposite ends of the chromosome, and the intermediate genes are located with reference to the two ends by means of their cross-over values with the two end genes respectively. This scheme works out so consistently that the majority of biologists have now been forced to admit the validity of the hypothesis and the results obtained through its application. Extraordinary as it may seem, it now appears highly probable that we can actually locate particular genes not only in a particular chromosome but can say exactly where in a given chromosome each gene lies with reference to all other known genes in the same chromosome. Chromosome maps have been published, showing the locations in the chromosomes of all genes so far discovered (Fig. 203). This discovery represents one of the most signal accomplishments of biological science.

There are many still more significant ramifications of modern genetic practice that have been intensely interesting to those who have followed the advances step by step, but without a familiarity with the data involved it is difficult to understand them. Suffice it to say that the newer discoveries are consistent with the old and all tend strongly to support the general chromosome theory of heredity. For present purposes we have probably gone as far as would be profitable into the intricacies of modern genetic advance.

7. *Summary and Conclusion*

In this and in previous chapters the CHROMOSOME THEORY OF HEREDITY has been presented as though it were a fact; and such it is to all intents and purposes. The evidences favoring this theory are overwhelming and at present appear to be incontrovertible. The most recent and most technical of these evidences are the most conclusive of all. Nowadays, only an occasional biologist remains unconvinced of the main features of the theory; a good many balk at the implications of the linkage and crossing-over phenomena; while only a few are sufficiently in command of the details of the evidence thus far adduced to be in a position adequately to pass judgment upon the validity of this new analysis of hereditary phenomena. The present status of our knowledge of the exact mechanism of Mendelian heredity has been attained after one of the most rapid and most spectacular advances ever made in the history of biological science, comparable with recent advances in phys-

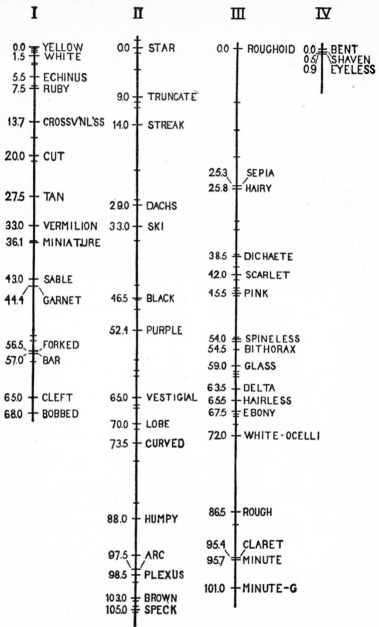

FIG. 203. Chromosome map of *Drosophila melanogaster*, showing the location of the genes in the four chromosomes: I, the x-chromosome, and II, III, IV, the three autosomes. (From Morgan.)

ics along the lines of theories as to the ultimate nature and structure of matter.

Suppose, for the sake of discussion, that we admit that it is now possible to locate with accuracy the position of each gene in its appropriate chromosome, what light does this throw on the nature of genes or the way in which genes produce characters? Here we have to admit almost complete ignorance, but there is not a little evidence favoring the idea that the gene is a minute mass of colloidal protein material with catalytic or enzymic properties, capable of influencing certain specific chemical processes in the cytoplasm of certain cells. The end result that we call a character is the product of the activation of a particular cytoplasm, located at and conditioned by a particular level of the organism, by the particular activator present in the gene. Thus, it now seems highly probable that the exact specificity of a character depends upon three equally necessary coöperating factors: (a) the level of the cells concerned with reference to the different metabolic gradients of the organism; (b) the inherited specific activating substances, or genes; and (c) the particular environment. If any one factor be changed, the end product, or character, will be changed from its typical expression, or may not be able to develop at all. Thus, we may conclude that there are three coöperating factors in the development of the specific characters of an organism: the genes, the axiate relations of the organism, and the environment. There is now every reason to believe that these same factors coöperate in racial development, or organic evolution.

CHAPTER XLII

INTERRELATION OF THE CAUSAL FACTORS OF EVOLUTION

A. The Five Causal Factors

In the three preceding chapters some of the primary causal factors of evolution have been described and discussed. It is our purpose in this concluding chapter to deal with the whole complex of factors as one interoperating mechanism in which each part is essential. If all parts of a mechanism are essential it can hardly be said that one is more important than another.

When we use the term "factors" in connection with organic evolution what do we mean? Strictly speaking, factors are the agencies or mechanisms that make evolution proceed as it has done in the past and is doing today. Factors are the interoperating parts in the evolution machine. Our problem is that of discovering just what rôle each factor plays and in what ways each factor is related to the others.

There are five principal factors:

1. The persistence factor: *heredity*
2. The change factor: *variation*
3. The accelerating factor: *sex*
4. The guiding factor: *selection*
5. The dividing factor: *isolation.*

Certain other factors might be named, but there is no general agreement as to their reality or their mode of operation. Hence it seems best for the present purpose to confine our attention to factors that are known to be real and about which we have adequate information.

HEREDITY as a factor tends to preserve continuity of structure and function. With heredity operating alone and undisturbed by other factors the organic world would go on unchanged throughout the ages. With VARIATIONS appearing at their pres-

480

ent rate, and no heredity of these, the generations would all differ from one another and the organic world would be a chaos. With mutations as they are and heredity as it is, the evolution of new types would be relatively extremely slow, were it not for the speeding up afforded by SEX in connection with the processes of gametic reproduction. As we have already seen (Chap. XLI), through the shuffling and dealing of various combinations of the differing characters of the parents there may be brought together in one individual all sorts of new combinations of characters that had formerly been present in different individuals. Thus the favorable mutations that arise in hundreds of separate individuals may ultimately all be combined in one individual. Such an individual might be expected, on account of its superiority, to produce more offspring than others, and thus come to be the characteristic type of the species. If, therefore, evolution had to proceed without sexual reproduction, it would take a very much longer time for favorable variations to accumulate in any one line of descent.

If the first three factors were in full operation and all variations and combinations were preserved by heredity, the world would be full of monsters and defectives. Hence, it is obvious that if organisms are to become more fit, better adapted to their conditions of life, there must be a SELECTION among the novelties presented by mutation and recombination. As has been shown, only an occasional mutation is truly beneficial; the vast majority are harmful, or at best of negative value. If the individuals having the worst mutations, or the poorest combinations of mutations from different lines of descent, were to fail to reach adult life, it is clear that their germ plasm would die with them and thus the species would get rid of its worst hereditary traits. The individuals with the occasional favorable mutation, or the rare combination of previously separate good characters, would have the best chance to survive and transmit their characters to offspring.

Under relatively easy conditions, however, many inferior and nonprogressive types would continue to survive and propagate their kind, but when a period of hardship comes, the struggle for existence would tend to eliminate more and more of the poorly adapted types, and only the fittest would survive. The survival of the fittest, or NATURAL SELECTION, is then the most important positive guiding factor.   It is, however, not a creative factor nor a perpetuating factor; it merely acts as an arbiter among the hereditary differences provided by the factors previously considered.

Imagine, if you will, all of the four factors already discussed operating in a homogeneous world, a world without any diversity of environment and without barriers between its various parts.   Assume, for the sake of argument, that life arose from one source and in one place and then proceeded to evolve in the direction of increased fitness in all respects.   What would be the outcome?   A little reflection will show, I think, that in a homogeneous world there could be but one kind of environment and but one kind of fitness; hence there could be but one goal for evolution and but one kind of organism would arise.   The result would be one course of evolution and only one, and also but a single type of organism.   There would be no multiplicity of types adapted to a great variety of environments such as we actually have today.

In order then to introduce diversity of types, and give us the numerous phyla, classes, orders, families, genera, and species, a DIVIDING FACTOR is necessary.   Several agencies of quite different sorts may result in splitting up a single group into two or more groups, but they all operate on the principle of ISOLATION.   If one part of a species be isolated from another in a way that will prevent free interbreeding between the two divisions, the stage is set for divergence of the two branches.   The mere geographic isolation of a few members of a species will of itself tend to initiate a new type, which in the course of time may diverge to such an extent as to constitute a distinct species.   The reasons for this are not difficult to understand.   In the first place, each individual possesses not all of the hereditary genes of the species, but only a particular assortment of them.   If but one or a very few individuals are isolated from the main stock, the average assortment of genes will differ from the assortment possessed by the species.   In the second place, inbreeding for some generations would be inevitable, and we know that inbreeding tends to bring to light many recessive characters previously hidden by dominant allelomorphs.   This would give rise to many new types, of which some might happen to be better adapted to the new environment than were the older types.   In the course of time a standardized type would be produced that would differ materially from the parental stock. The isolated stock would continue to produce mutations, as would also the parental stock; but under changed conditions, even were the mutations in the two stocks identical, there would be a different survival standard in the two environments, involving the persistence of one kind of mutations in one stock and another kind in the other. Thus the two stocks would inevitably become less and less alike until the classifier would call them two different species, or even two different genera.

Geographic isolation is not the only effective method of dividing a stock into two noninterbreeding groups. Another effective method is one that involves a separation in time rather than one in space. If, for example, a few individuals of a species of insects were to be precocious in reaching sexual maturity, so that they would be the first ones ready to mate, it is certain that these would mate among themselves rather than with the more slowly maturing individuals. If the sexual precosity be hereditary, their offspring would also be isolated from the offspring of the main stock and would form an inbreeding group. The results would be the same in most respects as those described for geographic isolation.

Even a change of feeding habits on the part of some members of a species would tend to cause their segregation from the main stock and their closer association with others having the same food preference. This would introduce an element of selective mating that would be an effective agent in isolating a portion of a species from the rest, and would in time lead to specific divergence.

The two great classic theories of dealing with the methods of evolution are those of *Lamarck* and of *Darwin*. No account of the factors of evolution would be adequate without at least a brief discussion of these two theories.

B. LAMARCK'S THEORY

Lamarck's theory is commonly spoken of as that of THE INHERITANCE OF ACQUIRED CHARACTERS. Specifically, he held that somatic changes, either structural or functional, resulting either from the use or disuse of organs or from changed environment, are transmissible to offspring. According to this view, a highly perfected adaptation has arisen as the result of use in a particular line of activity. Thus, the neck of the giraffe was believed to have been the result of stretching after high branches of trees for a long series of generations, each generation inheriting from the last a neck a little more stretched. Similarly, the blacksmith, because of continuous heavy exercise of his arms, becomes large muscled and very strong. This acquired strength is believed to be passed on, to some extent at least, to the blacksmith's children.

If the effects of use and disuse be heritable, we need look no further for an explanation of most adaptations. What simpler explanation could be imagined than that improvements, acquired through practice and passed on from generation to generation, would in the end render an organ or an organism perfectly adapted? Unfortunately, however, this explanation, so natural and so obvious that it is generally assumed to be a fact, has failed to gain the adherence of more than a small minority of biologists. The reason for this is that it lacks experimental verification.

Much confusion has been caused by a failure to state the problem in exact terms. The question at issue is just this: "Can a modification of the body, or soma, arising in the lifetime of the individual and itself in no way due to inheritance, affect the germ cells in such a way that the offspring developed from them will exhibit a corresponding modification of the soma?"

Weismann was the first prominent biologist seriously to oppose the Lamarckian Theory. His opposition rested on the ground that germ cells give rise, by processes of cell division, to body cells, but body cells do not give rise to germ cells. The only way in which inherited characters can be transmitted is through cell division, and therefore germ cells cannot inherit anything from body cells. The latter merely furnish shelter, protection, and food for the former. The germ cells, moreover, are considered by Weismann as being set apart early in ontogeny and as having a life history independent from that of the soma.

Against Lamarck's theory it must be said that, although countless experiments have been made to test its validity, not a single one has furnished a positive demonstration. Many experiments appeared at first sight to favor the theory, but in every case some flaw in method or in interpretation of results has made it necessary to discard the data or at least to interpret them in a different way, thus making them of no avail as evidence of the inheritance of acquired characters.

In favor of Lamarck's theory, however, we have the recent experiments of **Guyer** and **Smith,** which seem to demonstrate at least one thing quite clearly: that germ cells are not immune to changes occurring in the soma. It was shown by these two investigators that hormones or antibodies injected into the blood of pregnant female rabbits bring about particular alterations in the soma of offspring, and that, either at the same time or subsequently, the germ cells are so changed that they produce other offspring with equivalent somatic alterations. The investigators do not claim to have proven the inheritance of acquired characters; the results merely serve to indicate that the germ might in some way reflect induced somatic changes.

In view of these new developments, which are considered by many as favoring the Lamarckian theory, it seems advisable for the present not to discard the theory altogether, but to remain open minded and to await further developments. The prevailing attitude among biologists at present is one of skepticism toward the Lamarckian Theory; and their conclusions are embodied in the Scotch verdict: *not proven.*

C. Darwin's Theory (Natural Selection)

The most satisfactory theory to account for adaptations that has ever been presented is the theory of Natural Selection. According to this, the main reason why organisms and organs are usually well adapted is that in each generation only the best adapted individuals have survived, and that these have passed on their adapted characters to their descendants. This theory was the result of decades of hard thinking and search after evidences. It was no sudden inspiration, prematurely published; for Darwin withheld any statement until he believed his theory adequately supported by an overwhelming mass of evidence. The theory is built upon a certain number of apparently self-evident postulates, together with certain conclusions which may legitimately be drawn from these postulates. Stated briefly, the postulates are as follows:—

1. All organisms tend to increase in geometrical ratio. Even the slowest-breeding species, such as the elephant, tend to produce during their lifetime at least two offspring to each parent.

2. There is neither food nor space for the numbers of offspring that would result from such a rate of increase.

3. All individuals of a species vary among themselves in a vast number of respects. Some of these variants will inevitably be better adapted to the conditions of life than others.

4. As a result of overproduction, some individuals must be eliminated; and, in the long run, those with the most favorable combinations of variations will survive in larger numbers than those with less favorable combinations of variations. Many of the least favorably equipped individuals must inevitably fail in the struggle for existence.

5. The survivors of one generation naturally become the parents of the next, and will pass on to their offspring whatever hereditary characters they may possess.

6. This second generation is then a selected group and, so long as the conditions of life remain unchanged, the competition will be keener than before and will demand of survivors a higher degree of adaptiveness. Each successive generation finds the criteria of success a little more severe. Thus, through the struggle for existence and the survival of the fittest, organisms tend to become more and more completely adapted to the prevailing conditions of life.

7. If the conditions of life undergo slow or rapid alteration, the basis of selection may become changed and the individuals that formerly were best adapted (those most highly specialized for the former set of conditions) may be the first to perish; while the more generalized or plastic types will have the best chance to vary in directions likely to fit the changed conditions. This would explain the extinction of many great specialized groups of the past and the survival of the more generalized types from age to age.

The above statement is not exactly a literal rendering of Darwin's theory, but is a justifiable modernized paraphrase and one with which Darwin would probably have agreed. In this form the theory is open to little objection. Biologists today are almost unanimously of the opinion that Darwin's explanation of the phenomenon of adaptation, when divested of misconceptions that have accumulated about it or have been read into it by some of its over-zealous adherents, is the most satisfactory that has yet been offered. There is at present no real rival theory in the field; for Lamarckism is as yet not sufficiently strongly supported by evidence to offer any real rivalry to Natural Selection.

Criticisms of Natural Selection.—While there is little ground for opposition to the general conception advanced by Darwin, criticism has been aimed at some of the minor implications of the theory. Darwin, for example, believed that all variations were hereditary, including somatic modifications due to changed environment and the effects of use and of disuse. We now believe that only germinal changes are inherited, and we are skeptical about the possibility of somatic changes being transferable to the germ cells. Darwin, again, underestimated the value of mutations as the raw material of evolution, considering them too infrequent to admit of the possibility of the right variation occurring just when needed to meet changing conditions. Now that we know how frequent mutations really are, Darwin's objection seems not to have been well considered. It has been said, furthermore, that Darwin's theory fails utterly to explain the ORIGIN of adaptive characters. It may reasonably well explain their SURVIVAL, but does not account for their ARRIVAL. Darwin, to do him justice, claimed only this much for Selection, and attributed the origin or "arrival" of improvements to the phenomenon of variation. Variation was looked upon as self-evident, needing no particular explanation, and changes were supposed to occur more or less at random and in every direction. This was enough, Darwin thought, to furnish all of the material necessary for selection to work with. Selection was, therefore, merely an arbiter among the better and the worse combinations of characters.

Today we still believe that Selection plays a directive rôle in evolution; but consider that the only materials that are of evolutionary value, and therefore suitable for natural selection to work with, are germinal variations, or mutations. The substitution of mutations for fluctuations does no violence to the essential features of Darwinism. Thus, Darwin's central theory of Natural Selection holds its own after more than half a century of critical examination. It is, in fact, more firmly intrenched than it was at the beginning of the present century.

APPENDIX

BIBLIOGRAPHY

(The following list of books and monographs has been a constant source of reference for the author and would form a fairly comprehensive working library for a teacher of general Zoölogy.)

BABCOCK, E. B., and CLAUSEN, R. E. *Genetics in Relation to Agriculture.* 2nd edition. McGraw-Hill Book Co., 1927.

BAYLISS, W. M. *Principles of General Physiology.* 3d edition. Longmans Green & Co., 1921.

CALKINS, G. N. *Biology.* Henry Holt & Co., 1917.

CALKINS, G. N. *Protozoölogy.* Lea and Febiger, 1909.

CAMBRIDGE NATURAL HISTORY, THE (a treatise in ten large volumes, covering the whole field of animals; valuable especially as a reference). The Macmillan Company.

CASTLE, W. E. *Genetics and Eugenics.* 3d edition. Harvard University Press, 1924.

CHILD, C. M. *Individuality in Organisms.* The University of Chicago Press, 1915.

CHILD, C. M. *Senescence and Rejuvenescence.* The University of Chicago Press, 1915.

COCKERELL, T. D. A. *Zoölogy.* World Book Co., 1920.

CONKLIN, E. G. *Heredity and Environment in the Development of Men.* 4th edition. Princeton University Press, 1922.

CONKLIN, E. G. *The Direction of Human Evolution.* Charles Scribner's Sons, 1921.

DAHLGREN, ULRIC, and KEPNER, W. A. *Principles of Animal Histology.* The Macmillan Co., 1908.

DARWIN, CHARLES. *The Origin of Species.* London, 1859. 6th edition, 1880.

DARWIN, CHARLES. *The Descent of Man.* London, 1871.

DARWIN, CHARLES. *Variation in Animals and Plants under Domestication.* London, 1868.

DENDY, ARTHUR. *Outlines of Evolutionary Biology.* D. Appleton & Co., 1911.

DREW, G. A. *Invertebrate Zoölogy.* 3d edition. W. B. Saunders & Co., 1920.

GEDDES, P., and THOMSON, J. A. *Sex.* Henry Holt & Co., 1914.

GUYER, M. F. *Animal Micrology.* 2d edition. The University of Chicago Press, 1917.

GUYER, M. F. *Being Well-Born.* Revised edition. Bobbs Merrills Co., 1925.

HEGNER, R. W. *An Introduction to Zoölogy.* The Macmillan Co., 1910.

HEGNER, R. W. *College Zoölogy.* Revised edition. The Macmillan Co., 1926.

HEGNER, R. W. *The Germ-Cell Cycle in Animals.* The Macmillan Co., 1914.

HEGNER, R. W. *Practical Zoölogy.* The Macmillan Co., 1915.

HENDERSON, L. J. *The Fitness of the Environment.* The Macmillan Co., 1913.

HERTWIG, R., and KINGSLEY, J. S. (translator). *A Manual of Zoölogy.* 3d edition. Henry Holt & Co., 1912.

HOLMES, S. J. *Biology of the Frog.* Revised edition. The Macmillan Co., 1925.

HOLMES, S. J. *The Trend of the Race.* Harcourt, Brace & Co., 1921.

HUXLEY, T. H. *Collected Essays.* D. Appleton & Co.

HYMAN, L. H. *A Laboratory Manual for Elementary Zoölogy.* The University of Chicago Press, 1919.

JENNINGS, H. S. *The Behavior of the Lower Organisms.* Columbia University Biological Series, 1906.

JENNINGS, H. S. *Life and Death, Heredity and Evolution in Unicellular Organisms.* Gorham Press, 1920.

JORDAN, D. S., and KELLOGG, V. L. *Evolution and Animal Life.* D. Appleton & Co., 1908.

KELLICOTT, W. E. *General Embryology.* Henry Holt & Co., 1913.

KELLOGG, V. L. *Darwinism Today.* Henry Holt & Co., 1908.

KINGSLEY, J. S. *Comparative Anatomy of Vertebrates.* 2d edition. P. Blakiston's Son & Co., 1917.

LANKESTER, E. R. (editor). *A Treatise on Zoölogy* (in 8 volumes). A. and C. Black, London.

LILLIE, F. R. "The Freemartin; A Study of the Action of Sex Hormones in the Foetal Life of Cattle." *Jour. Exp. Zoöl.,* Vol. 23, 1917.

LOCY, W. A. *Biology and Its Makers.* 3d edition. Henry Holt & Co., 1915.

LOCY, W. A. *The Main Currents of Zoölogy.* Henry Holt & Co., 1918.

LOEB, JACQUES. *The Organism as a Whole.* New York, 1916.

LOEB, JACQUES. *Forced Movements, Tropisms, and Animal Conduct.* J. B. Lippincott, 1919.

LULL, R. S. *Organic Evolution.* The Macmillan Co., 1917.

MCFARLAND, J. *Biology, General and Medical.* 3d edition. W. B. Saunders Co., 1918.

MOORE, B. *The Origin and Nature of Life.* Henry Holt & Co., 1912.

MORGAN, T. H. *Evolution and Adaptation.* The Macmillan Co., 1903.

MORGAN, T. H. *Heredity and Sex.* Columbia University Press, 1913.

MORGAN, T. H. *The Physical Basis of Heredity.* J. B. Lippincott & Co., 1919.

NEWMAN, H. H. *Vertebrate Zoölogy.* The Macmillan Co., 1920.

NEWMAN, H. H. *Readings in Evolution, Genetics and Eugenics.* Revised edition. The University of Chicago Press, 1925.

NEWMAN, H. H. *The Biology of Twins.* The University of Chicago Press, 1917.

NEWMAN, H. H. *The Physiology of Twinning.* The University of Chicago Press, 1923.

NEWMAN, H. H. and others. *The Nature of the World and of Man.* The University of Chicago Press, 1926.

NUTTALL, G. H. P. *Blood Immunity and Blood Relationship.* London, 1904.

OSBORN, H. F. *From the Greeks to Darwin.* The Macmillan Co., 1894.

OSBORN, H. F. *The Origin and Evolution of Life.* Charles Scribner's Sons, 1917.

PARKER, T. J., and HASWELL, W. A. *Textbook of Zoölogy.* 3d edition. The Macmillan Co., 1922.

RITTER, W. E. *The Unity of the Organism.* Richard G. Badger, 1919.

SCOTT, W. B. *The Theory of Evolution.* The Macmillan Co., 1917.

SEDGWICK, W. T., and WILSON, E. B. *General Biology.* Henry Holt & Co., 1895.

SHARP, L. W. *Introduction to Cytology.* McGraw-Hill Book Co., 1921.

SHELFORD, V. E. *Animal Communities in Temperate America.* The University of Chicago Press, 1913.

SHIPLEY, A. E., and MACBRIDE, E. W. *Zoölogy.* The Macmillan Co., 1901.

SHULL, A. F., *et al. Principles of Animal Biology.* McGraw-Hill Book Co., 1920.

THOMSON, J. A. *Darwinism and Human Life.* Henry Holt & Co., 1908.

VERWORN, MAX. *General Physiology.* The Macmillan Co., 1899.

WALTER, H. E. *Genetics.* The Macmillan Co., 1922.

WARD, H. B., and WHIPPLE, G. C. *Fresh-Water Biology.* John Wiley & Sons, 1918.

WEISMANN, A. *The Germ Plasm.* Charles Scribner's Sons, 1892.

WHITMAN, C. O. "The Inadequacy of the Cell Theory." *Woods Hole Biological Lectures,* 1893.

WILSON, E. B. *The Cell in Development and Heredity.* 3d edition. The Macmillan Co., 1925.

WILSON, E. B. "The Problem of Development." *Science,* N. S., 1905.

WOODRUFF, L. L. *Foundations of Biology.* 3d edition. The Macmillan Co., 1927.

GLOSSARY

ABIOGENESIS. The abandoned doctrine that living organisms or living matter may or does arise from nonliving matter; same as SPONTANEOUS GENERATION.

ABORAL. Opposite the mouth.

ABORTIVE. Unsuccessful; incapable of functioning.

ACCLIMATION. The process of becoming habituated to environmental conditions not native.

ACHROMATIC FIGURE. That part of the mitotic figure that does not stain deeply, namely, the spindle together with the central body and asters.

ACTINIC RAYS. The chemically active rays of sunlight or other lights.

ADAPTATION. The mutual fitness of organism and environment; a structure or reaction fitted for a particular feature of the environment or for a particular function in the body; the process of becoming fitted to an environment.

ADDUCTOR. One of the large muscles attached to the valves of a mussel shell, by means of which the shell is closed; any muscle which draws a structure toward the median axis.

ADIPOSE. Pertaining to fat.

ADRENALIN. The specific enzyme secreted by the suprarenal (adrenal) glands.

AFFERENT NERVE. Any nerve that conducts impulses from the peripheral sense organs to the central nervous system.

AGRONOMY. The science of agriculture.

ALGÆ. A large and heterogeneous group of lower plants in which the body is unicellular or consists of a thallus.

ALIMENTARY. Pertaining to digestion or to the digestive tract.

ALLANTOIS. An embryonic membrane of land vertebrates, used primarily for embryonic respiration.

ALLELOMORPHS. Genes similarly situated on homologous chromosomes which produce alternative or contrasting characters.

ALTERNATION OF GENERATIONS. See METAGENESIS.

ALVEOLAR. Of the nature of an emulsion.

ALVEOLUS. One of the separate droplets of an emulsion. Also one of the ultimate air spaces of the lung.

AMBULACRAL. Literally, resembling an alley; a term applied to the grooves on the oral surface of echinoderms in which are found the tube feet.

AMBULATORY. Pertaining to walking.

AMINO ACID. One of a number of organic acids in which one hydrogen ion is replaced by the amino radical (NH_2). These acids are known as the building stones of proteins.

AMITOSIS. Cell division not involving the formation of discrete chromosomes or a spindle; direct cell division.

AMNION. A thin membrane surrounding the embryos of reptiles, birds, and mammals.

AMŒBOID. Usually applied to cell movements resembling those in Amœba; movement by means of pseudopodia.

AMPHIASTER. The figure produced by the two asters and the spindle in the dividing cell.

AMPHIBIA. A class of vertebrates including frogs, toads, newts, salamanders, etc.

AMPHOTERIC. Substances (like many proteins) that can absorb and therefore neutralize either acids or alkalis.

AMPULLA. The flask-shaped bulb associated with the movement of the tube feet of echinoderms. Also, a bulbous enlargement at the base of a semicircular canal in which lie the sense cells of equilibration.

AMYLOPSIN. A starch-digesting enzyme produced by the pancreas.

ANABOLISM. The constructive phase of metabolism.

ANAL. Pertaining to the anus.

ANALOGOUS. Similar in function.

ANAPHASE. All stages of mitosis during which the chromosomes, after longitudinal division, are passing from the equatorial plate of the spindle to the ends of the latter.

ANATOMY. The science which treats of the structure of animals; especially that which may be made out by dissection.

ANIMAL POLE. That part of an egg in which the protoplasm is concentrated, which has the highest rate of metabolism, and which in most organisms goes to form the nervous system and sense organs.

ANNELID. A member of the phylum Annelida, the segmented worms.

ANTENNA. One of a pair of jointed appendages belonging to an arthropod, usually sensory in function.

ANTERIOR. Pertaining to the front or head-end of animals with an axis of polarity. In human anatomy, the ventral side.

ANTHROPOID. Manlike. Referring especially to manlike apes.

ANUS. The posterior opening of the alimentary tract.

AORTA. A large trunk artery carrying blood away from the heart.

AORTIC ARCHES. Arteries arising from the ventral aorta and supplying the gills in aquatic vertebrates; also found in the embryos of the higher (terrestrial) vertebrates.

APHIDS. Small sucking insects, commonly called "Plant Lice" and usually green in color.

APICAL. Pertaining to that part of the axis of an axiate organism which has the highest rate of metabolism and exercises a dominance or control over other parts of the axis.

APPENDICULAR SKELETON. That part of the skeleton of a vertebrate which consists of the limbs and the limb girdles.

ARCHENTERON. The primitive digestive tract of a gastrula. The primitive gut.

ARISTOTLE'S LANTERN. The elaborate masticatory apparatus of a sea urchin.

ARMADILLO. An armored mammal belonging to the order Edentata.

ARTERY. A blood vessel conducting blood from the heart.

ARTHROPOD. An animal belonging to the phylum Arthropoda, which includes Crustacea, Arachnida, Myriopoda, and Insecta.

ARTIFICIAL PARTHENOGENESIS. The artificial activation of an egg to develop without fertilization.

ASEXUAL. Sexless. Without the use of gametes.

ASSIMILATION. The conversion of digested foods and other materials into protoplasmic substances.

ASTER. The starlike figure composed of the central body and the radiations from it; or the central body may be absent.

ASYMMETRY. Absence of symmetry; more particularly, the development on one side of a bilateral organism of structures not present on the opposite side. An aberration of bilateral symmetry.

ATLAS. The first vertebra on which the skull rests.

ATTRACTION SPHERE. A differentiated portion of the cytoplasm, usually lying near the nucleus, and usually containing a central body. The whole structure is associated with mitotic cell division.

AUDITORY. Pertaining to the sense of hearing.

AURICLE. The anterior chamber of the heart of fishes, and one of the two anterior chambers in that of higher vertebrates. Also the lateral sense organs on the side of the head of a flatworm.

AUTOSOME. Any one of the chromosomes of a cell except the X- or the Y-chromosome.

AUTOTOMY. Self-mutilation, as in the voluntary cutting off of the arm of a starfish or the chela of a lobster.

AVES. The class of vertebrates consisting of birds.

AVOIDING REACTION. The more or less stereotyped protective reflex induced in an organism by an adverse stimulus.

AXIAL GRADIENT. The orderly arrangement of regions of differing metabolic rate in which the apical end has the highest rate and there is a steady decrease in rate as one proceeds from apical to basal levels of the axis. The name of a theory of organic individuation.

AXIAL SKELETON. That part of the skeleton of a vertebrate consisting of the cranium and the spinal column.

AXIS OF POLARITY. An imaginary line running from the anterior to the posterior end of an organism.

AXIS OF SYMMETRY. Double or twin metabolic gradients running from the mid-dorsal (mid-ventral in invertebrates) region laterally and ventrally (dorsally in invertebrates).

AXOLOTL. The name applied to the pædogenetic larva of the tiger salamander, *Amblystoma tigrinum*, which reproduces in the larval state.

AXON. The projection from a nerve cell that usually conducts impulses away from the body of the cell.

BACTERIA. Microscopic unicellular plants, some of which are responsible for diseases in host organisms and others for the decay or decomposition of organic matter.

BARNACLE. A kind of degenerate sessile crustacean, usually covered by a hard shell and found on rocks, piles, and ship bottoms.

BASEMENT MEMBRANE. A thin layer of noncellular material separating the ectoderm from the endoderm in Hydra and its relatives.

BILATERAL SYMMETRY. An arrangement of the parts of an organism such that the halves on opposite sides of a sagittal plane are mirror images of each other.

BILE. The fluid secreted by the liver in vertebrates.

BILE DUCT. The tube through which the bile is discharged into the intestine.

BILOBED. Divided into two lobes or segments.

BINARY FISSION. The division of a cell, especially of a unicellular organism, into two daughter cells.

BINOMIAL NOMENCLATURE. The accepted scientific method of naming species of organisms by two Latin or Latinized words, the first designating the genus and the second the species. *E.g.*, the dog, *Canis familiaris*.

BIOLOGY. The branch of science that deals with living organisms, both animals and plants; more technically, the study of the manifestations of matter in the living state.

BIOPHYSICS. The study of the physical aspects of biology.

BIPARENTAL. Derived from two parents, male and female.

BISEXUAL. Having both sexes. See HERMAPHRODITE.

BLADDER WORM. One stage in the life cycle of the tapeworm.

BLASTOCŒLE. The cavity of the blastula.

BLASTOMERE. One of the cells produced by the early divisions (cleavage) of the egg.

BLASTOPORE. The opening through which the cavity of the gastrula communicates with the exterior.

BLASTULA. An early developmental stage typically consisting of a hollow ball of cells.

BLOOD CORPUSCLE. A detached cell present in the fluid plasma of the blood. There are two principal kinds, red and white.

BOWMAN'S CAPSULE. The expanded end of the kidney tubule, in which a glomerulus is located.

BUCCAL CAVITY. Mouth cavity.

BUCCAL MASS. The complex of muscles, jaws, radula, and digestive glands making up the anterior part of the digestive tract in certain mollusks, such as the gastropods and cephalopods.

BUD. An undeveloped lateral branch of an organism, e.g., the bud of a Hydra of a plant.

BUDDING. The division of an organism in such a way that the main part is left intact and the secondary part is relatively small and usually has an axis at right angles to the parent organism.

CÆCUM. A blind, sac-like extension of the large intestine in vertebrates.

CALCAREOUS. Composed of salts of calcium or lime.

CALCIFEROUS GLANDS. Glands which are supposed to secrete calcium carbonate into the œsophagus of the earthworm, believed to serve the function of neutralizing the acidity of the food.

CALCIFIED CARTILAGE. Cartilage in which there is a deposit of salts of calcium.

CAMBRIAN. The name applied to one of the earliest of the geological periods and the earliest from which fossils have been taken.

CAMOUFLAGE. The art of concealment by the use of colors or patterns that deceive the eye.

CANALICULUS. One of the numerous minute channels radiating from a lacuna in bone, through which extend slender processes of the bone cells.

CAPILLARY. One of the ultimate branches of the blood vessels that carry blood directly to the tissues and cells of the body.

CARBOHYDRATE. Any one of a class of organic substances, such as sugars, starches, cellulose, etc., composed of carbon, hydrogen, and oxygen, and usually with two atoms of hydrogen to one of oxygen.

CARDIAC. Pertaining to the heart.

CARNIVOROUS. Flesh eating. See HERBIVOROUS.

CARTILAGE. A flexible, somewhat translucent tissue composed of cells embedded in a matrix.

CAST. A sort of fossil produced by a mass of rock forming in a mold left in soft mud by an organism.

CASTE. One of several distinct types of individuals of one species in a diversified animal community, such as that of ants or termites.

CATABOLISM. The breaking-down or destructive phases of metabolism.

CATACLYSMIC THEORY. A doctrine held during the Middle Ages to the effect that the stratification of the earth, the formation of mountain ranges, etc., had come about as the result of a series of vast and violent disturbances that destroyed all existing animals and plants, necessitating repeated special creations to repeople the world.

CAUDAL. Pertaining to the tail, or near the tail.

CELL. A small mass of protoplasm containing a nucleus or nuclear material.

CELL MEMBRANE. A specialized surface layer of protoplasm surrounding a cell. Plasma membrane.

CELL THEORY. The theory that all animals and plants consist of similar units called cells. According to this theory a protozoan organism is equivalent to a tissue cell of a metazoan organism.

CELL WALL. A nonliving structure secreted by the surface protoplasm of a cell, and commonly composed of cellulose or chitin.

CELLULOSE. A substance, one of the carbohydrates, out of which the walls of plant cells are composed.

CENOZOIC. Pertaining to the most recent geologic period. The age of mammals.

CENTIPEDE. A member of the class Myriapoda, phylum Arthropoda.

CENTRAL BODY. That structure which forms the focus of the aster in mitotic cell division. An older term for this structure is CENTROSOME.

CENTRAL NERVOUS SYSTEM. The brain and spinal cord; the principal ganglia and their connectives.

CENTROSOME. See CENTRAL BODY.

CENTROSPHERE. Same as ATTRACTION SPHERE.

CEPHALIC. Pertaining to the head.

CEPHALIZATION. The process of head formation. More particularly, the evolution of the larger and more elaborate brain and head of the higher organisms from the smaller and less specialized head of lower forms.

CEPHALOPOD. A member of the class Cephalopoda, of the phylum Mollusca.

CERCARIA. The tailed larval form of the liver fluke Fasciola and allied forms.

CEREBELLUM. A division of the brain in the vertebrates developed from the dorsal side anterior to the medulla oblongata.

CEREBRAL. Pertaining to the Cerebrum.

CEREBRUM. The anterior portion of the brain in vertebrates; in man, the main bulk of the brain.

CHÆTÆ. Spines or bristles embedded in the body wall or in the parapodia of the annelids.

CHELIPED. The fourth thoracic appendage in the crayfish and its allies; usually in the form of a pincher.

CHEMOTROPISM. The response of an organism to chemical stimuli.

CHITIN. A horny substance forming the exoskeleton of insects and other arthropods.

CHITINOUS. Composed of chitin.

CHITON. A genus of primitive mollusks, having a longitudinal series of eight dorsal shells.

CHLORAGOGUE CELLS. The cells of the outer layer of the intestine in the earthworm.

CHONDROCRANIUM. A skull or cranium composed of cartilage; found in adult sharks and in the embryos of higher vertebrates.

CHORDATE. Pertaining to the phylum Chordata. A member of the phylum Chordata.

CHROMATIN. A deeply staining protoplasmic substance characteristic of the nucleus, forming chromosomes, etc.

CHROMOMERE. One of the beadlike granules that are arranged in a chain or linear series to form a chromosome.

CHROMOSOME. One of the deeply-staining rodlike or rounded bodies into which the chromatin network resolves itself during mitosis.

CILIA. Delicate whiplike protoplasmic projections from the surface of a cell, used either as organs of locomotion or as a means of transporting substances in ducts or passages.

CILIATE. Provided with cilia; pertaining to the class Ciliata; a member of the protozoan class Infusoria. Same as CILIATED.

CIRCULATION. The movement of blood through the system of blood vessels.

CIRCULATORY. Referring to organs of circulation.

CIRRI. Soft tentacle-like projections or appendages.

CLASS. A division of a phylum; a group superior in rank to an order.

CLEAVAGE. The mitotic division of an egg to form blastomeres.

CLEAVAGE CAVITY. Same as BLASTOCŒLE or SEGMENTATION CAVITY.

CLITELLUM. A thickened glandular region of the body wall of the earthworm and other annelids, used in the formation of the cocoon.

CLOACA. A common passageway or vestibule into which the intestine, the kidneys, and the sexual organs discharge their products; present in some fishes, in amphibia, in reptiles, in birds, and in some of the primitive mammals.

CNIDOBLAST. A type of formative cell which, in the Cœlenterata, forms nematocysts.

CNIDOCIL. The delicate sensory projection or "trigger" of a nematocyst.

COCHLEA. The spirally-coiled portion of the membranous labyrinth of the inner ear of higher vertebrates in which lie the auditory sense cells and their accessories.

COCOON. A sac or case in which eggs are stored and in which larvæ develop; also the silky covering around a pupa.

CŒLENTERATE. Pertaining to the phylum Cœlenterata; a member of this phylum.

CŒLOM. The true body cavity, lying between the digestive tract and the body wall; lined with and formed from mesodermal tissue.

CŒLOMATE. Pertaining to the cœlom; any member of the animal kingdom possessing a cœlom. All animals without a cœlom are referred to as ACŒLOMATE.

COLLOID. A state of matter in which particles larger than molecules are held in suspension in a fluid or semifluid medium.

COLLOIDAL. Pertaining to a colloid.

COLONY. A group of individuals of the same species organically connected with one another. These sometimes are so closely integrated as to form a superior unit or individual.

COLUMNAR EPITHELIUM. A type of epithelial tissue in which the individual cells are somewhat elongated or column-shaped, and have their greater axis at right angles to the surface.

COMBINATION. A heritable variation due to the recombination of genes during maturation or fertilization.

COMBUSTION. The oxidation of chemical substances, usually accompanied by a release of heat or some other form of energy.

COMMENSALISM. The association of members of two or more species in which neither may be strictly parasitic upon the other in the sense that one feeds upon the tissues of its associate.

COMMISSURE. A group of nerve fibers connecting two ganglia.

CONJUGATION. A temporary union of two protozoa during which nuclear exchanges take place; the sexual phase in the life cycle of Infusoria.

CONNECTIVE TISSUE. A tissue composed of cells and materials excreted by cells, which in its simpler forms binds other tissues or organs together. In its broader sense it includes cartilage, bone, adipose tissue, tendons, and ligaments.

CONTINUOUS VARIATION. That type of variation in which the variates are merely plus or minus deviations from the mode and which may be seriated in the form of a simple chance curve.

CONTRACTILE VACUOLE. A vesicular reservoir in Protozoa in which water and waste products collect and are discharged to the outside by means of a contraction of the vacuole. Same as PULSATING VACUOLE.

CONUS ARTERIOSUS. A portion of the circulatory system of vertebrates lying between the heart (ventricle) and the aortic arches. ·

COPULATION. The sexual union of two individuals, during which spermatozoa are introduced into the oviduct of the female.

CORACOID. A bone found in the pectoral girdle of most vertebrates.

CORTEX. A name sometimes applied to the layer of the ectoplasm beneath the cuticle in Paramecium and its allies. More generally, any layer just beneath the surface layer.

CRANIAL NERVES. Nerves that arise from the brain.

CRANIUM. Same as SKULL. The bony or cartilaginous case that incloses or partly incloses the brain.

CRETIN. A defective (subnormal) type of animal or human being, resulting from either congenital or operative deficiency of thyroid secretion.

CRINOID. A member of the class Crinoidea of the phylum Echinodermata, commonly known as sea lilies.

CROSSING-OVER. The rearranging of linked characters as the result of exchanges of genes between homologous chromosomes during synapsis.

CRUSTACEAN. Pertaining to the class Crustacea of the phylum Arthropoda. A member of this class.

CUTICLE. A surface layer of cells or a noncellular layer; more particularly, the dead surface cells of the epidermis.

CUTTLEFISH. A kind of cephalopod mollusk related to the squid and the octopus.

CYPRIS LARVA. The characteristic larva of the order Cirripedia of the class Crustacea. Seen in the barnacles and in Sacculina.

CYST. A small capsule or sac.

CYSTICERCUS. The bladder-worm stage in the life cycle of the tapeworm.

CYTOGENIC REPRODUCTION. That type of reproduction that is effected by means of unicellular germ cells, which by growth and division give rise to a new multicellular body. In contrast with SOMATOGENIC REPRODUCTION.

CYTOLOGY. The science which deals with the structure and function of cells, especially of germ cells.

CYTOPLASM. The protoplasmic material of which the cytosome consists. Formerly used in same sense as CYTOSOME.

CYTOPLASMIC INCLUSIONS. Any materials not strictly living that lie in the cytoplasm.

CYTOSOME. That part of the cell that lies outside the nucleus. An older term for this is CYTOPLASM.

DARWINISM. The theory of Natural Selection, proposed by Charles Darwin. Wrongly used as a synonym for EVOLUTION.

DE NOVO. A common Latin expression used in biology to indicate an origin from no known source or from no similar structure.

DENDRITE. A projection from the body of a nerve cell which ordinarily conducts impulses toward the body of the cell.

DERMAL. Pertaining to or arising from the DERMIS.

DERMIS. The deeper skin beneath the EPIDERMIS.

DETERMINATE CLEAVAGE. The early divisions of an egg in which each blastomere can be traced to some prospective organ or tissue and in which the cells from the first are arranged with reference to the prospective axes of the organism.

DETERMINER. Same as GENE.

DIAPHRAGM. A muscular partition between the thoracic and abdominal cavities in mammals.

DIFFERENTIATION. A process of becoming structurally or functionally unlike the original condition. Similar to SPECIALIZATION.

DIFFUSION. The spreading of molecules of one substance among those of another.

DIGESTION. The conversion of food into soluble substances which may diffuse through the tissues and into the protoplasm.

DIHYBRID. The offspring of parents differing with regard to two given characters. A kind of cross involving two different pairs of genes.

DIŒCIOUS. Having the male and female organs in separate individuals. The opposite of MONŒCIOUS.

DIPHYLETIC TREE. A schematic representation of the supposed ancestral relations of the various animal phyla. The tree has a short common trunk and two main branches.

DIPLOBLASTIC. Composed of two fundamentally different layers of cells, ectoderm and endoderm.

DIPLOID. The maximum or full (duplex) number of chromosomes, found in body cells (soma) and in the unmaturated germ cells. See HAPLOID.

DIRECT CELL DIVISION. Same as AMITOSIS.

DISSEPIMENT. A thin partition, derived from the segmental cœloms, between two adjacent cœloms in annelid worms. Same as SEPTA.

DIZYGOTIC. Derived from two eggs, or zygotes. Said of certain kinds of twins. See MONOZYGOTIC.

DOMINANT CHARACTER. One of a pair of alternative characters which appears to the exclusion of the other in the F_1 generation in Mendelian heredity.

DORSAL. Pertaining to the back; hence, usually, upper.

DORSAL AORTA. The chief artery distributing pure blood to the body.

DUCTLESS GLAND. See ENDOCRINE GLAND.

DUODENUM. The anterior of the three divisions of the small intestine.

DYAD. The double body formed by the division of a tetrad into two parts.

ECDYSIS. The shedding of the exoskeleton in the Arthropoda.

ECHINODERM. A member of the phylum Echinodermata. Pertaining to the latter.

ECOLOGY. That branch of biology dealing with the relation of organisms to their environment.

ECTODERM. The outer layer of cells of the gastrula stage of development; the cellular derivatives of this layer in later stages of development.

ECTODERMAL. Derived from or pertaining to the ECTODERM.

ECTOPLASM. The outer layer of protoplasm in a protozoan organism. Sometimes called ECTOSARC.

EFFERENT NERVE FIBER. A fiber carrying impulses away from the central nervous system toward the periphery or toward an organ; a nerve fiber carrying motor impulses.

EGG. A female germ cell after the process of maturation has been completed. Same as OÖTID.

ELEMENTAL THEORY. The doctrine that the whole or the individual is to be fully explained as the result of the summation of the characteristics and activities of its ultimate parts. To be contrasted with the ORGANISMAL THEORY.

EMBRYO. An undeveloped organism while still within the egg membrane and nourished by the substances stored in the egg or by nutritive materials derived from the uterus. To be contrasted with LARVA.

EMBRYOLOGY. The science which deals with the development of the embryo.

EMBRYONIC. Pertaining to an embryo.

ENCYSTMENT. The process of becoming inclosed in an impermeable envelope or CYST.

ENDOCRINE GLAND. A gland whose secretion passes directly from the cells into the blood stream without passing through ducts. Sometimes called DUCTLESS GLAND.

ENDODERM. The inner layer of cells of the gastrula; or the derivatives of this layer in later stages.

ENDOMYXIS. A nuclear reorganization in Protozoa, e.g., Paramecium, which does not involve conjugation or the exchange of nuclear materials between different individuals. Similar to PARTHENOGENESIS in Metazoa.

ENDOPLASM. The inner mass of protoplasm in cells, particularly the Protozoa, in which the outer layer is differentiated into an ECTOPLASM.

ENDOPODITE. The inner of the two distal parts of the typical biramous crustacean appendage.

ENDOTHELIUM. A layer of cells of endodermal origin lining the passages of the alimentary tract and its derivatives.

ENTOMOLOGY. That branch of Zoölogy that deals with the study of insects.

ENZYME. An organic substance which brings about or hastens a chemical reaction but is not consumed in the process. Usually secreted by glands.

EPIDERMIS. The outer layer of the skin, derived from the ectoderm.

EPIGENESIS. The doctrine that the germ cell is absolutely, or relatively, structureless and that differentiation arises de novo through the interaction of the protoplasm and the environment. To be contrasted with PREFORMATION.

EPITHELIAL. Pertaining to an epithelium.

EPITHELIUM. A layer of cells at the outer or inner surface of an organ or passage.

EQUATORIAL PLATE. The flattened group of chromosomes at the equator of the spindle in a dividing cell.

EROSION. The wearing away of rock or soil through the action of water or other agencies.

EUGENICS. The science which applies the principles of genetics for the purpose of race improvement. See EUTHENICS.

EUSTACHIAN TUBE. A passage in air-breathing vertebrates, connecting the pharynx with the middle ear. A survival of the first gill slit of the embryo.

EUTHENICS. The science dealing with the improvement of the human race by improving the environment. See EUGENICS.

EVAGINATION. The folding of a layer of cells outward from an inclosed cavity. See INVAGINATION.

EVISCERATE. To remove or cast out the internal organs from the body cavity.

EVOLUTION, ORGANIC. The theory that animals and plants have undergone gradual changes through the process of descent with modification, and that the species of today have been derived from those of the past. The antithesis of the doctrine of SPECIAL CREATION.

EXCRETION. The process of elimination of the dissolved waste products of metabolism. The waste products themselves.

EXCRETORY. Pertaining to excretion.

EXCURRENT. An excurrent canal, pore, siphon, or other structure is one that conducts water or other fluid away from an individual, organ, or cavity. Opposite to INCURRENT.

EXOPODITE. The outer of the terminal segments of a typical biramous crustacean appendage. See ENDOPODITE.

EYE SPOT. A light-sensitive pigmented area connected with the central nervous system and playing the rôle of a simple eye.

F_1. An individual or generation of individuals resulting from the crossing of two unlike parents. An abbreviation for *first filial*.

F_2. An individual or generation of individuals resulting from the intermating of individuals of the F_1 generations. An abbreviation for *second filial*.

F_3. An individual or generation of individuals resulting from the intermating of the individuals of the F_2 generation.

FACTOR. An agent or agency influencing the development of an individual or the evolution of a race. In genetics, the same as a GENE.

FAMILY. A taxonomic group of higher rank than a genus but below an order.

FATS. One of the chief groups of foodstuffs; one of the ingredients of protoplasm. A compound of glycerol and one or more fatty acids.

FATTY ACID. One of a group of organic acids, such as acetic, butyric, and stearic acids.

FAUNA. The animals of any given geographic area or geological period.

FAUNISTIC. Pertaining to faunas.

FERTILIZATION. The union of the egg with the spermatozoön. More broadly, the union of a pair of gametes.

FIBRIL. A very slender fiber. More particularly, one of the longitudinal contractile threads of a voluntary muscle fiber.

FIBRILLAR. Pertaining to fibrils; composed of fibrils.

FISSION. The division of an organism into two approximately equal parts. More generally, division of any sort that involves the cutting off of any part of an organism already formed, in order to produce two individuals or two organs.

FLAGELLATE. Possessing flagella; pertaining to flagella. As a noun, a member of the Class Mastigophora of the Subkingdom Protozoa.

FLAGELLUM (pl. FLAGELLA). A long whiplike motile projection from a cell.

FLAME CELL. A cell with a hollow interior in which there is a bunch of vibratile cilia; part of the excretory apparatus of the flatworms.

FLATWORM. One of the members of the phylum Platyhelminthes.

FLUCTUATIONS. Somatic variations resulting from differences in environment or in function, and not hereditary.

FLUKE. A parasitic flatworm belonging to the class Trematoda.

FŒTUS. An advanced embryo of a mammal. Same as FETUS.

FOOT. Technically, the basal muscular part of a mollusk. More generally, the terminal part of a leg, the basal disk of a Hydra, etc.

FORMATIVE CELL. One of the undifferentiated cells of the ectoderm of a Hydra.

FOSSIL. The preserved remains or other indication of a prehistoric organism.

FREEMARTIN. The partially masculized female member of a pair of cattle twins.

GALL BLADDER. A sac-like receptacle in the liver for storing bile.

GALVANOTROPISM. The response of an organism to an electric current.

GANGLION. An aggregate of nerve cells.

GASTRIC. Pertaining to the stomach.

GASTROVASCULAR. Serving the double function of digestion and circulation.

GASTRULA. A stage in the development of metazoan animals in which the embryo consists of a two-layered sac, with an archenteron, or primitive intestine, and a single opening, the blastopore.

GASTRULATION. The process of invaginating or infolding the vegetal-pole cells of the blastula into the blastocoele. The process of forming a gastrula.

GELATINE. A colloidal substance obtained by boiling cartilage, bone, etc.

GEMMULE. A reproductive body composed of a number of cells, in sponges.

GENE. A factor or element in the chromosomes of germ cells or other cells which conditions a character of an organism.

GENETICS. Experimental evolution. The science of variation, heredity, sex-biology, etc.

GENITAL. Pertaining to, or concerned with, reproduction.

GENOTYPIC. Pertaining to the germinal or hereditary constitution of an organism. See PHENOTYPIC.

GENUS. A taxonomic division composed of one or more species that have a large number of characters in common and are therefore believed to have been derived from a common ancestor. A main division of a family.

GERMINAL CONTINUITY. The concept of an unbroken stream of germ plasm from generation to generation back to the beginning of life.

GERM LAYER. A primary embryonic tissue, such as ectoderm, endoderm, mesoderm, from which the tissues and organs of an organism develop.

GERM PLASM. The specific hereditary material forming the bridge between successive generations. More particularly, the chromatin of germ cells. In contrast with SOMATOPLASM.

GILL BOOK. A type of external respiratory organ found in aquatic Arachnida, composed of a series of leaves bound together by one edge and free elsewhere.

GILL SLIT. One of the openings connecting the pharynx with the outside; found in chordates. Also called GILL CLEFT or PHARYNGEAL CLEFT.

GLAND. An organ which secretes or excretes some special substance.

GLOCHIDIUM. A bivalve larva of clams or their relatives, which commonly lives for some time parasitically imbedded in the gill tissues of fishes.

GLOMERULUS. A coil of capillaries at the end of each nephric tubule in the kidneys of the higher vertebrates.

GLOTTIS. A slitlike opening in the pharynx leading to the trachea.

GLYCEROL. One of the alcohols. It enters into the composition of fats. Same as glycerin.

GLYCOGEN. Animal starch. A common form of stored carbohydrate food in animal tissues.

GONAD. The organ (ovary or testis) in which germ cells are produced or lodged.

GONOPHORE. An individual which bears gonads or reproductive organs, as in Hydroids.

GULLET. Same as ŒSOPHAGUS.

GUSTATORY. Referring to the sense of taste.

HABITAT. The environmental complex in which an organism lives.

Hæmocœle. A specialized part of the cœlom or body cavity used as a blood channel or reservoir.

Hæmoglobin. The red coloring matter of the blood.

Haploid. The reduced (one half) number of chromosomes present in gametes. See Diploid.

Heliotropism. The response of organism to the direction of light.

Hepatic. Pertaining to the liver.

Herbivorous. Plant-eating. See Carnivorous.

Heredity. Organic resemblance based on descent.

Hermaphrodite. An individual organism possessing both ovaries and testes.

Hermaphroditism. The state of being hermaphroditic. Same as Monœcious.

Heterogamy. The union of unlike gametes, as that of eggs and sperm.

Heterozygous. Producing gametes which fall into equally numerous classes with respect to the genes (allelomorphs) for a pair of alternative characters. See Homozygous.

Hibernate. To pass the winter. Usually to go into a dormant state during the winter.

Histology. The science which deals with the structure and function of tissues.

Homology. Fundamental structural resemblance based on inheritance, and often modified to subserve a variety of functions.

Homozygous. Producing gametes that are all alike with respect to any given pair of alternative genes or allelomorphs. See Heterozygous.

Hormone. An internal secretion, usually from a ductless gland, that circulates in the blood and acts as a stimulus to other organs or to growth processes.

Host. An organism that harbors a parasite.

Humerus. The upper arm bone of the terrestrial vertebrates.

Hyaline. Glassy or semitransparent.

Hybrid. The offspring of two parents unlike in some heritable character.

Hydra. A small tubular fresh-water cœlenterate with a crown of tentacles.

Hydrocœle. A specialized portion of the cœlomic system of an echinoderm larva, from which arises the radial water canals and which is responsible for the radial symmetry of the adult.

Hydroid. A colonial cœlenterate, the individuals of which resemble a Hydra.

Hymenoptera. An order of insects comprising the bees, wasps, ants, etc.

Hyoid. A group of bones or cartilages located at the base of the tongue.

Hypertonic. Possessing greater osmotic pressure than some other solution, e.g., sea water or blood, with which it is being compared.

HYPNOSIS. A form of sleep or somnambulism brought about by artificial means, in which there is usually suspension of some powers and unusual activity of others.

HYPOSTOME. The crater-like elevation about the mouth in Hydra.

HYPOTONIC. Possessing lower osmotic pressure than some other solution with which it is compared. See HYPERTONIC.

ILEUM. The last and usually the longest of the three divisions of the small intestine.

ILIUM. The dorsal bone of the pelvic girdle in the amphibia and higher vertebrates.

IMMUNITY. Resistance of an organism to disease-producing organisms.

INCURRENT. An incurrent canal, pore, siphon, or other structure is one that conducts water or other fluid toward or into an individual, organ, or cavity. Opposite of EXCURRENT.

INDETERMINATE CLEAVAGE. Segmentation of the egg in which the prospective fate of the individual cells is not readily traced and in which there is no great specialization of the blastomeres.

INDIRECT CELL DIVISION. Same as MITOSIS.

INFUSORIA. A class of Protozoa, usually possessing cilia.

INGESTION. The taking in of food.

INSTINCT. An unconscious, stereotyped series of reflex actions, due to an inherited nervous pattern.

INTEGRATION. The process by means of which units of a lower order become united and correlated to form an individual of a higher order.

INTERCELLULAR. Between cells.

INTESTINE. That portion of the alimentary tract leading from the pyloric end of the stomach to the anus.

INTRACELLULAR. Within a cell.

INVAGINATION. The folding of a layer of cells inward into a cavity.

INVERTEBRATE. An animal without a backbone or vertebral column. See VERTEBRATE.

IRRITABILITY. Susceptibility to the influence of stimuli.

ISOGAMY. The union of like gametes. See HETEROGAMY.

ISOLATION. In genetics, the prevention of promiscuous interbreeding between a mutant or a new variety and the main body of the species.

ISOTONIC. Having the same osmotic pressure as another solution with which it is compared.

JEJUNUM. The second of the divisions of the small intestine.

JUGULAR VEIN. A large vein returning blood from the head.

KARYOKINESIS. Same as MITOSIS.

KERATIN. A substance forming the characteristic material of horn, hair, nails, hoofs, etc. Similar to CHITIN.

KIDNEY. The chief organ of excretion in vertebrates and in some invertebrates.

KRAUSE'S MEMBRANE. A transverse partition of a voluntary muscle fiber.

LABIAL PALPS. Liplike, ciliated troughs leading into the mouth in many clamlike mollusks.

LABIUM. The upper lip in insects, as for example, the grasshopper.

LABRUM. The lower lip in insects.

LACUNA. A small space in the matrix of bone that, in life, contains a bone cell.

LAMARCKISM. The doctrine of the Inheritance of Acquired Characters.

LAMELLA. A thin layer.

LANCELET. A chordate belonging to the genus Amphioxus.

LANUGO. A coating of embryonic hair that appears in the human fœtus at about the sixth month of pregnancy, covering the whole body except the palms and soles. It is lost before birth.

LARVA. An immature and more or less active stage in the development of an organism; with certain adaptive characters that have no prospective significance so far as adult structures are concerned.

LARYNX. The enlarged anterior end of the trachea, containing the vocal cords.

LENTICULAR. Pertaining to, or shaped like, a lens.

LEUCOCYTE. A white blood corpuscle.

LIGAMENT. A tough band of fibrous connective tissue attaching a muscle to a bone, or two muscles together.

LIMPET. A small type of gastropod mollusk with a simple uncoiled shell.

LININ. An achromatic substance that forms a network of threads in the nucleus.

LINKAGE. The tendency for certain characters to be inherited in groups, presumably because the genes for these characters occupy the same chromosome.

LIPIN. A kind of fat.

LUMBAR. Referring to that part of the region of the spine of vertebrates back of the ribs.

LUNG BOOK. An inclosed respiratory organ composed of thin sheets of tissue bound together like the leaves of a book. Found in spiders and scorpions.

LYMPH. A clear fluid containing colorless cells found in lymph vessels. Essentially, blood without its corpuscles.

MACROGAMETE. The larger of the two kinds of gametes in species that exhibit heterogamy.

MACRONUCLEUS. The large nucleus in Infusoria, believed to be chiefly concerned with the vegetative activities of the cell.

MADREPORITE. The sievelike external opening of the water-vascular system in the echinoderms. Same as MADREPORIC PLATE.

MALARIA. A disease due to the presence of a sporozoan parasite in the red blood corpuscles.

MALPIGHIAN BODY. A structure in the vertebrate kidney composed of a combination of the Bowman's capsule and the glomerulus. Same as MALPIGHIAN CORPUSCLE.

MAMMAL. An animal belonging to the vertebrate class Mammalia.

MAMMARY GLAND. The milk gland of a mammal.

MANDIBLE. A jaw. More particularly, the third pair of appendages of the head of the crayfish and its allies.

MANTLE. A specialized layer of tissue that secretes the shell in mollusks.

MARSUPIAL. A mammal having a pouch in which the young are carried.

MATRIX. The noncellular substance in which are embedded the living cells of cartilage or bone.

MATURATION. The process through which germ cells pass in preparation for fertilization, usually accompanied by a numerical reduction of chromosomes.

MAXILLA. One of the members of the fourth or fifth pair of head appendages of the crayfish and its allies.

MAXILLIPED. One of the members of any of the first three thoracic appendages of the crayfish and its allies.

MECHANISM. Any more or less complex groups of organs, systems, or minor parts of an organism that work in a regulated fashion and that subserve a useful function in the preserving the life of the individual or the race. In order to be considered as a mechanism such a complex need not necessarily be wholly intelligible in terms of the physics and chemistry of lifeless materials.

MECHANISTIC VIEW. The view that life is explainable in terms of natural transformations of energy and of matter without introducing any immaterial or extra-natural "vital forces." This view is in distinct contrast with VITALISM.

MEDULLA OBLONGATA. The most posterior of the principal divisions of the vertebrate brain.

MEDULLARY PLATE, GROOVE, TUBE. Three phases or types of the central nervous system of vertebrates.

MEDULLARY SHEATH. A fatty insulating layer covering a nerve fiber or axon.

MEMBRANOUS LABRINTH. The system of sacs and canals that make up the inner ear apparatus in vertebrates. It includes the sacculus, the utriculus, and the semicircular canals.

MERIDIONAL. In a plain parallel with the axis of polarity.

MESENTERY. A double sheet of tissue, continuous with the peritoneum, which supports an organ, such as an intestine, from the body wall.

MESODERM. The layer of cells between the ectoderm and the endoderm.

MESOGLŒA. A noncellular gelatinous layer in cœlenterates, lying between the ectoderm and the endoderm.

MESOZOIC. The Age of Reptiles. The geologic period between the Palæozoic and the Cenozoic.

METABOLISM. The sum total of the chemical processes that go on in the living body.

METAGENESIS. The alternate appearance of two forms in the same species, one of which reproduces sexually and the other asexually. See ALTERNATION OF GENERATIONS.

METAMERE. One of the series of homologous segments in metameric organisms.

METAMERISM. The process or condition of embryonic transverse fission resulting in the segmental structure seen in annelids, arthropods, and vertebrates.

METAMORPHOSIS. The transformation of a larva into an adult.

METAPHASE. The climax of mitosis involving the longitudinal splitting of the chromosomes.

METAZOA. A subkingdom of animals characterized by somatic specialization and unity of organization. Commonly, multicellular animals.

MICROCHROMOSOME. The very small fourth chromosome in Drosophila. More generally, any very small chromosome.

MICROGAMETE. The smaller of the two types of gametes in species exhibiting heterogamy.

MICROMERE. One of the quartet of smaller cells at the eight-cell stage of cleavage in the egg of the frog, etc., destined to form the ectoderm.

MICRONUCLEUS. The smaller of the two nuclei in Paramecium and its allies, supposed to function chiefly in reproduction. See MACRONUCLEUS.

MIMICRY. The resemblance of a defenseless species to a well defended one, presumably as an adaptation for protection.

MIRACIDIUM. The earliest larval form of a trematode worm such as the liver-fluke.

MITOCHONDRIA. Organized cytoplasmic bodies in animal cells.

MITOSIS. Cell division involving the formation of chromosomes and a spindle.

MOLLUSK. A member of the phylum Mollusca.

MONŒCIOUS. Same as HERMAPHRODITIC.

MONOHYBRID. The progeny derived by mating two individuals differing in but one pair of alternative characters or genes.

MONOZYGOTIC. Referring to twins or larger numbers of offspring derived from a single fertilized egg or zygote. See DIZYGOTIC.

MORPHOLOGY. That branch of biology which deals with the form or structure of organisms.

MUTATION. Any heritable modification initiated in the germ plasm.

MYRMECOPHILOUS. Literally, ant-loving. Technically, commensal with ants.

NARES. Internal or external openings of the nasal passages.

NATURAL SELECTION. Charles Darwin's theory of Evolution, which has been paraphrased as "The Survival of the Fittest."

NAUPLIUS. The type of larva typical of the more primitive Crustacea.

NEMATOCYST. One of the stinging bodies characteristic of cœlenterates.

NEMATODE. A roundworm belonging to the class Nematoda.

NEOTENY. The retention of larval characters throughout life; becoming sexually mature while retaining larval characters.

NEPHRIC TUBULE. The structural unit of a vertebrate kidney. Similar to a NEPHRIDIUM.

NEPHRIDIUM. A tubular excretory organ, characteristic of many invertebrates.

NEPHROSTOME. The funnel-like opening at the inner end of a nephridium.

NEURAL GROOVE, TUBE. Same as MEDULLARY GROOVE, TUBE.

NEURILEMMA. The delicate external membrane covering a nerve fiber.

NEURON. A nerve cell, including the cell body and all of its processes.

NEWT. A tailed amphibian.

NODES OF RANVIER. Places in a nerve fiber where the medullary sheath is interrupted.

NONDISJUNCTION. The failure to separate after synapsis on the part of homologous chromosomes, so that both of the latter go to one daughter cell and none to the other.

NOTOCHORD. Typically, a cylindrical rod of cells in chordates, lying ventral to the spinal cord and dorsal to the alimentary tract.

NUCLEOLUS. The true nucleolus, as distinguished from the chromatin nucleus. The same as the PLASMOSOME.

NUCLEOPLASM. The protoplasm of which the cell nucleus is composed. In contrast with CYTOPLASM.

NUCLEUS. A specialized protoplasmic body in all typical cells.

OCCIPITAL CONDYLE. A part of the base of the skull that serves as a pivot by means of which the head is articulated with the first vertebra.

ŒSOPHAGUS. The passage leading from the pharynx to the stomach.

OLFACTORY. Pertaining to the sense of smell.

ONTOGENY. The developmental history of the individual. See PHYLOGENY.

OÖCYTE. A fully grown ovarian egg cell prior to the second maturation.

OÖGENESIS. The process of the development of the mature egg from the primordial germ cell.

OÖGONIUM. One of the early germ cells of a female prior to the beginning of the processes of maturation.

OÖTID. A mature egg. Comparable with SPERMATID.

OPERCULUM. A fold of skin covering the gills in the tadpole larva of the frog. Also, a plate used for closing the shell in gastropod mollusks.

OPTIC LOBES. Thickenings of the dorsal surface of the mid-brain.

OPTIC NERVES. The nerves connecting the eye with the brain.

ORAL. Pertaining to the mouth.

ORDER. A taxonomic group ranking below a class and above a family.

ORGAN. A complex of tissues subserving a specific function.

ORGANELLE. A specialized structure in a unicellular organism playing a rôle equivalent to that of an organ in a metazoan organism.

ORGANISM. A living individual, whether animal or plant.

ORGANISMAL THEORY. A doctrine that emphasizes the idea that the organism is a unit and that its unity consists in the centralized control of one dominant region over all subordinate regions. See ELEMENTAL THEORY.

ORTHOGENESIS. Definitely directed variation. The idea that repeated variations in the same direction occur in a race or a species, and that these changes are due to internal causes.

OSMOSIS. Diffusion of dissolved substance through a semi-permeable membrane.

OSMOTIC PRESSURE. The pressure exerted in a solution by the dissolved substance.

OSTIUM. A valvular opening through the wall of the heart in arthropods. Also the opening in a sponge through which it takes in water.

OVARY. The organ in which the germ cells of a female are formed or lodged.

OVIDUCT. A tube through which eggs leave the ovary.

OVIPARITY. The condition of being oviparous.

OVIPAROUS. Egg-laying. See VIVIPAROUS.

OVULATION. The process of giving off full-grown eggs from the ovary.

OVUM. An egg. A mature female gamete. Same as OÖTID.

OXIDATION. The chemical combination of any substance with oxygen.

OXYHÆMOGLOBIN. Hæmoglobin combined with a certain amount of oxygen.

PÆDOGENESIS. Precocious sexual maturity. Sexual maturity in an embryo or larva.

PALÆONTOLOGY. The science of ancient life. It deals with fossils of prehistoric organisms.

PALÆOZOIC. Pertaining to the geological era prior to the Mesozoic; commonly called the age of invertebrates and fishes.

PANCREAS. A gland opening into the intestine that secretes several important digestive enzymes.

PARAPODIUM. A flat, fleshy segmental projection characteristic of marine annelids, used for locomotion and respiration.

PARASITE. An organism that lives in or on another (the host) at the expense of the latter.

PARENCHYMA. A kind of loose, spongy mesodermal tissue found in some of the lower types of animals.

PARIETAL GANGLION. One of the ganglia characteristic of mollusks.

PARTHENOGENESIS. The development of an egg without fertilization.

PATHOLOGIC. The condition of being diseased.

PECTORAL GIRDLE. A group of bones or of cartilages serving to connect the fore limbs of vertebrates to the axial skeleton. See PELVIC GIRDLE.

PECULIAR. When used to describe a species it means that such a species is not found anywhere else except in the place designated.

PEDAL DISK. The basal attachment disk of a Hydra.

PEDAL GANGLION. A ganglion associated with the activity of the foot in mollusks.

PEDICELLARIÆ. Minute automatic pincher-like structures characteristic of the surface of starfishes and sea urchins.

PELLICLE. A thin protective layer on the surface of a cell.

PELVIC GIRDLE. A group of bones connecting the fore limbs to the main skeleton.

PENIAL. Pertaining to the penis.

PENIS. The copulatory organ of many species of animals.

PEPSIN. The enzyme of the stomach that acts in the digestion of proteins.

PEPTONE. A substance derived by digestion (hydrolysis) of proteins.

PERICARDIUM. The peritoneum lining the pericardial cavity.

PERIOSTEUM. The living epithelial membrane on the outer surface of bone that functions as a producer of new bone cells.

PERIPHERAL NERVOUS SYSTEM. That part of the nervous system of a vertebrate that is made up of the spinal and cranial nerves.

PERISTOMIUM. The second segment in the body of an annelid worm; the segment into which the mouth opens.

PERITONEUM. The membrane lining the cœlom of vertebrates. This is continuous with the mesenteries.

PETRIFICATION. The process of substituting mineral matter for organic matter during the disintegration of an animal or plant. A method of fossilization.

PHARYNGEAL CLEFT. See GILL SLIT.

PHARYNX. That part of the digestive tract that belongs to the head; in invertebrates, that part of the digestive tract between the mouth and the œsophagus.

PHENOTYPIC. Pertaining to the somatic or expressed hereditary characters of an organism or group irrespective of their germinal constitution.

PHOTOTAXIS. Response to light on the part of organisms.

PHYLOGENETIC. Pertaining to the ancestral history of a species or race.

PHYLOGENY. The ancestral history of the race. See ONTOGENY.

PHYLUM. One of the main taxonomic divisions of a kingdom or subkingdom.

PINEAL BODY. A small glandular structure on the dorsal side of the brain in vertebrates; believed to be a vestige of a third eye.

PITUITARY BODY. A glandular body beneath the brain, derived partly from the nervous system and partly from the alimentary tract.

PLACENTA. An embryonic structure characteristic of the higher mammals serving as an organ by means of which the mother imparts nourishment to the fœtus.

PLACOID SCALE. The type of scale characteristic of the elasmobranch fishes.

PLASMA. The fluid part of the blood; blood from which all solid or semisolid ingredients have been removed.

PLASMAGEL. The relatively solid, or viscous, phase of protoplasmic colloids. Opposite of PLASMASOL.

PLASMA MEMBRANE. The surface membrane of the cytosome, composed of living protoplasm, and having the property of being semipermeable. To be distinguished from CELL WALL, which is outside of the cytosome and not a part of the latter. Same as CELL MEMBRANE.

PLASMASOL. The relatively fluid phase of protoplasmic colloids. In contrast with PLASMAGEL.

PLASMASOME. The true nucleolus. A formed component of the nucleus, not composed of chromatin. Of unknown function. To be distinguished from karyosomes, or chromatin nucleoli.

PLASTID. One type of formed component of the cytosome, fairly massive in form and functioning as a localized area of specific chemical transformation.

PLEURAL CAVITY. That part of the cœlom which contains the heart and lungs in mammals.

PLEURAL GANGLION. One of the characteristic ganglia of the mollusks.

PLEURO-PERITONEUM. A membrane lining the pleural cavity.

POLAR BODY. A small nonfunctional cell or gamete produced during the maturation divisions of the egg cell. An abortive oöcyte or oötid.

POLIAN VESICLE. A bulbous organ connected with the water-vascular ring in echinoderms.

POLYMORPHISM. The occurrence of several types, or castes, of individuals in a colony or community of individuals belonging to the same species and derived from the same parent or parents.

Polyp. One of the hydra-like or feeding individuals in a hydroid or coral colony.

Posterior. Pertaining to that part or end of an organism opposite to the head.

Predaceous. Characterized by preying on other organisms.

Preformation. The doctrine that the adult organism is represented in miniature in the germ cell. See Epigenesis.

Pregnancy. The state of being with young.

Proboscis. A tubular extension of the nose or of the lips.

Proglottid. One of the individuals in the chain of zoöids produced by transverse fission in a tapeworm.

Prophase. That period of mitosis prior to the metaphase.

Prostomium. The first segment of the body in annelid worms; the segment anterior to the mouth.

Proteid. Pertaining to proteins. Same as Protein.

Protein. A class of complex chemical substances containing nitrogen, making up an essential part of protoplasm.

Proteose. Any one of a number of substances derived from the hydrolysis of proteins.

Protista. A group consisting of both unicellular animals and plants.

Protoplasm. The physical basis of life; the living matter of which organisms are composed.

Protopodite. The basal segment of the typical biramous appendages of the crayfish and its allies.

Prototroch. The equatorial band of cilia in the Trochophore larva.

Protozoa. A subkingdom (phylum) of animals characterized by being unicellular.

Protozoölogy. That branch of animal biology that deals especially with Protozoa.

Proventriculus. The first division of the stomach in the birds.

Pseudopodium. The blunt fingerlike projections used by Amœba and its relatives for locomotor or feeding activities.

Pulmonary. Pertaining to the lungs.

Pupa. A quiescent stage in the development of insects, between the larval and adult stages.

Pure Line. A group of individuals possessing identical genes and derived from a homozygous ancestor.

Pyloric Valve. A muscular constriction between the stomach and the small intestine.

Quadrate. One of the bones of the skull in some vertebrates.

Quadruplet. One of a set of four offspring derived from a single zygote.

Radial Canals. The water-vascular canals radiating from the water-vascular ring in echinoderms.

RADIAL SYMMETRY. The arrangement of the principal parts of an organism like the spokes of a wheel.

RADIO-ULNA. The fused radius and ulna bones of the frog.

RADIUS. The bones of the fore-arm located on the thumb side of the limb.

RADULA. A ribbon-like rasping organ used for purposes of mastication in certain mollusks.

REALM. A large geographic division of the animal kingdom.

RECAPITULATION, LAW OF. The doctrine that the life history of the individual is equivalent to a much abbreviated résumé of the ancestral history of the race.

RECESSIVE. Referring to a gene that does not express itself in the soma in the presence of a contrasting dominant gene.

RECTUM. The terminal portion of the large intestine.

REDIA. An individual belonging to the second type of larva found in the life history of the liver flukes and their kin.

REDUCTION. The cell divisions in the germ cell cycle in which chromosomes, at one division, do not split lengthwise, but merely separate after associating for some time in pairs. Refers to a numerical reduction of chromosomes to one half that typical for the soma.

REFLEX ACTION. An action performed as the result of an impulse that travels over a reflex arc. It is involuntary and may be quite unconscious.

REGENERATION. The process of, or power of, replacing a lost part; the development of a whole individual out of a part.

RENAL. Referring to the kidneys.

REPRODUCTION. The process of producing, or power of organisms to produce, offspring.

REPTILE. A member of the vertebrate class Reptilia.

RESPIRATION. The process of obtaining energy from food, involving at least some phases of oxidation.

RESTING CELL. One which is not undergoing mitosis.

RETICULAR THEORY. A theory of the ultimate structure of protoplasm, according to which all structures are composed of networks of fibrils.

RETINA. The actual sensory part of the eye, composed of layers of light-sensitive cells.

RHABDITES. Rod-like bodies in the epidermis of flatworms whose function is not fully understood.

RHEOTROPISM. The reaction of organisms to currents.

ROTIFER. Any one of the small aquatic animals belonging to the phylum Trochelminthes.

RUGOSE. Ridged or furrowed.

SALAMANDER. One of the tailed Amphibia belonging to the order Urodela.

SALIVA. The fluid secreted by the SALIVARY GLANDS.

SALIVARY GLANDS. Glands emptying into the mouth of an animal, which secrete saliva, a digestive juice that starts the processes of digestion.

SARCODE. The term first applied to protoplasm, by Dujardin.

SARCOLEMMA. The delicate membrane surrounding a voluntary muscle cell.

SARCOMERE. One of the apparent segments into which each muscle fibril is transversely subdivided.

SARCOPLASM. The protoplasm of a striated muscle cell.

SCOLEX. The head, or attaching individual, in the linear series of individuals making up a tapeworm.

SECONDARY SEXUAL CHARACTERS. Morphological, physiological, or behavioral differences between the sexes other than those involved in the gonads, or primary sex organs.

SEDENTARY. Referring to organisms with sluggish habits that move about only to a minimal extent.

SEGMENTATION. Same as METAMERISM. Sometimes used as a synonym for CLEAVAGE.

SEGMENTATION CAVITY. The hollow of the blastula. Same as BLASTOCŒLE.

SEGREGATION. The separation of contrasting genes into different gametes.

SEMICIRCULAR CANALS. That part of the verterbate ear devoted to the sense of equilibrium.

SEMINAL RECEPTACLES. Sac-like bodies within the body of the earthworm which receive sperms from another worm and hold them until the eggs are ready for fertilization.

SEMINAL VESICLES. Large reservoirs associated with the testes in the earthworm whose function is to harbor the sperms during most of the period of spermatogenesis.

SEMIPERMEABLE. Permitting the passage of solvents but being relatively or entirely impermeable to dissolved substances.

SENSORY. Pertaining to sensation. Applied to a nerve cell which transmits an impulse resulting in a sensation.

SEPTA. The partitions that divide the cœlom of the earthworm into metameric chambers. See DISSEPIMENT.

SERIAL HOMOLOGY. The homology of one metameric structure to another in a different metamere; e.g., the various appendages of the crayfish are serially homologous.

SERTOLI CELLS. Modified testicular cells that seem to act as nurse cells for immature spermatozoa.

SERUM. The clear fluid of the blood that is left after the blood has clotted and the clot is removed. It contains many specific materials in solution.

SESSILE. Attached directly, as distinguished from stalked. More commonly, attached, as opposed to free-living.

SETÆ. Same as CHÆTÆ.

SEX CHROMOSOME. The odd or X-chromosome whose presence or absence determines whether a gamete shall be male-producing or female-producing.

SEX-LINKED. Associated in inheritance with one or the other sex; referring to characters whose genes are located in the X-chromosome.

SILICIOUS. Composed of silica (Silicon dioxide).

SINUS VENOSUS. A large thin-walled blood chamber on the dorsal side of the heart into which empty the main trunk veins and which, in turn, opens into the right auricle through the sinu-auricular valve.

SIPHON. A passageway for currents of water; as the openings between the right and left mantle of clams and mussels, where the edges do not meet.

SOMA. The body of an organism, contrasted with the germ cells.

SOMATIC. Pertaining to the body, or soma.

SOMATOGENIC REPRODUCTION. That type of reproduction that is effected by a division of a multicellular body, or soma, by means of fission, budding, etc. In contrast with CYTOGENIC REPRODUCTION.

SOMITE. One of the segments or metameres of a metameric organism such as the earthworm.

SPECIAL CREATION. The doctrine that each of the species as we know them today was specially created.

SPECIALIZATION. Structural or functional emphasis upon one or a few functions.

SPECIES. A group of individuals so nearly alike that they might have been derived from the same parents. In classification, the main subdivision of a genus.

SPERM. Same as SPERMATOZOÖN. A male gamete.

SPERMARY. Same as TESTIS.

SPERMATID. A male germ cell after the second maturation but before becoming specialized to form the typical spermatozoön.

SPERMATOCYTE. A male germ cell resulting from the last generation of spermatogonia; also male germ cells after the first maturation division.

SPERMATOGONIUM. An early male germ cell prior to the onset of changes leading to maturation.

SPERMATOZOÖN. The definitive male gamete in animals. See SPERM.

SPICULE. A needle-like skeletal structure seen in sponges.

SPINAL COLUMN. The series of vertebræ in vertebrates.

SPINAL CORD. That part of the central nervous system of vertebrates posterior to the brain and largely inclosed in the neural canal of the vertebræ.

SPINDLE. The assemblage of threads or fibers that are associated with the chromosomes in mitosis and that assume a more or less spindle-like form.

SPINDLE CELL. One type of cell characteristic of frog's blood.

SPIRACLE. In frog tadpoles, the opening on the left side through which water passes from the gill chamber to the outside.

SPIREME. The coiled thread or threads of chromatin seen during the pro-phases of cell division.

SPLEEN. A vascular ductless organ characteristic of most vertebrates. Lies near the stomach and has a function connected with the develop-ment and destruction of red blood cells.

SPONGIN. A horny material forming the skeleton of bath sponges.

SPONTANEOUS GENERATION. Same as ABIOGENESIS.

SPORE. A reproductive cell liberated from a parent, capable of giving rise without fertilization to a new individual. A reproductive cell which is not a gamete.

SPOROCYST. A sac-like individual formed from the miracidium of a liver fluke.

SPOROZOITE. A stage in the life cycle of the malaria organism (and allied forms) before it enters the red blood cell of man.

SPORULATION. The process of forming spores.

SQUAMOUS. Scaly. Referring to a kind of epithelium composed of flat scalelike cells.

SQUID. An animal belonging to the class Cephalopoda, phylum Mol-lusca.

STATOBLAST. A group of cells constituting the asexual reproductive unit of the Bryozoa. A sort of internal bud.

STIMULUS. Any condition which calls forth a response in living matter.

STOMODÆUM. That part of the lining of the mouth which is formed by an inturning of the ectoderm.

STRATIFIED. Arranged in strata or layers.

STRIATED. Cross-striped or cross-banded. Referring to one of the prin-cipal types of muscle fibers. See UNSTRIATED.

SUPRARENAL GLAND. A ductless gland in vertebrates that lies above the kidney. Same as ADRENAL GLAND.

SURFACE TENSION. A term describing the fact that the surface layer of fluids is under a tension. This results in the tendency of small masses of fluid to reduce the surface to a minimum and thus to assume the form of spherical droplets or vacuoles.

SWIMMERET. A primitive biramous appendage beneath the abdomen of crayfish.

SYMBIOSIS. The living together of two species supposedly for mutual benefit.

SYMPATHETIC NERVOUS SYSTEM. Two longitudinal nerve cords, together with a series of associated ganglia, in vertebrates.

SYNAPSE. A point of contact between two neurons.

SYNAPSIS. The pairing and lying in contact of homologous maternal and paternal chromosomes prior to maturation of the germ cells.

SYNCYTIAL. Pertaining to a SYNCYTIUM.

SYNCYTIUM. An undivided mass of protoplasm containing many nuclei.

SYNGAMY. The union of gametes to form a zygote.

TADPOLE. The larva of a frog.

TAPEWORM. A member of the class Cestoda, phylum Platyhelminthes.

TAXONOMY. The science of classification.

TELOPHASE. The final phase of mitosis, during which daughter nuclei are reconstructed.

TEST. The hard outer shell of the sea urchin or other animals.

TESTIS. The male gonad. The organ in which male germ cells are formed or are lodged. See SPERMARY.

TETRAD. A quadruple chromosomal body composed of paired homologous chromosomes each of which has precociously divided.

THALAMENCEPHALON. A part of the vertebrate brain derived from the primitive forebrain.

THERMOTROPISM. The response of organisms to changes of temperature.

THIGMOTROPISM. The response of organisms to mechanical contacts.

THROMBIN. A specific material, probably an enzyme, that causes clotting of the blood.

THYROID EXTRACT. An extract of the active principle of the thyroid gland, whose essential constituent is iodine.

THYROID GLAND. An endocrine gland in the neck region of vertebrates that has the function of regulating the rate of growth, metabolism, etc., of the whole organism. An extremely important chemical regulatory mechanism.

TISSUE. A group of cells of similar structure and function making up a continuous mass or layer.

TRACHEÆ. Tubes carrying air to and from the lungs in vertebrates. Also air tubes used for respiration in various arthropods.

TRIAL AND ERROR. The name applied to the theory that organisms find their way to favorable regions by continually avoiding less favorable regions. In contrast with the TROPISM THEORY.

TRICHOCYSTS. Minute rodlike bodies lying in the cortex of Paramecium, and other Infusoria, that are supposed to play a protective rôle.

TRIHYBRID. The offspring of parents differing with regard to three alternative genes or characters.

TRILOBITE. A kind of extinct arthropod.

TRIPOBLASTIC. Having the three primary germ layers: ectoderm, endoderm, and mesoderm. See DIPLOBLASTIC.

TROCHOPHORE. A nearly spherical type of ciliated aquatic larva characteristic of flatworms, annelids, mollusks, etc.

TROPISM. A response of an organism to a particular stimulus. Referring to a theory of animal behavior sometimes known as the "machine theory." See TRIAL AND ERROR.

TRYPANOSOME. A parasitic protozoan belonging to the class Mastigophora. The biological basis of sleeping sickness.

TRYPSIN. A ferment produced by the pancreas which has the power of digesting proteins.

TSETSE FLY. A species of fly which carries the germs of sleeping sickness.

TUBE-FEET. Tubular locomotor organs characteristic of echinoderms.

TUNICATE. A member of the class Ascidiacea, phylum Chordata.

TWINNING. The process of symmetrical longitudinal fission of a cell or of an organism resulting in the production of two equivalent individuals, or twins.

TYMPANIC MEMBRANE. Same as eardrum.

TYPHLOSOLE. A median dorsal invagination along the whole length of the intestine of the earthworm, whose rôle seems to be that of increasing the digestive surface.

UNIT CHARACTER. A character inherited more or less like a unit and independently of other characters.

URETER. The duct carrying urine from the kidney to the cloaca or to the surface of the body.

URINE. The secretion of the kidneys.

UROGENITAL SYSTEM. A complex system of organs in vertebrates concerned with both excretion and reproduction.

UTERUS. The lower, usually enlarged, portion of the oviduct in which incubation of eggs takes place; in mammals, the womb.

VACUOLE. A region within a cell occupied by fluid other than protoplasm.

VAGINA. The passage leading from the uterus to the exterior.

VALVE. A flap or pocket in the heart or main arteries of vertebrates or other animals whose function it is to prevent back flow of the blood. An entirely different use of the term is that in connection with the shells of bivalve mollusks; each of the two shells is called a valve.

VASCULAR. Pertaining to blood vessels or blood supply.

VAS DEFERENS. A duct conveying sperms from the testis to the exterior.

VEGETAL POLE. The pole of the egg where the rate of metabolism is lowest. That pole opposite to the ANIMAL POLE.

VENTRAL. Literally, pertaining to the belly. Referring to the lower side.

VENTRICLE. The muscular pumping part of the heart of vertebrates and other animals.

VERTEBRAL COLUMN. See SPINAL COLUMN.

VERTEBRATE. An animal possessing a spinal column, or backbone.

VESTIGIAL. Rudimentary, or reduced to a mere vestige of a one-time size or functional importance.

VISCERA. Internal organs of animals.

VISCERAL MASS. One of the chief subdivisions of a mollusk, containing the chief organs of nutrition, excretion, circulation, and reproduction.

VISCERAL SKELETON. That part of the skeleton of the vertebrates consisting of the bones of the jaws, of the tongue, and of the branchial arches.

VISCOSITY. Quality or state of being viscous, or imperfectly fluid, a quality characteristic of protoplasmic colloids that are more or less in the plasmagel state. A characteristic feature of a viscous material is that it flows relatively slowly.

VITALISM. The doctrine that attributes at least some of the phenomena of life to the interplay of forces different from those which prevail in the lifeless world. See MECHANISTIC VIEW.

VITAMINE. A substance of unknown chemical constitution, but essential for the maintenance of life and of health.

VITELLINE GLAND. An organ producing yolk to be supplied to growing eggs.

VITELLINE MEMBRANE. A membrane surrounding an egg.

VIVIPAROUS. Producing young from eggs that are retained in the uterus until they are hatched and able to move about of their own accord. In some animals the young are nourished in the uterus up to an advanced stage through a nutritive communication between the maternal and fœtal tissues.

VOMER. One of the bones of the under side of the vertebrate skull.

VOMERINE. Related to, or upon, the vomer.

X-CHROMOSOME. The peculiar chromosome in a germ cell that determines the sex of the zygote.

Y-CHROMOSOME. A peculiar chromosome often the partner of the X-chromosome and having to do with the fertility of males.

ZOÖGEOGRAPHY. That branch of zoölogy that deals with the geographic distribution of animals.

ZOÖID. An individual belonging to a colony such as that of hydroids. A term also used for subordinate individuals formed by transverse fission in Planaria and its relatives.

ZYGOTE. A fertilized egg. A cell produced by the union of gametes.

ZYGOTIC. Pertaining to a zygote.

INDEX

INDEX

Abactinal surface, 278
Abalone, 91
Abiogenesis, 5, 31–35
Aboral surface, 278
Acarina, 244
Achromatic figure, 73
Accœlomata, 199
Acquired characters, theory of inheritance of, 483–485
Actinal surface, 278
Adaptations, 7, 47, 251; chapter on, 371–390; suggested explanations of, 372–374; two categories of, 374–375; remarkable inherited, 375–388; individual, acquired, or contingent, 388–390; offensive and defensive, 376–380; adaptive behavior, 380, 381; reproductive, 381–383; theories of causes of, 483–487
Adaptive radiation, 231, 232
Adductor muscles, 227
Adenoid tissue, 331
Adhesion Theory, 121–122
Adipose tissue, 333, 334
Adolescence, of frog, 346
Afferent nerves, 327
Age and natural death, problem of, 143
Age of the Earth, 427
Aglossa, 296
Albumen cells, 167
Albumen gland, 222
Alimentary tract, of Nereis, 200; of earthworm, 205, 206
Allantois, 301
Alternation of generations, 97, 178
Alveolar Theory, 65
Amblystoma tigrinum, 408, 409
Ambulacral groove, 279
Amino acids, 42
Amitosis, 6, 69
Amœba, 94, 114–128; general characters, 114, 115; general anatomy, 115–118; physiology of, 118–127; nutritive processes, 120; locomotion, 121–125; behavior, 125–127; reproduction, 127–128

Amœba binucleata, 128
Amœba proteus, 114–120
Amœba verrucosa, 119, 123
Amphiaster, 73
Amphibia, 101; orders of, 296; characters of, 301, 302
Amphineura, 99
Amphioxus, 100
Amphipoda, 238
Amphoteric, 355
Ampulla, 281; of the inner ear, 365
Amylopsin, 320, 356
Anabolism, 46
Anadonta, 226, 227
Anal cirri, 197
Anal opening, 135
Anal spot, 130
Analogy, principle of, 20; versus homology, 413–415
Anaphase, 75, 76
Anatomy of frog, 302–318
Anaximander, 12
Anaximines, 31
Animal kingdom, the, 90–101
Animal pole, 64, 339
Annelida, classification of, 99; chapter on, 195–216
Annelid-arthropod assemblage, 105
Annelids, 99, 195–216
Anopheles, 265
Antennæ, 248–250
Antennules, 248–250
Anthozoa, 97, 176
Anthropoid apes, 3
Antibody, 419
Ants, 258–263; subterranean life, 258; polymorphism, 258–260; social life, 243, 259, 261; commensalism, 261; slavery, 261; feeding habits, 261, 262; compared with human societies, 262, 263; leaf-cutting, 262; honey ants, 262
Anura, 294
Anus, 130, 269
Aortic arches, 206, **207**
Apical end, 85
Apical region, 85

529